BETTY PILGRIM

A Journey from Epiphany to Christmas

by

EPPIE BARTLETT

O Lord, we beseech thee, let thy continual pity
cleanse and defend thy church: and, because it cannot
continue in safety without thy succour, preserve it
evermore by thy help and goodness: through
Jesus Christ our Lord. Amen.

The Collect of the sixteenth Sunday after Trinity

AVON BOOKS
1 DOVEDALE STUDIOS
465 BATTERSEA PARK ROAD
LONDON SW11 4LR

Printed and bound in the U.K.

Avon Books

London
First Published 1997
© Elspeth Bartlett 1997
ISBN 1 86033 520 9

With love and gratitude to Gordon whose idea it was that this book should be written and for whom I wrote it. All is due to his rare mixture of fun and true holiness which impressed itself on me from the beginning and also to his gentle prodding which encouraged me, ever wavering, forward along the Pilgrim Way. He also provided for this story the *ensample* of Father Edward, though *he* has not surprisingly turned out to be of his original a rather pale and static shadow.

NOTES

1. Many words of gratitude are due to the Scottish Episcopal Church much of whose structure and excellent Kalendar I have borrowed on which to hang my tale.
2. The letter quoted on page 161 of this book as being from 'Newspot' was in real life part of an article by Canon Arthur Fielder published in the Sunday Telegraph of 27 December 1987. I am grateful to him for having written these words which express my thoughts much better than any I could have chosen myself and for allowing me to use them in this book.
3. All the dreams recounted here were dreamt by myself except the one of Mike and his dog. I have heard every sermon mentioned except two: one preached at Christopher's first Mass and the other on St John the Evangelist's Day.
4. In this story the geography of Scotland has been somewhat altered. I hope no one will be offended.

THE GOOD BOOK LIST

The Bible	Mostly AV.
The Scottish Prayer Book 1929	
Canon A M. Alchin,	
Sister Eileen Mary	
Sister Mary Paul and	
Sister Benedicta SLG	*Julian of Norwich.*
Alexander Cruden	*Complete Concordance.*
Sister Eileen Mary SLG	*Pilgrimage and Possession.*
	Conversion in the writings of St Teresa and St John of the Cross.
Austin Farrer	*Saving Belief.*
	The Glass of Vision.
St John of the Cross	*Collected Works.*
C G Jung	*Answer to Job.*
Julian of Norwich	*Enfolded in Love.*
C S Lewis	*Mere Christianity* (and others).
M.D. Hooker	*The Gospel According to Mark.*
A.M. Hunter	*Interpreting Paul's Gospel.*
Dr. E L Mascall	*Christ, the Christian and the Church*
Canon Kenneth Mason	*George Herbert, Priest and Poet*
Thomas Merton	*Contemplative Prayer.*
	Life and Holiness.
H F D Sparks	*A Synopsis of the Gospels.*
Pierre Teilhard de Chardin	*The Mass of the World.*
St Teresa of Avila	*Collected Works.*
Wolfgang Trilling	*A Conversation with Paul.*
Simon Tugwell	*Prayer : Living with God.*
	Prayer : Prayer in Practice.
Esther de Waal	*Seeking God (St Benedict).*
Bishop Kallistos Ware of Diokleia:	*The Power of the Name.*

ABOUT THE AUTHOR

Eppie Bartlett was born just before the First World War in a house overlooking the mouth of the River Mersey and Liverpool Bay towards New Brighton and the Welsh Mountains. She didn't shine in any special way at school nor go to any university and was married just after the beginning of the Second World War. Her husband, a mechanical engineer, served in REME as a Lieutenant Colonel and later had a job in industry.

The Bartletts have five children, four boys with a girl at the end, all bright and mostly practical. They are now aged between forty-two and fifty-five. There are six grand-children; for a short while there were seven but sadly a grand-daughter was lost in recent years.

On her husband's retirement they went to live, for a complete change, near Inverness where he, amongst his other voluntary occupations, was treasurer for the Diocese of Moray and then for the Cathedral. Here Eppie Bartlett learnt that a treasurer's wife is not expected to express any views of her own, though she could always help with the accounts on the then newly-invented Amstrad.

After twenty-two very happy years in Scotland they have now returned to live in the Wirral again, (a distance of at least 400 miles from any of the family being considered too far for ease of access either way in any crisis).

This book was written eight or nine years ago but since then not much has changed. Women priests and modern language services are still lively topics.

POSTSCRIPT

Since this was written the Bartletts have lost their son Bill, who passed away peacefully in May this year.

CONTENTS

EPIPHANY

The Day Itself   1
Resolutions   5
The Dashwoods   10
The Morlands   13
Edward's Arrival   16
Betty's Story   22
Drummore   30
Trig Point Hill   35
St Paul   39
Some Collects   45
Christopher   51
Creation   54

LENT

A Springtime Picnic   58
St Benedict   65
At Philip's   71
Sunday and Sermons   75
At Ruth's   81
Dreams   89
To John's   97

EASTER

In the Glen   101
The Road to Emmaus   107
To Derva Cottage   111
With Angela   116
The Sloe Lane   123

WHITSUNTIDE

Catastrophe   129
The Holy Spirit in Action   134
The Spirit in the Scriptures   138
Trinity Sunday   142
Corpus Christi   148

Christopher's Priesting   156
Christopher's First Mass   162
At Jane's again   166
Edward to Lunch   171
Jung and a Dream   174
Jung Again   179
The Wrath of God   185
Prayer and Belief   190
Two Spanish Saints   195
At the Rectory   198
Holy Women   202
A Fun Sermon   207
Friends and Voices   212
Olva Comes to Ardness   218
All Angels   224
Betty has a Cold   228
More Books   236
The Sloe Lane Again   245
More Sermons   249
All Saints   253
All Souls   257
An Autumn Picnic   260

ADVENT

St Andrew   265
Christmas Preparations   270

CHRISTMAS

The Eve and The Day   278
Boxing Day   281
St John the Evangelist's Day 285

EPILOGUE
291

EPIPHANY: THE DAY ITSELF

It was the sixth of January, Epiphany. I'd woken too late to say all my usual morning prayers before it was time to get up and make tea for Nicholas and myself. It's not a good idea to rush one's prayers so I said just two, one for other people generally and one for Nicholas and the family and myself.

Epiphany. That means the salvation which God has prepared for everyone, a light to lighten the Gentiles. Our ancestors were gentiles, we have been given this light which is Christ and must take it in our turn to lighten other gentiles. Christ, our salvation, prepared by God his Father, our Father, Jesus Christ, who comes to be a Light for us.

I thought of this day, the day we celebrate the coming of the Three Kings. I'd always thought of them as kings, it's only natural they didn't travel wearing their crowns. Perhaps I should have thought of them more often as Magi, magicians, but I hadn't. After breakfast I brought the little figures out from their hiding place behind the potted palm, not like a real palm tree at all, (but not to worry), that stood beside the crib on top of the hall cupboard, and placed them carefully looking at the Baby Jesus who lay between his Mother Mary and Joseph. The shepherds and their two lambs had to be moved to just outside the stable, they must look as if they were leaving, though reluctantly, looking back at the Babe. I didn't want to remove them altogether, they were so decorative, appearing happy. They'd been with the Holy Family and the ox and the ass from Christmas time. The crib would stay out for another week, until the octave of Epiphany was over. Then, sadly, all would have to go away into their box and be put up in the loft to wait until next Christmas. I'd have to take the decorative fronds of ivy now spread over the top of the stable, which was really only a carton covered with foil inside and out, to the compost heap. The little Christmas lights, too, which had lit up the lovely scene, would have to go carefully away with all the rest.

The three gentile kings came from afar, from further to the east beyond Palestine, following a star. They were gentiles, (that's to say not Jews), looking for a king, bringing gifts for him. They brought gold for his kingship, frankincense as a sign of their worship and myrrh for anointing his dead body.

There's so much meaning hidden in this story. so much that's mysterious. That's why I loved to stand and stare for minutes on end, neglecting my household jobs. Here were kings looking for a king to whom, when they found him, they would offer kingly gifts. Then, after following the guiding star, they came to a Baby for whom such gifts were outwardly unsuitable. But we know how fitting they were to become. Jesus truly a king though not of this world. Jesus certainly the object of our worship always, and Jesus crucified and his body anointed with myrrh.

When I'd made these necessary alterations I went to write letters at my desk. Through the sitting room window I watched a flock of chaffinches. For the last week or so they'd been feeding on the stubble in the fields which spread out below our garden and beyond the Long Wood to the loch. Suddenly amongst all the familiar chaffinches I saw a bird with a white rump. That's what I'd been hoping for all winter. There it was at last, a brambling. I called to Nicholas who was working, as usual, at his own desk across the room at another window with a different view. He was pleased for me.

"Well done," he said, but he was not enthusiastic enough to get up and look for himself.

Then I thought about Epiphany again.

'I have sent you to be a light to the Gentiles, that you may bring salvation to the uttermost parts of the earth. And when the Gentiles heard this, they were glad and glorified the word of God.'

I thought about the uttermost parts of the earth. That means ourselves, for we on this island are very much at one far end of the old known world. Christ has been given to us as a light. How fortunate we are. I hoped we'd be glad about this and that we would, too, glorify the word of God.

That evening Nicholas and I drove into Strathlyon for the Eucharist at St Andrew's. It was a peaceful, happy service. The choir sang cheerfully, and we joined in, creating an atmosphere of rejoicing. The lights shone brightly over us all, it was not a time for gloom.

"Happy Epiphany," said Edward afterwards to us, to our best friends Jane and Jack and to everybody.

2

"Happy Epiphany," we all replied.

Yes, it really was something to be happy about, I thought to myself as we drove home through a light snow shower. If it weren't for Epiphany we wouldn't be here. If the Jews had kept Christ all for themselves, there wouldn't be this marvellous Christian heritage all around us. But that couldn't have been. He was meant for people for all time. It would have been even better though if the Jews had also believed in him. Afterwards, later on, of course. The worldly establishment of Jews and Romans had to fulfil itself by causing the death of Jesus so we should understand that his kingdom was not of this world.

"Not many people came to the service," said Nicholas after we'd driven through the almost deserted town and over the bridge towards home.

"People don't understand," I replied. "They don't understand, for one thing, how important Epiphany is to them. They don't think of themselves as being far flung gentiles as you and I do. They don't feel any motivation to come out on a winter weekday evening for a lovely Eucharist with everyone giving thanks with full hearts. They don't know what they're missing."

"That's true," said Nicholas. "And it doesn't matter in a way. It's the fact that the service happened that's important."

I went on thinking to myself. We'd been to a Mass and so had helped increase the Holy Spirit's presence in the world. In fact, I decided, if one thought about it, the Spirit is going out over all the world from every church all the time. Often, when I went into St Andrew's on a weekday, I saw people praying rather than just staring and admiring. Probably some were praying even when they looked as if they were just walking around. It's difficult for some people to kneel down and pray if they're not used to it. I used to be like that.

"Jack read the Epistle very well," said Nicholas as we turned off the main road into the single track lane which led through the fields to Ardness.

"Jack always reads well. Not only do you easily hear every word, but he doesn't just begin at the beginning and end at the end, the whole thing has a shape and the sense develops as he goes along."

"And that's not an easy bit of Paul."

3

"It isn't. I like the unsearchable riches of Christ though."

I went on musing to myself. From experience I knew Nicholas wouldn't really see the point if I'd thought aloud. I could see the unsearchable riches meant there were so many riches in existence that, however long or hard we searched, we would never find them all. It was this lovely old language which in fact works marvellously, in spite of what's often said about it. And I thought especially of the last sentence of all in the Epistle: 'In whom we have boldness and access with confidence through our faith in him.' I said to myself it means that, because of our faith, we can be bold enough and confident enough to come to God. We've access to him, we can, even must, overcome our natural diffidence. Paul is often good in what he says, he puts some things so clearly and he gives the right amount of emphasis you can't miss his point, even, or especially, in the old translation. Though I must say that sometimes he is, or his translators can be, rather discouragingly difficult to understand.

EPIPHANY: RESOLUTIONS

The next day, in the afternoon, I was walking along the lane that led out of Ardness to the west, beyond our house. I was on my own, a preferred state of affairs when I was wandering slowly along on one of my favourite walks. On my left was what Nicholas and I called The Wood, as it was nearer our house than any other of the local woods, the Long Wood for example. Most of its trees were tall oaks, though in places a sprinkling of birches lightened the more open parts with their white trunks. On that day at the beginning of the year of course, all the trees were bare of leaves but they were still beautifully interesting, their intertwining twigs and branches silhouetted against the sky and, lower down, nearer my own height, overlapping each other away into the distance. On my right on the other side of the road was a large field with only a few sheep, quiet creamy-grey Cheviots, munching the wintry grass. The day was one of those comfortable non-days which I loved; they came often in the winter, there, dispersed among several wet or stormy ones: no wind, no sun, no frost, no rain nor any other kind of precipitation, not even any damp misty fog.

As well as my body, my mind was wandering on in its usual vague way too, when, after a bit, I found myself again considering my New Year Resolutions. Edward our rector had by then been with us for nearly two years and he had made a great difference to the way I thought about such things. It's easy to have lots of ambitious ideas on this subject, especially at that time of year, but unless those ideas are carefully thought out, they don't carry one on through all the following twelve months. They get forgotten at the end of March or so. Disappointment and discouragement are no spur to progress. My resolutions were basically meant to leave me at the end of the year a better person than at the beginning, a better person for God. Therefore they had to be possible, within the possibility of achievement, not too grand. It was more helpful too if they included something practical, something I could visualize, and then as the months went past I might see myself growing into a noticeably different person. I'd have changed for the better.

5

I began to wonder about what outward changes there might be in our lives this coming year. If life were to be different, would it be for good or bad? Would it change for all of us or for some, or for only one of us, for Nicholas or myself or for either of the boys, Philip or John, or their families? Or, if life this coming year in a general way were to be not all that very different from this last one, which of my resolutions would turn out in the end to have been successful? I'd always wanted, even in past years, even in my uncertain-about-God years, to be able to love God more, to pray more from the heart, with more of my heart involved: I'd wanted to be able to praise God more, to remember more often to be thankful for all he had done for me and for all those I loved. This, I hoped, should bring me a chance of some success at least in a small way, for we are told, I remembered, in a collect (which one is it?) that, when we ask for such things as please God, we shall obtain our petitions. And so then presumably when a resolution is successfully accomplished we'll know we have asked for something good.

Resolutions, I was thinking, shouldn't be too vague or there may be nothing achieved. They should be definable in only a few words. I must try again to be nicer to everybody and especially to awkward people, that's to say those I found awkward. It was often most difficult to be so. I had to remember that difficult people are basically like myself (well, not like myself, that was the trouble, but they were people all the same). They were probably awkward only in my view of them, they were probably struggling to cope with life's problems in their own way just as I was in mine. It wasn't their fault they annoyed me and I probably annoyed them. In fact in some cases I knew I did. I wasn't really a very nice person, that's another trouble. Also, anyway, as we were taught to do, we did need to pray for our enemies as well as for our friends, though mostly those I knew well were not really my enemies. I didn't think I actually had any enemies of my own, it was those who made Nicholas's life difficult whom I was inclined to think of as enemies.

I'd by this time come to a gate on my left where I turned down into the wood, half hoping to see a woodcock. Mary-next-door had seen one earlier in the week when she too had walked through the wood with Boofie and Blot, her Jack Russell terriers, and they had put one up. (Blot's name came from her having a large black patch in the middle of her back and Mary-down-the-road was sure all the buzzards she saw were harriers).

I thought it was interesting that last year, after I'd persuaded myself to begin to pray for my so-called enemies, I really had found them much easier to meet and much more satisfactory to chat to than before, easier than I had imagined they would be. These difficult people had become friendlier and my conversations with them much more relaxed. I'd felt much better about them altogether, though of course their changing for the better might have had nothing to do with my praying for them but with praying for myself. Very likely it was due to my own changing that I saw them differently.

Also I discovered that now, when some of my so-called enemies had some good luck come to them, I found I was really pleased. I could remember wanting my enemies to be miserable, but after I'd begun to pray for them they seemed to be brought over more onto my side as it were and I'd begun to be able to wish them well. It was very mysterious how all this happened but I certainly felt much happier about my enemies than I'd used to.

I never saw a woodcock that afternoon, nor any bird at all - woods are generally very empty in the winter - until I'd got back into the garden where tits and chaffinches and a robin were feeding on the food we'd put out for them. That's a job we did every morning all winter through. It seemed important to remember the hungry birds and the cold weather in that part of the world's going on for many weeks longer than we'd ever expected. Spring was always long in coming, it forgot our progress through the months on the calendar. Some winters we saw only our old bird friends, or more likely their descendants, but other years in December or January we were thrilled to see a blackcap feeding on the seed, though its visit never last more than a few days. I wished we might be going to see one that winter but we had not been lucky so far. I found it odd that rare birds were exciting. But then I realized that their presence is an event, a good event, and therefore welcome and one can't help rejoicing.

On my return I didn't go directly into the house but walked through the nearer parts of the garden to admire the jasmine and viburnums and other early flowering shrubs such as the witchhazel and the winter flowering cherry. Every one of these was giving a better show, I thought, than they had done any winter before. This was natural really as the bushes and trees were all becoming more adult, better grown in their habits. I saw also the little green shoots of muscari popping up through the soil and the white buds of snowdrops soon to be opening if we didn't have a sudden snowy or frosty spell to set them back. I tried not to notice the weeds, mostly awkward persistent docks and dandelions, and the general overgrownness of odd patches all around. I made myself concentrate firmly on looking only at the encouraging and exciting signs of spring.

Then I went indoors and soon Nicholas came up from the bottom of the garden where he'd been cutting down and clearing up the gorse, bracken and suchlike 'weeds', the countryside invading the garden, which needed strong action. We had a welcome cup of tea by the fire and then I settled down in my comfy chair to read a book on prayer which Father Lyall had lent me. He was our young curate, a deacon still, very keen on his job with us at St Andrew's. He'd already a collection of what I thought would be very helpful books and I'd begun by borrowing this one.

Straightaway it made me think of an on-going resolution I'd had, not specially this New Year but more a perpetual intention, of not eating or drinking too much, not more than I needed, and above all not indulging myself generally. This problem was always much on my mind. I'd decided long ago that I was a naturally greedy person, but would God help me? However much I indulged myself it would make no difference to the happiness of the world in general. On the other hand I though he might feel somewhat involved in my ideas for improving my moral strength as one might call it. I was then and still am a very feeble person in that direction I'm afraid.

However, in this book I was reading, I was encouraged to learn that with more experience we should be able to pray for bigger as well as for smaller things. As our heart grew stronger we would begin to have enough love to pray for such big things as the peace of the world, and (very important for me) we should also discover that the smaller things were not too trivial for God to help us with.

I thought: well, that's good news. At the same time I wasn't certain that God would really help my greed to go away. It could be that he didn't want me to be cured of it. Perhaps like St Paul I was meant to have my weakness, then I couldn't boast. I couldn't be self-righteous. Not that I in any way raised myself up to St Paul's grand level. Also in being stuck with a sin as down to earth as being feeble-minded about food and drink, I should all the better understand other people's struggles with their sins. Of course St Paul's weakness is thought to have been something seriously handicapping, whereas my indulging myself is of minimum importance and could soon be overcome if I would only develop enough motivation.

EPIPHANY: THE DASHWOODS

Nicholas is a Dashwood which after all looks and sounds like an English name and his father had originally come to Seaborough from the Midlands. His mother's family however had come from the northeast, my father's from Scotland and my mother's from Ireland; her father's name was Smith which might come from anywhere. Our fathers had worked in Seaborough so we were born there and thought, if we thought about it at all, of ourselves as 'mixed' rather than English.

When Nicholas retired from his engineering firm we decided to go to live somewhere that would be a real change, somewhere for the first time of our own choosing. After all when one's young one lives with one's parents and later on near one's work, and up till that year Nicholas and I had spent all our married life at Westlake, a few miles along the Irish Sea coast from Seaborough. Now that our parents were no longer alive and our boys grown up and married, no longer needing us to be near them, we were free to live anywhere. We thought of Scotland mainly because we had so much enjoyed ourselves on holiday there and we knew even the Highlands could be reached by car in a day. (It soon took an even shorter day as the motorways grew). So when finally after a long search we chose to build a new house at Ardness near Strathlyon where there are miles and miles of beautiful and exciting surroundings in every direction we knew that we wouldn't be out of reach of the family.

This consists of two boys, Philip and John. They were then both in their early forties, and both married. Philip to Joyce with two young boys and John to Christine with a boy and a girl about the same age. The two fathers were settled in their jobs, Philip worked for the Northnat Bank, not behind the counter but with the care and organisation of buildings, the equipment of branches, security and suchlike which involved him in quite a lot of travelling. John worked for British Electricity at a power station at Quince. He did shift work and so had lots of daylight hours to spend how he wished at home. The two boys lived only about twenty miles apart, Philip in a leafy inland village and John still by the sea at Westlake where he'd been born.

"They don't need us to be living near them any more," said Nicholas. "They'll get on much better without our interfering. We can go and see them every year." And we usually did at least once, though usually in the spring, and they both came up to see us sometime during every summer, though not both families at once, I'm glad to say. I'm not marvellously good with young children. I never have been, much preferring them when they're old enough for fairly sensible conversation and I suppose Nicholas is much the same. So I didn't feel I was depriving them or myself of much when we left them for the north.

At Ardness, a small place to the north-west of Strathlyon, we found some new bungalows being built. These were much more suitable for us than the old manses or unwanted grotty crofts needing conversion which were what we had up till then mostly been offered. So we were the first people to live in our house, which was built in an embryonic garden on a steep slope with a lovely view. We called it Whinside after the mass of gorse which, when we first arrived, grew all down the garden in between a few young birch trees. There were tiny seedlings and larger ones up to enormous old craggy, bent and overgrown bushes. One of the first jobs was to remove as many as possible, also a few of the trees so as not to block our view as they grew up. Gorse is lovely to look at but not to live with or share a garden with and it was some descendants of these original bushes that had been occupying Nicholas while I was out on my walk.

Although we were living right in the country, with wonderful views to the west and south-west and almost no other houses in sight, it took only about fifteen minutes in the car for us to reach the centre of Strathlyon. There was first of all a narrow lane between fields of oats or sheep or unoccupied grass, then came a dash down the main road and finally in a more leisurely way we crossed the river into the town. It wasn't the sort of country we'd experienced on our Scottish holidays. I'd been expecting to live closely surrounded by heather and mountains, bracken and real dashing streams, the wild and exciting country which had made for us a real change from our flat, seaside homeland. From our Whinside windows we could see the mountains but they were quite a few miles away, not just at arms' length, and the dashing streams weren't visible at all though we knew they were there.

11

Ardness itself wasn't a village but just a collection of old farms and crofts and small modern houses like our own scattered over quite a large area of fields and small woods.

Ours was the last in a narrow lane which led on to The Wood. The garden faced south-west and was very informal, not demanding much of our attention after the first hectic year or two of tidying and planting. We left quite a lot of it to nature so all that we needed to do in later years to keep it under control was a little gentle pottering. (Apart that is from the grass-cutting in the summer months which took a lot of Nicholas's spare energy, though various modern implements helped him a lot). In spite of the slope we had a small patio below the house where we could sit out in the sun and relax. That's to say until in the high summer the temperature shot up into the 90s and we had to retreat into the shade on the other side of the house and sit on the front door step.

Strathlyon was not only our nearest town but the county town of Cairndhu and consequently the most important place for many miles around. We found it very pleasant and enjoyed our visits there, usually twice on a Sunday to church and on one other day for shopping. The centre was elegantly spacious with wide roads running along both sides of the river Lyon. There were fine old trees, mostly limes, along its banks and often there were fishermen with great long waving rods standing in their waders thigh deep in the rushing water.

The town was also the centre of the Diocese of Cairndhu which covers a great area of mountains as well as much farming country. Here members of the Old Church in Scotland, to which we soon discovered we belonged, could find St Mary's, the Cathedral, and two other churches, St Columba's and St Andrew's. (This last was the one we eventually chose as our own). There were many more churches of many other denominations, but they don't affect my story.

EPIPHANY: THE MORLANDS

Just as breakfast was finished a day or two later, the phone rang. It often rang at this hour of the day for Nicholas, for at that time people knew he might most surely be got hold of. That morning, though, it was Jane ringing for me, just to tell me that I'd better not go over to see her that day as we had arranged, because workmen were coming to work on two or three windows that had been leaking and she thought she'd better be there with them on their own.

Jane and Jack Morland were two of the friends who'd encouraged us to come to St Andrew's church. Jack had been a farmer, but was now retired, though still working as a consultant, and this pleasant job took him all around the country. Both he and Jane had been born and spent most of their lives in Isla, in the Diocese of St Fergus away to the east. On Jack's retiring, they'd come westwards to enjoy the gentler weather. They had bought an old farmhouse, Drummore, near Easter Kilcoy on the far side of the river Lyon from ourselves but still not so far away we couldn't visit each other quite easily. Which we often did, and as I would have done that day if Jane had not rung.

I was very fond of Jane, and I still am. She was the kind of person I would rather like to have been if I could have chosen. She was artistic and yet not scatterbrained. In fact she was a very organized person, her house was very well run, everything happened at the right time without any apparent fuss. Drummore was a very comfortable old house and not a bit inconvenient. Everything was beautiful and welcoming. Their furniture wasn't startlingly new, neither was it old and shabby, but chosen primarily for long-lasting comfort. On the walls there were lovely pictures, old and modern, some painted by Jane or the uncles and aunts of her artistic family. I always felt happy when I was there, some houses are like that. There were usually jolly flowers in Jane's house, just a small bunch or two even in the winter. She loved them and often painted them. At Whinside, in contrast, I hardly ever had any at all. This was mostly, though, not because I didn't like them around me but so often I would forget to look after them and I'd suddenly find a vaseful of droopy flowers with smelly

13

water in it or no water at all. I much preferred plants in pots as they were less fussy about being forgotten for two or three days at a time.

I had soon got to know Jane. She had a very simple and certain religious faith which appealed to me. From the moment we became friends she did me a tremendous amount of good. She had from her youngest memories always believed in God, in Jesus and in the Holy Spirit. She doesn't remember anything else, any conversion from another belief or non-belief, so what she did believe was securely part of her basic self. In a way her religion was a bit like Nicholas's, it was in her nature, but *her* nature was quiet and accepting, totally different from his. She took change as it came and hoped to accustom herself to it, whereas Nicholas had a hidden fieriness which burst out from time to time. He would fight for his God who was for him the same yesterday, today and tomorrow, as also should be his church, unchanging and secure.

Jane didn't, unlike me, even now, spend her life looking for questions and answers, she was content to accept what was already in her heart. Therefore she was never either overwhelmingly happy with new-found love and faith, or, a week or month later, fall into a mood of despondency. She was younger than myself by a few years, but that was no drawback to her being a great help to me. In lots of ways she seemed older, an anchor of steady kindness, someone who listened, and would do so for ever to any problems and discoveries I had. She'd often encouraged and cheered me up when necessary, but mostly she just listened calmly. I admired that marvellous calmness, it was real and deep.

Jack, on the other hand, was, I thought, a very difficult person to describe. He was really just a very good person, full stop, just the sort of man to suit Jane. He was kind and intelligent and capable and yet not stuffy. In fact he was very good company and he got on well with Nicholas and vice versa, which was helpful all round. I know he was constantly setting the world to rights, but then aren't we all, or we'd like to?

They had two children, David and Prue, who'd arrived comparatively late in Jane's life. David was, at the time I'm writing about, a well-off bachelor and seemed content to be so. He worked for a firm of stockbrokers in London, and shared a flat with a friend. Prue was brainy too, she'd won a scholarship to read history at Oxford. Then before she got there she'd fallen in love with, to her, a charming young man who'd suddenly whisked her off into the unknown. Jack and Jane heard nothing for some weeks, and when at last they had, Prue'd announced that she'd decided not to go to Oxford, but would be living with Martin and they would soon be getting married.

Jane, naturally, had wanted to dash off at once to see Prue, but Jack persuaded her to wait a little while. In the end she did go. She'd found them living in a minute gloomy flat in the south of London. Martin was indeed charming. Prue was working, she was bright enough to get a job any time she wanted. Martin was not working so he organised the food, visited the launderette and so on. No, they were not yet married. Jane hoped they never would be, which was, in her, a victory for common sense over principle. She felt Martin's charm was not backed by any depth of personality, which in the end must make him an unsatisfactory companion for a whole lifetime, especially for Prue. She returned home in no way more satisfied than before she'd left, except that she'd seen her beloved daughter and found she was still well in body even if confused in mind and spirit.

EPIPHANY: EDWARD'S ARRIVAL

As soon as we came to Strathlyon we were made especially welcome by members of the Old Church in Scotland and went to St Margaret's at Dunmarkie, a lovely oldish church in an oldish, small and unspoiled town a few miles to the north of Ardness. We chose this because we'd met the rector when we'd been here on holiday and he, in his normal kindly way, came along to say hello and invite us to join his congregation. It was a friendly church, everyone was kind to us, and, after two or three years there, Nicholas was chosen to be People's Warden, whose not very arduous duties he'd very much enjoyed. He was often able to help people with their non-religious problems, the more practical ones, and we thought of ourselves as quite settled there. Then the rector, still a youngish man, felt a call to be a missionary and he went off quite suddenly to Papua New Guinea. One couldn't argue with him about the idea. His leaving seemed a compulsion which had come from his inner nature, not to have been imposed from outside by anyone or even by anything he had read.

"I'm sure it was right for him," I remember saying at the time. We hadn't tried to dissuade him, but it was hard for us all the same. It's always upsetting to have unwanted, unexpected changes.

After this, we found ourselves making more friends in Strathlyon itself, and, at the same time, beginning to feel restless at St Margaret's. The new rector, a few months after his institution, had begun to make changes, one of which was to replace, though gradually at first, the old Liturgy with the new. This much upset Nicholas who was especially conservative in his religion. On his arrival in the Highlands he had not taken long to get used to the Scottish Grey Book, which contained, on the whole, the familiar words of the Book of Common Prayer and it was easy for him to adapt himself. If one had tried to simplify the BCP 1662 service without seriously altering the language one would have produced something very like the Grey Book. He could not see himself ever getting used to the strange, awkward and rather bare bleak language of the new Blue Book. How, he thought, could these very ordinary words in short sentences ever express the greatness and glory of God and his love for us and all those other holy truths? For

Nicholas, and for many others too it appeared, these truths needed a noble and rather special language.

So, after some hesitation, we decided to leave St Margaret's and go to St Andrew's in Strathlyon itself, where the Grey Book was still used and seemed likely to be so for some time, or even, one hoped, indefinitely. In most other ways too, things were done there in the traditional manner.

Both of us were relieved to make the change. We soon felt at home and were even becoming good friends with our new rector. We had much in common with him, not least our ages. He was a true father to his flock, who loved him in return, and he much enjoyed his pastoral duties and seemed in no hurry to retire. Then, suddenly, he received the offer of a small house in the old cathedral city in England where he had spent his boyhood and in a few months he too was gone.

I couldn't help thinking that although some changes are helpful and interesting and for the better, others are disruptive to one's peace of mind. Here we were having another change in our church just as we had changed our church. I was sorry about this, for I'd been quite happy and contented with how things had been turning out. But it's often no good not doing one's best to adapt, to wait patiently for things to settle down again. It might after all turn out to be all for the better. However disturbed one feels at first, not all changes are for the worse in the end. .

Before the appointment of a new rector was decided upon, though, there was another alteration in our lives. The long-standing and experienced St Andrew's treasurer left Strathlyon for a new job in Aberdeveron in the St Fergus diocese, and Nicholas was elected his successor.

When we'd first moved up from Westlake, Nicholas has been still secretary to a sailing association, the Swift Owners. The Swift was a small sailing boat, a cabin cruiser, which, in spite of its name, was not very fast but very suitable and safe for beginners and families. He'd enjoyed the administrative side of the work and also writing to and hearing from owners from all over the world. He'd been able to use the organising skills he'd learned in the practical world of engineering, he was able in clear, simple language to explain the details of arranging all the equipment of the boat and the manoeuvres of sailing it. Also he could do all this from his home wherever that might be, Westlake or Ardness.

On his seventieth birthday, however, he decided that a mostly young person's sailing association should have a younger secretary, and he handed all over to the present owner of his old Swift, a bright young man in his early forties not overdone with work. And so he was suddenly free to look around for another voluntary job, something to fill up his time and be an interest to him as well as of benefit to others though not necessarily in a grand way. And he didn't have long to wait.

It seemed to me that almost straightaway, almost too quickly, he was pounced on. He was asked to be Treasurer of St Andrew's.

"It's too good to be true," said one of the St Andrew's congregation, "that your husband should be free, just when we need him."

So Nicholas took over as treasurer and, finding things not altogether well organised, gradually through the next months brought in a more intelligent and useful routine of work and administration. It was a challenge and hard work, but he was the sort of person who dislikes boredom more.

"Nothing to do, nothing to get your teeth into, that's a terrible thing. What's better than a challenge, if it's within possibility of achievement. It's a spice for life."

During this same time, the choice of our new rector was proceeding very slowly, but in the end the name of Edward Rankin was heard in the parish for the first time. He had come to Strathlyon a month or two before just for the day from Eaglesburgh, to preach at a Society of Mary service, held at St Columba's. Nicholas, and not only he, remembered this priest and his very good sermon. Up to that time his name had been quite unknown to most of us, but now we were wondering why we had never thought of him before. Why should we not invite him to be rector of St Andrew's? Would he come? That became the question.

Father Rankin, now known to all as Edward, was also at first uncertain of the answer, but after a few days of hesitation he decided to accept.

"I thought at the time," he told us later, "that not only would it be a real change from the Lowlands to the Highlands, but from a capital city to a county town. A different atmosphere. Also it would be a change from my being one priest amongst many to one of only three. Anyway after ten years in one church it's possible that it's about time for a change. And there's always the challenge, too, of making St Andrew's a more shining example of what a church can be. I was hopeful!"

In many ways Edward was rather a dark horse. Nicholas was beginning to wonder if we were doing the right thing. Whomever he spoke to or wrote to, each had something different to say, sometimes good, sometimes less so. Nowadays I laugh at myself when I think of this mystery man. He who became one of our best friends and a much needed and much loved spiritual guide.

"No more a dark horse, he's as clear as daylight, at least he is to me."

So Father Rankin, that's to say, Edward, came to Strathlyon and then began those interesting years. He was about the same age as Philip and John and so communication with him came naturally to Nicholas and myself; not straightaway of course but easily and almost imperceptibly. We talked to him, we discussed things with him, we asked his advice, we laughed with him, and moaned and groaned with him, just as if he were one of the family. I needn't have worried that this change might have been for the worse or even been awkward or difficult.

Gradually, though we hardly realized it at first, St Andrew's did change from a rather struggling parish with a rather complacent and uninterested congregation into one which took a pride in itself. It hadn't seemed such a rundown church at the time, though when I looked back on it all from later I saw many things in the buildings or even in the services which had been not so good or even awful. Lots of people, as well as ourselves, began to have bright ideas and even to put them to work, and with Edward's encouragement and Nicholas's financial sense, we began to achieve much we would previously have thought impossible; we were successful beyond our imagining.

I remember Nicholas's saying, when he was hesitating about taking on the treasurer's job, that he'd never done anything in that way before. He'd been an engineer which is, outwardly at least, a very different type of occupation. One is a practical and active affair, using objects in one's hands, the other static, though the two do meet somewhere in the middle, and managing money even in his old job was always important to Nicholas.

Fortunately he had been brought up in a family of very keen church people, his father had been a much revered churchwarden in Seaborough, and his mother was a daughter of the vicarage. My parents on the other hand had been only what I should call token Christians. Going to church on Sundays was a thing only other people did. The Sunday papers and Sunday lunch were the highlights of the day.

Perhaps because of this, even from a child I'd been restless and dissatisfied with the shape of life. There never seemed to be any serious point, or aim, or goal, or whatever I felt there should be in a life. Each day followed the one before but they were not joined by any strong thread which could have brought a feeling of purpose, something to draw me on, something to give every effort a point. I'd often hoped to find a guide, someone who would orientate my efforts, but I never had.

Later on, after the tensions of the war and the years of living with two small exhausting boys, things had become easier in many ways. At last we had more time to look about us. Nicholas had always been looking forward to having more time for the church and by the time we came up to Strathlyon it had become again an important part of his life. He had become enthusiastic, and even I found more time and energy to enjoy going to services with him, services which I found on the whole not over-boring.

All the same, up to the time of Edward's arrival, I was still a very doubting person. I loved reading about THINGS, about the basic things of life and what was to come after. I wasn't, and am still not, a student of theology, or at least I've never thought of myself as one. A theologian would hardly have forgotten all his Latin, or never learned any Greek, not even the alphabet. But I'd always felt the need to learn about God. He must be the most important Person we do need to learn about. I knew I must do this so I could learn truly to love him and then life *would* have a purpose. 'Religion in man is everything' I read in

20

one of Dr. Mascall's books that Edward lent me a month or two after his coming to Strathlyon.

After Nicholas became treasurer and Edward had arrived at St Andrew's, the days seemed to fly past, Nicholas was always busy with church affairs, or the garden, or his other interest, the local scouts, of whose leaders he was chairman. My own outward interests and activities had always been more diffuse, rather nameless, disconnected one from the other, not obviously important, rather hard to describe, usually existing in bursts of enthusiasm followed by periods of great forgetfulness and lack of interest. I always felt it was easier to tell people what I didn't do rather than what I did. I never did, and still don't, help with the food needed at the church, (usually a taken-for-granted woman's role), I still don't know how the tea urns work, nor could I ever construct an empire biscuit nor make the cream and jam stay inside their scone. I don't knit any longer. I don't sew except the minimum of mending, my needle always unthreads itself or the thread ties itself into hopeless knots. I don't enjoy cleaning the house. I enjoy gardening only up to a point - the point being when the weather outside becomes too cold or too hot. But I write the notices for the St Andrew's notice boards. I do enjoy that, though it doesn't sound very much. And I enjoy looking at birds, though that's not *doing* anything, it's only watching. And I love taking photos of the wonderful scenery that's all around us. Anybody could do these things, except perhaps the notices. But that's not a difficult skill, it's only a knack. And I love reading, but not silly books, they must be something nourishing and well-written. And I'm still glad I don't want to be a woman priest. Worship of God is fine, it's basic, but I'm not temperamentally suited to leading others to do so. Anyway it's an impossible proposition, women as priests. Entirely mistaken, I would have thought. and it's not that I've not thought about it quite a lot.

EPIPHANY: BETTY'S STORY

It seems a good idea at this point in my story to explain a bit about myself. After all if it weren't for what happened to me there would be no story at all.

I was telling you why we'd changed our church and gone from St Margaret's in Dunmarkie to St Andrew's in Strathlyon. Somewhat naturally after all these changes I was even more unsettled than I might otherwise have been, hesitating in my ideas about God and what I could or would or should include in my concept of him. I'd begun to feel a bit differently about life. What I believed and didn't believe had taken on a new importance for me. I'd begun to puzzle about my soul, if it were my soul I was thinking about; I wasn't even sure about basic things, and I could come to no satisfactory solution.

If I could have seen more clearly what was happening to me, if I'd have stood back, or forward, or away, or at any rate outside myself somewhere; if that had been possible I might have been able to see where I was going. I could remember the years when I believed almost nothing, except, rather vaguely, in God. But at the same time it was my ambition to be a person of great faith and devotion to him. I used to try to involve God in my life, but it was like talking to someone on a long distance phone call. Was he, I used to worry, making me wait for the moment he would choose to come to me or let me come to him? If so, why was he waiting? And if that moment was to come, when would it be? All that sounds very contradictory and I couldn't help feeling this contradiction. So all that time, the time I'm writing about, I used to be a hopelessly doubting person, and yet I was longing to have a firm faith like Nicholas had, or Jane. Though of course I didn't know Jane at that time. Her example came to me later at some unrecognised moment. However a change did begin in me, very slowly at first, and since then such marvellous and good things have happened. The best of which has been my growing to believe that it's true that Jesus is Christ, the Son of God, and himself God, from all time, he who became one of us.

Gradually at first it happened; but in the end quite suddenly, in a rush, the real believing, what I'd been hoping for all those years, arrived. This great and exciting dawning, the true light, came into my soul after a great long time of darkness. A long and dreary night was followed by a real dawn. And this understanding is still growing in me. The long time it took is really what confused me - my coming to believe didn't happen in one clear-cut moment, as it had to St Paul for instance, but was spread out over several months, even over several years; though the final moment of realization was an event I remember still.

I was alone in the house one evening. Nicholas had gone to a Vestry meeting at St Andrew's rectory in Strathlyon. Should I put on a record, I wondered, and try to think, or would I think better in silence? I'd try some music anyway. I felt I needed to understand in what order everything had happened. Life had been indeed very exciting but I'd found it difficult to understand. I'd come through to feeling very different from how I'd ever felt before.

I chose Elgar's first symphony. I love this, there are some lovely tunes in it. I didn't concentrate on the music. It wasn't unfamiliar or demanding, but more on my problem. In what way or ways did I feel changed? Could I remember how I'd come to be changed? I remembered I'd long been a searching kind of person, wondering about what might be called eternal truths. I'd been baptised and confirmed into the Church of England, so naturally I'd turned there first of all, but had found nothing definitely helpful and I became rather lost and confused. I didn't feel I was being led along a path to anywhere. I realized after some thought that it wasn't so much the fault of the church but rather of the times we were living in. All through our school days we'd been taught to use our brains, our intelligence, when weighing things up. Feelings were frowned on, rather neglected. In this way, so we were taught, we girls might be able to show ourselves as equals to those boys, our brothers, (only I didn't have any brothers). But after I'd left school all this was more or less forgotten. My father wouldn't let me train for a job and I wasn't brave enough to break out as one would nowadays. He expected me to become a wife and enjoy housekeeping which actually it's not my nature to be or do). Though my younger sister escaped. The difference of two years and a brighter temperament were a great help to her. Feeble minded are words I often apply to myself. I can see now it was with my brain I'd always been searching for God's love and of course I found nothing very much to encourage me, to help me with my life.

As I've said, I wasn't brought up in a religious family. I'd never seen, close at hand, religious faith in action. Such an idea was always away to one side, something I knew existed but wasn't in touch with. At school I couldn't help absorbing the beauty of the chapel, the words and music of Matins and Evensong and the excitement every Sunday of anthems whose music seemed to come directly down from heaven, and carols in the weeks before Christmas. I loved the carols especially, but that's not faith in action, it's on the fringe, not basic, it's a lovely decoration to one of the high points in the Church's year. This holy music, all the same, left a strong impression on me, a memory which has lasted even to this day. Even if parish carols can never equal school carols in personal commitment or perfection of performance, they still move me. Does this explain anything?

In all the long years between my growing up and our children's growing up, my energy was spent mostly in looking after them, trying to do as much as possible as well as possible on as little money as possible. And coping with rationing. Thanksgiving is due still to our good fortune of not being actually starved as others were. I wasn't really a strong enough person for all this. I suppose my being so busy with family life left me high and dry so far as religion was concerned. Each day rushed past with little time and no energy to spare for contemplation. I can see clearly now that I was in need of another dimension in life which would wake up the depths of my soul and nourish me when it was awakened. But I had no idea how to begin to find such a thing as my depths. Nor had I any idea where to look for any outside help.

Always, since I could remember, I'd believed all things to have been made by God. He is God the Creator of everything. He made heaven and earth, the stars, the universe, all animals and plants and rocks, and, to do this he must have invented chemistry and physics and biology and of course mathematics, not forgetting astronomy with its bent space and black holes and quasars and all things not yet discovered. I could see we were here on this wonderful, beautiful, terrible world which *is*.

It exists; we can see it, hear it, feel it, we are part of it, it has been made, and the Mind or the Spirit which made it I called God. I believed all that. It seemed and seems still, so clear to me that we and everything around us has been created by this Mind or Spirit which must exist in another dimension from ourselves. We can only partly comprehend who or what we are trying to grasp. I have been, ever since I can remember, very enthusiastic about all this. I loved the world, or perhaps I mean the earth, all nature and the natural scenery around us. But I wasn't content. I was still searching for the key to it all, the source of all truth. This would be for me the answer to everything, the reason for everything.

One day, a few years after we'd come to Ardness, I'd realized I was no longer very enthusiastic about anything. This gave me a shock. It was as if I'd stopped reacting to anything. I seemed to be moving about in a world of cardboard figures and I myself was one of them. Well, maybe it wasn't as bad as that. Outwardly, I probably seemed just as keen on life as I'd been before. We, Nicholas and I, worked with great energy to create our garden out of a gorse-covered slope, we explored all the roads for miles around in every direction, days which kept the eyes open to the glory of the earth. All of this was excellent, though it could be, and it was, detached from any still-existing inner life. Occasionally I would look back and remember the self I had been who used to mind about people and things. I didn't understand why I had changed so much for the worse, why I had lost almost all feeling.

Perhaps, I thought, I was suffering from old age. I felt like one of those old shrivelled-up potatoes I'd often found at the bottom of the sack in the garage in March or April. I used to go to church every Sunday with Nicholas. He was thoroughly involved there spiritually and practically, and I was always hoping I might become so too. Even if I'd been on my own I think I should have felt the need for a church anyway, for I seemed to realize with part of myself, my unthinking self, that my hope lay there, even such a wobbly hope as my mind was able to produce. I found there a kind of basic nourishment. When I look back from where I am now, as I'm writing this, I can see that the Bread and the Wine were, every week, slowly joining me to the body of Christ and helping in my eventual rescue. It's true, I'm sure, that the Bread and Wine can work in us at a level below our consciousness, below our realization.

I read lots of books, a few brought hope, showing me that life for some people was full of love for God; life which for that reason, was exciting and worthwhile; the authors' or their subjects' hearts were beating with faith and hope and love. Many helpful books appeared to fall off the library shelf into my hands, it was magical. It seemed to be myself who chose them.

One day, in one of these books, I learned that having doubts about the place of Jesus in Christianity is not really a bar to becoming a Christian. Doubts could be respectable even in those who claimed to belong already to the Church. I was still looking for logical reasons for everything, imagining I could be intellectual about God, and, because of this, I had doubts by the hundred. It was very helpful to read that doubts were, as one might say, OK, that total belief in the creed wasn't necessary. (certainly not for beginners). I was encouraged. The author of this book, himself a bishop, was not without his own doubts. I'm not sure I could read this book now. It's lack of commitment would dismay me, which might be a sign that God did have a part in my choice of books and the timing of their arrival in my hands.

Shortly after this time a famous theologian was consecrated bishop of an important see and made the first of his famous pronouncements. Both these two bishops seemed to be saying, 'Look at us. We have doubts and look where we've got to in the church. Come and try.' Well, they didn't doubt their faith in the spirit of Christ, it was the traditional details they doubted, those which need a supernatural outlook in believers. They indicated that belief in these wasn't essential. Why should I not go as far as this, I thought. Though even then I felt there should be more than this to my conversion. (if I could use so grand a word for what was happening to me). I had a grave suspicion this partial acceptance of Christ with my mind only would probably turn out to be insufficient for my happiness or even contentedness. These two authors said nothing, or at least I didn't hear them, about giving up our lives, our hearts, our minds, our souls, even our pride to God and coming emptied of our old selves to him in humility. My understanding of this came much later. At that time it was just a hunch I had that a complete change was needed, a prospect I hardly dared contemplate.

Something in me was still missing. It had then no name, but soon I understood it was my heart that remained untouched. There was still no fire, no flame, no warm beating, no green shoots yet on the old potato. I was very despondent. I didn't see that it was my mind that needed someone or something to quieten it, so that other parts of myself could begin to help me, to let my heart realize its existence and begin to be heard beating.

I didn't realize this, put real words to it, until at last the day came when Father Edward Rankin, that dark horse, came to St Andrew's as our new rector. In his sermons Sunday after Sunday he spoke to us in clear straightforward language. Then I began to listen to him.

"It's not our reason which knows God, God speaks to the heart. God," he was saying, "is someone you love with your heart. When you're a child you don't reckon up your own father's feelings for you with your mind, with your intelligence, but return his love unquestioningly from your heart. What Christ has done in coming to earth. God born a man among us, born of Mary, is to teach us that it's with the heart we shall come to understand the mysteries of the everlasting things. Christ taught us about his Father who is our heavenly Father, that he himself, Christ, is in the Father, and the Father in him, and, since his coming here to earth, he is in our hearts and we, since that time too, are in his."

Edward told us about Christ's dying for us, God's dying for us, for our sins; he taught us about Christ's resurrection and his taking us up with him to heaven in his glorious ascension. "All these mysteries call to the heart, not to the mind, though afterwards the mind helps us to understand a little of their significance, to see these significances more clearly ." These were Edward's words.

He always spoke quietly. I could feel these words coming from *his* heart through the clear ordering of his mind, across the church into my ears, through my mind and down into *my* heart. At first I noticed only that I enjoyed listening to him, but very soon I discovered a new person growing in myself. One day I realized that my own heart was being woken up to life again. With Edward there in the church the whole service began to wake me up, to speak to my heart, his quiet seriousness tuned in with my mood. I began to take heart, as one might say.

It was astonishing how quickly I did take heart. I began to react to life as I'd used to all that long time ago. In one way my heart became a better heart than it had been before, it was more God-centred, less self-centred. I'm so grateful for the different ways in which all came together to help me at that time and since. I don't have ever to worry that ever again will I feel myself to be a cardboard cut-out person.

The Elgar symphony had come to an end long ago and I decided to put on the Enigma Variations. There was a pause in my thoughts while I changed the record. I'd not really been listening to the music but had enjoyed having the lovely sound in the room with me.

Then what else had happened? Could I remember? What had happened next? I suppose, in some way, my heart was beginning to work on my mind and my mind on my heart. I remember wondering how I was going to manage with all this unaccustomed love which was forming itself inside me. It needed a centre to focus on. Could I remember what happened then? Not very clearly. Life must often have progressed in a series of events followed by feelings and then more events and then more feelings and then other events, each following the other as a result of the ones before. My new warmth of heart led to my more quickly understanding Edward's words. They held a message I needed badly and therefore I remembered them. One day, one Sunday evening, he spoke about love binding all things together.

"Nothing works well without love," he said. "Nothing works well without Christ. And the two must work together. St Paul says:

'Whatever you do in word or deed, do everything in the name of the Lord Jesus, giving thanks to God the Father, through him.'"

I remember that Sunday night. I went to bed with my head in a whirl. I felt very much on my own, very much alone. There was no one to say 'Go on, it's all right' or 'Wait a bit, you're not sure.' Nicholas's faith was long-standing and so firm, he would have hardly seen that I should have any problems. In my mind I saw myself in a place of greyness like one's own road on a wet winter's evening before the street lights come on, friendly in a way because it's not a strange place, but not to be recommended as somewhere in which to stand around for long. Ahead of me, away in the distance, I could see an expanse of light where, I knew, in some way, there was not only sunshine but warmth. I could tell, in some way, too, it was nearer than it looked. It should not be beyond my strength to get there. And it seemed to me, if I did go, I would find myself no longer alone. Perhaps I'd only to walk towards and into this light and I would never ever be alone again, never feel lost, ever again.

Before I went to sleep I made up my mind to go where this light was. I could always come back again, into the old familiar greyness, if it didn't work out. It could easily not work out. I'd been disappointed before.

However, the Holy Spirit took loving care of me through the real night, and when I woke next morning all was settled in my mind. Jesus was Christ and he was in my heart, never to leave it again. I spent the day discovering how different the world looked. I felt happy and carefree. It was an ordinary day, a Monday, but the light and air seemed to be singing to me as the hours, full of everyday chores, went past.

The newness of my new outlook was refreshing. Any time I paused in my day's work to look back on the previous evening, I tried to hold all that had happened securely in my memory, travelling again in my mind the stages of my journey to Christ and his love. It hadn't been a leap in the dark I'd had to force myself to take. It wasn't that I'd had to make any great decisions about life. It was more like a gift from God. My new faith had come without my deserving it, or my expecting it, at that moment. I hadn't said, 'Tonight I shall try believing Jesus is God, and, if I've enough faith, it will turn out to be true!' It wasn't like that at all. I'd just put my head on my pillow and relaxed and let my heart take me a few steps forward towards that shining light. I'd peeled off a few defences, told my mind, as Edward had said in his sermon, to keep quiet, to shut up in fact, and my heart to bestir itself. The Holy Spirit did the rest.

The Enigma Variations - a very familiar favourite record of mine at that time and therefore not demanding necessarily any serious attention - had come to an end long ago. Nicholas had not yet arrived home, he'd probably stayed to talk over a few odd points with Edward as he often did. So I'd had long enough on my own to go through my own story and arrange it all more or less clearly in my mind. When Nicholas did come in I heard about some of the highs and lows of the evening and we had a few laughs and groans, then we had hot drinks and shortly went to bed.

EPIPHANY: DRUMMORE

The following week I did go over to Drummore to have lunch with Jane. Jack was away, and Nicholas was staying at home anyway. After he'd checked the St Andrew's bank statements against his accounts he would do some tidying up in the garden. He was used to getting his own lunch so long as it was straightforward and simple, as it usually was and he enjoyed the peace of being alone for a short time.

It was only about a quarter of an hour's drive to Jane's home in Easter Kilcoy, a larger collection of houses than we had at Ardness. At the far end on top of a slight hill I turned through a gate and along a short drive to the house. Drummore. It was an old and interesting farmhouse where the Morlands now lived. The house and its surrounding buildings were no longer attached to their old farmland, though cattle still grazed in the fields around, fields in places often divided from each other by strips of old Scots pine which intersected the landscape. Planted as windbreaks, these trees were now too tall to afford much protection to life at ground level, whether people or animals. However, the native cattle were very hardy and appeared to thrive there and people could and did take evasive action with windproof garments or they retreated into their cars.

"There'd have been plenty of shelter when the pines were younger and shorter," I'd heard Jack observe. "But with ten or twenty feet between one tree and the next their trunks don't provide much protection at ground level."

I found Jane busy letter-writing when I arrived.

"You aren't painting! Have you done any lately?" I asked as soon as I saw her. She was a very gifted amateur painter, usually in water-colours, usually in a small way and I'd often found her at work when I arrived. Her garden was specially planted to produce suitable flowers for every season.

"No," Jane replied, "it's not been possible. The days are still much too dark and gloomy. After all you haven't got to see only your work, you need to see your subject. So I must be patient for a while longer. Though there's not much to paint, is there, at present. I'm not missing much."

We talked for a bit about everyday things and then after lunch we went a walk over the nearby fields, taking Tess, her black labrador. The weather was somewhat overcast and gloomy though not actually raining, and in the west, we hoped, some bright gaps in the clouds might be approaching.

"Let's go round by the Snoopy Croft and come back by the lane," suggested Jane and so we did.

As we crossed the fields we several times had to climb over or squeeze through wire fences and encourage Tess to climb through too, but these accomplishments still came easily as we were both used to it and had never let ourselves get out of the habit of so doing.

"If we walked along roads only and not over fields for six months continuously, then we might find the fences a bit of a problem. We'd have got out of practice." I suggested.

"And we're fortunate both of us, I think, because we've both got comparatively long legs, though neither of us is especially tall."

"You certainly are tall," I said, "though perhaps not especially. And I'm certainly only medium in height. And for some reason or other, I don't find skirts catch on barbed wire any more than trousers do, if as much, which is odd. And fortunate."

Jane usually wore trousers on days like this but I hardly ever did any more, judging my seventy years to be a sign the time had come to decide not to end my days wearing them.

After a bit, the subject came unexpectedly into my head, and that it was Jane I needed to tell, I suddenly said,

"There's something else I should have arranged for this year. As well as my straightforward New Year resolutions I need to reorganise the list of people I pray for, my intercessions. I've got in a muddle. The whole thing's got out of hand. I've got such a long list of people I want to pray for that I never get through it without rushing and that's not much good."

"No! Not for yourself, nor for anyone on your list."

"I suppose I should divide them up somehow but how best to do so isn't clear to me. But I shall have to do something. What do you do?"

"I find it's quite a good idea to separate my list of people into days of the week and, of course, I pray for my nearest and dearest every day. But I've read you can have a list and every day take three or four names and concentrate on those but ask God to take care of the unnamed ones too. That sounds a good idea but I've not tried it. There can be quite a problem for us, can't there?"

"I thought I'd ask you, for I knew you might have a good idea or two. I find some people make me feel I'm meant to pray for them, so I do. And others one feels one ought to."

"I think it's important never to ask for anything specific for individuals. I just ask for each to be helped, to have the best for *them*. I mean, perhaps it isn't meant that someone should get better from an illness, how can we know? Or a boyfriend come back to a girl friend, or the other way round."

"But some people do, I mean pray for specific things."

"Yes. I remember meeting someone who was very keen on more or less demanding things or happenings from God. He said we should pray for anything that would make life easier for us, such as that there should be a space in a usually crowded car park. And if we were any good at prayer a space would appear for us as we drove up."

"That seems wrong," I objected. "Someone else might need the space more, for something more urgent than our own need. How could you know? I think that might be magic, not prayer. Perhaps that's a good definition of the difference between prayer and magic. Nicholas says he was taught that prayer should never be about things which are just for one's own convenience or vanity, but rather for the furtherance of God's kingdom. This could include one's own health because it's possible to need health and strength in God's service. I mean, I would love to have curly brown hair, but I've always had this straight stuff which has now gone grey, and I would think it not at all right to pray for it to be changed (and useless probably). My wanting to change would be for selfish reasons only and could make no difference to God's kingdom."

"The Lord's Prayer really covers much of the things we need to ask for, our daily bread, forgiveness of our sins and that we shall forgive those who've hurt us. In it we pray for the coming of God's kingdom and for his will to be done on earth as it's being done in heaven. And we start our prayer by blessing God's name, and calling him our Father. The main thing is for the words not to become too familiar, so that we should be able to see the meaning in them as if we'd come to them freshly. That's difficult. Or at least I find it so."

"I'm sure if we stick to the New Testament and the Prayer Book we shall be quite safe in how we pray." Jane's ideas were traditional but helpful.

"I expect, if we were careful in our search, we could find all we needed in those two books but I find other people's ideas very helpful, often. For instance, sometimes I think Thomas Cranmer was too keen to remove every mention of Blessed Mary and so I find books about her very helpful. I suppose he had to work in the narrow space between the Puritans and the Romans, but we can look further afield. I can see we shouldn't pray *to* Mary, we should pray to God, but she was a real person who's in heaven where she can help us with her prayers."

"I once read that prayers are pathways and God needs us to provide them for him so his actions may be able to take place in the world."

"Yes, I think that's a good way of looking at it. And I read, too, that although God knows what we want and we know too, it's necessary it all should be displayed, spread out, as it were, in words on a table so it all can be acknowledged between oneself and God. Then you can see clearly whether you're asking for something in which he can be involved and not something for yourself alone."

Then we were at the Snoopy Croft but there was no Snoopy teatowel hanging on the line in the garden. Only a large bathtowel with a colourful jungle scene.

Jane remarked, "I don't think we need change the name to the Jungle Croft, do you? It would hardly be suitable. What is there here really, actually? Two rowan trees, one and a half geans, some feeble whins and a lot of fencing." We used to refer to it as the croft on the corner of the lane, but after the arrival of the Snoopy teatowel, the Snoopy Croft was adopted as a shorter and more explicit name.

We then turned into the lane and walking became easier and harder at the same time, our shoes making more noise on the tarmac than they had in the fields, but we needed no longer to watch our steps.

"Look, buzzards," I called, 'two of them. It makes a change from a thousand rooks and crows and jackdaws. They're funny floppy things, aren't they? Except when they're soaring properly. But they do have a bit of glamour, being connected to the rarer birds of prey."

"I love the noise they make, especially the young ones in August. It's so nostalgic."

"Yes, it is. It reminds me of Devon where we went for holidays when we were children. Sounds are very nostalgic things, aren't they?"

"They are. So are smells. Pine cones on the fire, expensive soap in other people's bathrooms."

"Old furniture polish. I hate the new ones. I never use them. I never polish the furniture. Oh, dear. I am a hopeless housewife, wife, mother or whatever. But it can't be helped. It's too late for me to change."

By then the distant brightness had come nearer to us. We could see real sunlight gleaming through the clouds across the far mountains.

"It really is lighter this week. Look, it's nearly four o'clock and we can see things clearly, not only the hills but the trees and the house and the black dog too. And here we are safely home. Cheer up, Betty, on the whole good housewives are boring, I think."

"You aren't boring although you're a good housewife. And it would be possible to be boring *and* a rotten housewife as well. I expect there are plenty who are. Let's change the subject and then I'll go home."

EPIPHANY: TRIG POINT HILL

About a fortnight later Jane came over to lunch with us. As usual she brought her black labrador, Tess who like most of her kind, was hardly ever any trouble either indoors or our. She was only slightly alarmed by cattle and horses, and bored by sheep. She wasn't very excited by rabbits either, she hardly noticed their presence. This lack of interest didn't matter to Jane or Jack for they hardly had any rabbits in their garden, but our own garden netting mesh, though considered small enough to discourage normal adults, wasn't altogether successful against tiny baby ones in their springtime wanderings. When they got in amongst the vegetables we had to borrow Mary-next-door's Boofie and Blot, both of whom and especially Blot were very expert rabbiters.

After lunch Jane and I went for a walk, first of all along the lane at the edge of the wood. The sheep were still in the field on our right. Jane was tall with short black curly hair, assets which contrasted with my medium height and wispy straight grey hair. We both walked with springy steps that covered the ground easily, unhurriedly Tess, of course, rushed back and forth in the normal habit of dogs but was no trouble. In a little while, a bit further on than I'd walked the other day, we turned off to the right into a field we called the permafrost field. This was because the surrounding fairly tall trees were arranged in such a way that the sun was unable, at that time of year, to reach much of the grass for long enough to keep it from being almost permanently frozen.

"There are lovely butterfly orchids here in the summer," I said to Jane. "Though it's hard to imagine it today."

Beyond the field we followed a sheep track through a birch wood down to a small loch. It wasn't a true loch really, I supposed. It had been a reservoir of a kind and there was a very damp and disintegrating earth dam at the far end on which one could in summer sit comfortably leaning against a tree and wait to see dabchicks, moorhens and coots swimming around with their young. Downstream of the dam the original boggy surroundings were still there: strange shaped old willows nearly always standing with their roots in water, with strange growths of pale grey frilly lichen hanging from their branches. There

35

were great sphagnum moss hummocks, green and red, and on the slopes at the side where we walked a wonderful example of the three kinds of heather, cross-leafed at the bottom, bell at the top and ling in the middle. In the drier woody parts I'd sometimes been able to find coral root orchid and winter green. I'd begun to imagine myself turning into a serious botanist but the feeling didn't last.

The day I was with Jane, it was too damp to sit and relax anywhere and there wasn't much in the way of birds; all we'd seen so far were three chaffinches and a treecreeper, though we'd heard a wren. So after stopping for one or two minutes we turned and climbed up through the wood and then out into the open and up a gorse-covered hill.

"Have you any more news of Prue?" I asked Jane.

"Well, I'm not sure. We ring her at times, as you know, and at other times she rings us. It's just possible, I was saying this to Jack, there might be a slight change in the way she sounds. It might be wishful thinking on my part, of course, but she seems perhaps a bit more interested in what we are doing and she talks less about herself and Martin. She sounded to me to be less on the defensive too, I thought. At least that was my impression."

"Do you think he hoped brainy Prue would earn enough for the two of them or is he genuinely fond of her? Or perhaps he thought you would rush in to help them with some of your money, not that you've all that much."

"That's hard to say, isn't it? Jack and I, though I suppose it's myself mostly, are very disappointed Prue's decided not to go to Oxford. I'm so sorry she's missing this chance of getting a good degree, and I would have loved to have a child at a university, especially Oxford. David's being a stockbroker is marvellous for him, but not much glory rubs off on his parents. Of course I don't seriously mind for myself, but for Prue I do."

"I think she's so practical as well as clever she'll be able to use her brains to work at anything she's interested in, degree or no degree. I'm sure you needn't worry about that."

"That's true. No, I'm much more worried about her temperament not fitting in with Martin's. No, that's not true. I'm really quite pleased their temperaments are so unsuited. Prue may all the sooner decide to leave him. He really is all surface charm and no background, no serious education, though that sounds a snobbish thing to say. But with Prue's being so brainy they've really very little in common deep down. David, I need hardly say, can't stand him. But I hope I wouldn't despise a young man just because he'd had a bad start in life. Martin is, though, or seems to be, very insincere. It's impossible not to notice that every time he tells you about himself he tells you a different story. And you can recognise in a person's voice and manner, can't you, if they're really keen to make something of life and would be grateful for some helpful ideas and encouragement,"

We'd, by now, come to the top of the hill. The summit was clear of gorse and was smoothly carpeted with short sheep-eaten grass. It was a trig point hill with a smart white concrete pillar embedded in the ground and a metal triangle set into the top. From the garden at Whinside I could look up and see this mark and wish myself up there too looking out at the great expanse of distant peaks. This day we were there, really at the top, not just in my imagination. It was a lovely clear afternoon and I could see many of the familiar far away details of the mountains. Everything that day appeared as bright and gleaming as it ever had. Bringing our eyes away from the distance and onto nearer things, we could see some of our Whinside garden and most of Ardness itself.

Then we scrambled down the steep slope from the hill directly to the lane and were soon back home where we had some tea by the fire with Nicholas.

"It'll be the Conversion of St Paul and Candlemass soon," said Jane. "This year St Paul's day's on a Sunday. Candlemass was on a Sunday last year if you remember. What fun we had with everyone having candles given them as they came into church."

"Oh, yes, I do remember. And some people *weren't* so pleased, candles reminding them unwillingly of Rome. This year it'll be the Evensong of Candlemass and Sunday Evensong, both at the same time, if you see what I mean. So we'll have candles with less likelihood of complaints, there being so many fewer of us in church in the evening. I'd always wanted to go to a church where they had candles and now I do I'm pleased. I love flames - not menacing arsonist's flames of course, but gentle, quiet, aspiring-to-heaven ones like those of candles and night lights."

"I remember last year at Evensong we held our lighted candles while the choir sang the Nunc Dimmittis. It was lovely. For Candlemass is the Feast of the Presentation of Christ in the Temple and Simon is praying to God as he looks at the baby Jesus:

" 'Lord, now lettest thou they servant depart in peace, according to thy word. For mine eyes have seen thy salvation, which thou hast prepared before the face of all people, to be a light to lighten the Gentiles and to be the glory of thy people Israel.' "

"I remember. And Edward preached a sermon on light, light in religion. A candle burns itself out totally; when the wax is burnt away its flame dies, and nothing is left, there is no ash. So a candle shows us how our life is, we burn with brightness and then our light goes out, we go away, away to God. It is like this with Christ too, only more so. After he died on the cross and his Spirit rose to heaven he was buried and his Body rose from the tomb on the third day. The tomb was empty. He left no ash, as it were, no buried remains. He left nothing solid behind him and is altogether risen, ascended to his Father, glorified. But, of course, he's still with us on earth mysteriously. Perhaps we can think of it like a candle going out, it's turned into many gases which are dispersed into the atmosphere, always there to help us. A candle is a symbol of this mystery."

"Christ's Light lives on," Jane said. "When we light a candle in church and say a short prayer and have to go away because there are other thing we need to do, our prayer lives on only for a short while in the candle flame, but Christ is the Light of the world, he lives on forever."

"Do you remember Captain Douglas that Candlemass Day? He lit the candle he'd just been given with his own gas cigarette lighter instead of waiting for the server who was on his way down the aisle with *his* candle, giving a light to the person at each row end. It was so unexpected. The picture of his doing so has stayed in my mind ever since. It was funny. Captain Douglas probably wasn't concentrating. He could see the candle needed a light so he did what came naturally to him."

"It is good, isn't it, to have such days as Candlemass in the Church's year: landmarks to remind us of the many mysterious aspects of what we believe."

EPIPHANY: ST PAUL

On the day of St Paul's Conversion, that's to say the 25th January, I found myself thinking about his marvellous career and the great effect for good he has had on the world. There are some people who think Paul hasn't always had a good influence but I feel they're looking at the wrong things. His letters appeal to me greatly, they are very mysterious as well as a challenge. Almost every Sunday I can hear some part of one read as the epistle in church and I look forward to reminding myself of his ideas. He seems to have distilled the teaching of the Gospels (perhaps even before these were written), poured the resulting spirit into bottles, and here we are still partaking of the contents. All the same I found understanding him a not always easy task and sometimes felt there mightn't be much point my listening if I wasn't clear about what was being said.

One day a week or two before this I'd bought a small book about St Paul which definitely shed a clearer light onto the situation by explaining in simple language the main points of his teaching. I had enjoyed it very much and had learned a lot and realized that my friend Ruth would love to hear about it too. She and I were both interested in religious ideas and as she didn't read very much because of her rather weak eyesight I often wrote to her about what books I had discovered. So long as I explained things to her simply she usually was pleased to agree with me and was able to see things in a new light.

Ruth was about the same age as myself, she was one of a large family brought up in an English country rectory. Her parents in some way had known my parents, so, when she came to Seaborough to study physiotherapy, rather than travelling all the way to her home at weekends, she often used to spend them with us in Westlake. She especially enjoyed the family atmosphere and the non-institutional food.

She and I had much the same views about life and people so conversation between us was easy. Because of her upbringing in a rectory her interest in religion was natural and fitted in well with mine. It was one of our favourite subjects for discussion, though she said she no longer believed a lot of what she'd been taught at home. This was sad, I thought, for her, though I doubted it was really true, and sad also for myself who was still discovering my way into the faith and needed her informed guidance.

In a rather detached and superior way we were searchers, seekers after the truth, and whenever we met we recounted our progress. It seems clear to me now that we were full of pride. We thought if we used our brains enough we'd come up with the final truth about God. You can understand how much I needed Edward to help me.

After she qualified, Ruth went to work in a London hospital and soon after that Nicholas and I were married. So from then on we hardly ever managed to meet and as we were both busy people we wrote to each other only occasionally. (It was mostly myself who wrote anyway). Then Ruth retired early because her back had been troubling her for a long time and her hospital colleagues were unable to cure her enough for her to continue working.

Not long after this she went to visit her brother and sister-in-law at Much Milford, a small country town on the edge of Wales, where he had retired from his job in a Midlands city. If she went to live there too, she thought, she'd not be all alone, far from any other member of her family but away from London and, as she was used to an independent existence, she need not be a nuisance to him. So after a quick look round she found a little terrace house for sale inexpensively, decided to buy it and move into it as soon as possible. For quite a few years she'd lived there contentedly. She was near the shops, people were friendly, she had a little garden where her plants flourished and which, to begin with at least, was more a pleasure than a burden. And her nearness to her brother had worked out well. She saw him only from time to time but he was near when needed.

She got on well with her neighbours. 'I don't want to be a nuisance to anyone. I just want to help people as much as I can. I want to help the world as much as I can for as long as I can."

Then at last, with Edward's help, I discovered about the reality of Christ. When I'd taken this reality into my heart, the correspondence between Ruth and myself continued but with a difference. I'd thought it would need only a letter or two and she, in turn would suddenly understand all. She would realize our search was now at an end. But it didn't turn out like that.

Now I needed to write to her about St Paul, and one evening, having made up my mind to do so, I settled down comfortably with my pad of paper on my knee and my pen in my hand.

My Dear Ruth,
How are you? I've just been reading a new book I found about St Paul. It's good and not complicated. I learnt a lot from it. So I thought I'd write and tell you about a few of the things I'd read. Quite to the point as it's nearly the day of his Conversion. I know his words in the Bible can sound complicated, and in a way he himself is complicated. One of the reasons for this, I think, is because each of his letters is more or less complete in itself and so contains in different words much of what he writes in other letters. Therefore one can't sit down and take notes from Paul as if he were a lecturer giving say six lectures, each one following on logically from the last. But in a good book like this one I've just read the author has done the sorting out and the important points can be seen.

What ideas in this book have I found simple enough to grasp and yet solid enough to be worth remembering? We can easily remember his famous conversion on the road to Damascus. It's so dramatic, but what about the things he taught and what happened to him in his life?

A thing we can't forget is that his life was very eventful, he must have learned much from his experiences as they happened. He writes that he had five times received forty stripes save one from the Jews, three times he was beaten with rods, once he was stoned; three times he was shipwrecked including a night and a day 'in the deep'. On frequent journeys he was in peril from waters - were they floods? - from robbers, from his own countrymen as well as from the Gentiles; in perils both in the city and in the wilderness. He suffered from weariness and pain, from hunger and thirst, from cold and nakedness. he seems to enjoy reciting all these adventures, hoping we shall be impressed. And so we are. And he felt for others: 'Who is weak and I am not weak? Who is made to stumble and I do not burn?'

But when we come to what he writes about the things Christ taught, one of the simplest and yet most important points I read in this book is that he is pleased to have lost what he used to value in his past life. What he had lost is now, for him, just so much rubbish. His need for it all has gone away altogether, and, instead, he has gained Christ who lives in him. What he lost were influences based on the Jewish law and, in their place, he has the righteousness that comes through faith in Christ, a faith that comes from God. For this faith Paul needs to know Christ and the power of his resurrection. With this knowledge he can share in Christ's suffering and therefore, he will share too, in his resurrection.

The second idea I need to mention is that St Paul also insists on the importance of the cross. This idea is not so simple as the last but in a way it's much more worthwhile of our understanding. I've tried to make my mind clear about it, so I hope you will grasp a bit of what I'm saying. Paul writes that we should never think about Christ's resurrection without his cross. At the back of this is the idea that God's way is not (as I said before) the way of worldly success or even of what we think of as developing our own personality, being ourselves, which as you know is a very fashionable thing to think about these days. Doing our own thing. But God's way is the way of humiliation and helplessness, even of shame. We must be as if crucified in order to rise again. We must suffer our own cross before we can come to Christ and his resurrection. Christ's glory came after the Cross. In a way it's like how you can't get better until you've been ill first, you can't be rescued unless you're first captured and imprisoned by the enemy, or you can't be found unless you're first lost.

Paul is telling us that a good, quiet life, the sort some people want to live, so blameless as to be without risk to limb or life or even character, is no way to heaven. It's not what we were taught, is it? Our parents were inclined to say, 'Be a good girl always and you'll be taken straight to heaven when you die'. Perhaps they said this so we'd be as little trouble to them as possible; of course good children are less of a nuisance than naughty ones. We weren't taught to expect long struggles ahead; but there are, and they're not always a direct result of our disobedience. However much people try to be good, God will put a cross in their life. It's fascinating to think of this.

The third idea of Paul's I've got for you is about the foolishness and weakness of God. Even his foolishness and weakness are much wiser and stronger than the wisdom and strength of men. Of course, when we think at all about God's glory and power, we can see this must be so, and Paul helps us to understand it.

'My grace is sufficient for you, my power is made perfect in weakness.'

Paul boasted of his weakness. At first he prayed that God might take it away, but God didn't. So Paul understood he must be weak. All our strength comes from God anyway, we have none of our own, and always he'll give us enough for our needs. Then, if we realize what God is doing for us, there's no chance of pride taking root in our minds.

'For the sake of Christ I am content with weaknesses, insults, hardships, persecutions and calamities, for when I am weak then I am strong.'

Paul loves long lists, doesn't he? Think of all those sins. He seems to enjoy rolling them off his tongue. I'm having to look them up in order to get them right, to include them all for you, I hope.

'Adultery, fornication, uncleanness, lasciviousness, idolatry, witchcraft, hatred, variance, emulations, wrath, strife, seditions, heresies, envyings, murders, drunkenness, revellings and suchlike.'

(Perhaps it's just as well we don't - or I don't anyway - understand what each of these words exactly means nowadays). But Paul followed this list with one about the fruit of the spirit: here it is.

'Love, joy, peace, long-suffering, gentleness, goodness, faith, meekness and temperance.'

And after all it was St Augustine who, in the garden, in Milan, under the fig tree, heard the child's voice in the next door garden saying, 'Open the Book'. And he did and began to read St Paul's list of sins. Immediately he saw himself clearly as he really was, as God saw him, and so began his transformation into the saint whose writings have since touched all our lives. Paul says:

'...but put ye on the Lord Jesus Christ, and make no provision for the flesh, to fulfil the lusts thereof.'

What Paul says about weakness is very interesting. He says, if we remember we are weak, we will realize that anything we achieve will be achieved through Christ and not through our own efforts. My mother was always saying to me, "Oh, Betty, you're useless.' And she said it so often that the idea became part of myself. I used often to worry about this and think how much better I might have turned out if she had said encouragingly instead. 'Oh, Betty, you are very good at so and so,' or even 'Betty, you are improving.' But now I'm glad I am as I am, for if I do anything reasonably well or helpful, it's not hard for me to see it's not myself doing it, but Christ in me. Or anyway not myself, but something outside of me, working independently.

I hope you won't say all I've written is totally meaningless to you. Take it slowly. Do try to understand. Paul is good.

Not much news here. We hope to be coming south in March. Nicholas is deep in the church here and its finances, and he's perpetually having to humour people. I've been doing a little gardening at the church which seems stupid for our own garden needs much attention.

I'll write or ring you in about a month. We should be able to manage a visit to you when we're down.

Love
Betty

PS: On reading this through I think it really might appeal to you especially because of your weakness, of your being so conscious you can do so little.

You, of all people, can never be tempted to go round boasting of all the activities you take part in. Not like some. So I feel you're half way to godliness. God loves us for what we are, not for what we do. We don't need to worry that our handicaps are keeping us from serving him in active ways. Whatever we do, however little we do, it's done for him. He will always give us enough strength for what he wants us to do. You can pray and meditate just as well lying down as kneeling. I'm sure you're very good at this after all these years of practice. You do a lot by being friendly to people, having them in for a chat or asking them to do odd jobs for you. And you're good with young people, you know how to speak directly to them as if they were grown up, real people. They appreciate that.

I hope your roof isn't leaking again nor your kitchen being flooded and you haven't had any more jackdaws' nests in your sitting-room chimney.

EPIPHANY: SOME COLLECTS

It was my ironing morning. As I stood at the ironing board, I had a very good view of all that went on outside the kitchen window. Today there was no wind, but there was snow on the ground, on every bush, on every twig of every tree, on the gate and on the wire fence dividing the garden from the road. This white covering, though it looked dramatic, was only about two inches deep on the ground and even less on the trees. There were birds feeding on the nuts and seed and fat. Sparrows, fortunately only a few of them, were flicking the seed from the feeder onto the ground, where it was quickly picked up by other birds. That morning there were about three times as many individual birds present as there'd been the day before, there were chaffinches, greenfinches, all three kinds of tits, two robins now instead of one, two dunnocks and the half dozen sparrows come in from probably a nearby croft. Two blackbirds were enjoying the oddly shaped rather pathetic small apples I'd given them, the best the Bramley seedling had produced at the end of last summer.

Then I remembered I must ring Jane. There'd be no point her driving over here in this weather, nor my going there either. Then before I did anything about my thoughts the phone rang and it was Jane to say she wouldn't come here nor should I go there. We didn't stay on the line to chat, we were both busy and could keep any chit-chat for another time. Back at my ironing I was noticing the brightness of the birds that day, their colours very different from normal, more vivid, their undersides lit by the light relfected from the snow. I appreciated the unexpected difference.

As well as my ironing morning it was also the Monday after the fourth Sunday after Epiphany. So whilst I was bent over my work I was also learning the words of that Sunday's collect. We don't always have a fourth Sunday in Epiphany. Easter can come so early in the spring to allow time for all the Lent Sundays and the three (Septuagesima, Sexagesima and Qinquagesima), the fourth Sunday disappears which is a pity, its collect being one of my favourites.

The time spent with one's iron in the hand and one's eyes watching every movement of it is a good time for learning with the brain or even for reciting prayers already well-known to oneself. And it was time now to concentrate on this instead of daydreaming. My Prayer Book was just behind me on the table amongst the shirts and teatowels to remind me of the words when I hesitated.

'O God, who knowest us to be set in the midst of so many and great dangers, that by reason of the frailty of our nature we cannot always stand upright:'

I often feel like that, unable to stand upright. Oh yes, let's see what comes next:

'Grant to us such strength and protection as may support us in all dangers and carry us through all temptations.'

That's good and helpful, I thought to myself. Collects often tidy up for us our rather wandering prayers. Sometimes we can express our thoughts better in a Prayer Book prayer rather than in our own feeble and disorganised words. Of course there are some which satisfy me much more than others. I love best the ones with strange constructions, though, I suppose, I ought to prefer those with the best messages for us. But it's the odder, unexpected phrases which strike my mind and are irresistible. I suppose the plainer collects are much too much like those we might have made up for ourselves.

'O Almighty and most merciful God, of thy bountiful goodness keep us, we beseech thee, from all things that may hurt us; that we, being ready both in body and soul, may cheerfully accomplish those things that thou wouldest have done...'

'and because through the weakness of our mortal nature we can do no good thing without thee, grant us the help of thy grace, that in keeping of thy commandments we may please thee...'

'Almighty and merciful God, of whose only gift it cometh that thy faithful people do unto thee true and laudable service; Grant we beseech thee...'

'that as by thy special grace preventing us thou dost put into our minds good desires, so by thy continual help ...

'thy only begotten Son to take our nature upon him and as at this time to be born of a pure virgin...'

It's their unexpectedness which fascinates me. How could I not believe, or not be encouraged to believe their varied messages? And

46

also I love those sentences with pairs of words, the second half of the pair usually reinforcing the first half's meaning.

'through our sins *and* wickedness we are sore let *and* hindered ...'
'...Lord of all power *and* might who are the author *and* giver of all good things...' '...increase *and* multiply upon us they mercy ...' '...that thou being our ruler *and* guide ...' '...that we may both perceive *and* know ... thy bountiful grace *and* mercy may speedily help *and* deliver us...' '... also have grace *and* power faithfully to perform the same ...' '...so many and great dangers...' (this my favourite) '...most chiefly in showing mercy *and* pity ...' also '...in thy steadfast fear *and* love...' (that pair makes me stop to think, and remember,) '...strength *and* protection...'

A lot of the character and individuality of collects lies too in their dependent clauses. These often hang deliciously from each other in great strings where nowadays we would have several full stops and in this way they impinge on my brain. Then I invite them into my heart where they usually find a home with me, hopefully for the rest of my life.

Also, I love to bring to mind all those unknown people from the dim past as well as from the years only just gone by, those holy people whom we never knew, who worshipped in our churches over the centuries, all those who used these collects. When I think of them I feel joined to all the saints of the past who strove, obviously more successfully than myself, to follow in our Lord's footsteps. Sadly soon the collects I know I will no longer bind us all together. They'll be replaced by unfamiliar, unremarkable prayers. I feel that's sad. It's more than I feel about most things.

The last hanky was folded and pressed again and again and put in a pile with the rest of the ironing to be taken later to be put in their drawers. Ironing is not a bad job these days with all the help from modern materials. There's no reason really why I shouldn't stand upright. No need to wilt, and with God's help I shan't.

One evening soon after Easter when we'd sat down with the day's work finished. I'd turned my mind back to the collects and their words. I'd been very impressed with one just after Easter so I'll tell you about it now while the subject is fresh in my mind.

47

And I'd been thinking too that in the course of our lives some words acquire, in a way I don't understand, a life of their own, a power to work in us. These word from the old collects and in other prayers seems to work on our souls and produce something in us of great value that nothing else can. The *sense* of both old and new words may be the same so far as the dictionary's concerned, but the voltage, if that's a good way of expressing it, is usually many times more powerful and the actual words more beautiful in the old version of a prayer.

Last year Jane and I went to a friend's son's confirmation at the Cathedral, St Mary's. We were surprised not to hear the old words, those we knew from our own confirmations and our children's, and which we'd imagined would continue in a long line of confirmations stretching out forever into the precarious future. *That* has turned out more precarious than we expected. One can't forget;

'Defend, O Lord, this thy child, with thy heavenly grace, that *he* may continue thine for ever: and daily increase in thy Holy Spirit more and more, until *he* come unto thy everlasting kingdom."

This, I've always felt, is the lovely heart of the service. Something to be kept in mind, always. Instead we heard.

'Strengthen, O Lord, thy servant N, with your Holy Spirit. Equip him/her for your service and sustain him/her all the days of his/her life.'

How could anybody write those words as an improvement on the original? What here is our greatest loss? Is it that 'Defend' has given way to 'Strengthen'? 'Defend' is such a striking and unusual word and helps us to feel God is at our side supporting us with his heavenly grace, whereas 'Strengthen' is more about something coming into us. Quite good but nothing like *as* good. Or do we feel most the loss of 'thy heavenly grace'? Or that we have that sharp little word 'equip' which reminds me of 'quip' or 'whip', and the rather boring 'sustain', instead of our being 'thine for ever'? Is it that we are being asked to think no further than 'all the days of his/her life' instead of seeing the open doorway of coming 'unto thy everlasting kingdom'? But, after some discussion with Nicholas afterwards, when I'd got home, what I most regretted was the change of 'child' into 'servant'. We need to think of ourselves as God's children enfolded in his love. Thinking of ourselves as children of God is the mainspring of our lives. Jesus taught that we should call God our Father, and he also said that we are no longer servants but sons of God. St Paul, too, writes about our being no longer servants but sons, heirs of God through Christ. Even when we're grown-up we are still God's children. I've never had any trouble in thinking of myself as one of his sons. Neither sons nor daughters, at the time I was growing up, were ever thought the one to be more valuable that the other, it was just that they were created for different purposes. In God's eyes we are all for ever his children, for ever growing up, not yet adult. I picked up my prayer book and turned to the page. It read:

'O Almighty God, who alone canst order the unruly wills and affections of sinful men: Grant unto thy people, that they may love the thing which thou commandest, and desire that which thou dost promise, that so, among the sundry and manifold changes of the world, our hearts may surely there be fixed, where true joys are to be found: through Jesus Christ our Lord, Amen'.

I love this collect, it must be one of the best of all. The clauses are enjoyably involved but still not hard to understand. Here all is contained in one sentence though these days we'd probably use three or four. That's often the great attraction of a collect, it's something not quite ordinary. This one too gives us a very good example of the pairs of words I mentioned before. These pairs increase the meaning and at the same time allow our minds time to catch up with the sense:

'the unruly wills *and* affections' ... 'that they may love the thing which thou commandest *and* desire that which thou dost promise' ...'the sundry *and* manifold changes.'

How does it compare with its new equivalent? The old one has a lovely shape to it and the sense is not altogether arrived at in a direct and simple way. We need to concentrate our minds. The language is musical and intriguing, fascinating, and the words don't give us their sense at once. In fact there's everything here a collect ought to have, so much so that I'd have thought there was no need to write a modern version for modern ears. Let's though see what has happened:

'Almighty God, who alone can bring order to the unruly wills and passions (why *passions*?) of sinful men: give us grace to love what you command and to desire what you promise, that in all the changes

49

and chances of this world, our hearts may surely there be fixed where lasting joys are to be found.'

The old collect perhaps can be summarized: that besides asking God to grant that we may love the things he commands and desire those which he promises, we ask also that he will fix our hearts surely on them, because, among the sundry and manifold changes of the world, it's just these things that will prove to be our true joys. The new version has more or less the same meanig as the old but expressed in feebler words. 'Passions' is outwardly stronger than 'affections' but by annoying me loses its strength. 'What' is more ordinary than 'that which' and 'changes and chances' instead of 'sundry and manifold' is a real loss and 'lasting' for 'true' is change for change's sake, for if joys are true they will be lasting.

There may be some modern people who think that 'sundry' or 'manifold' are words too esoteric or exotic for today's worshippers to comprehend, and, therefore, they've been replaced by something more humdrum. But I'd disagree. I think both are strong and very descriptive words and would be good and useful additions to anyone's vocabulary. Our language is full of phrases from the Bible and the Prayer Book and we have had no reason to be sorry this is so.

I remember once reading that, even if we weren't religious, even if we didn't believe a word of what they're about, the old collects, when learned by heart, will give us a wonderfully firm basis for writing good English. They'd stand us in good stead all our lives. But how even better it is for us to believe also in their meaning as well as needing to write good English. We can read or hear some collects each week through the whole year. We shall rejoice not only in their lovely words and in the wonderful construction of their sentences, but most of all we can use them to ask God to grant us all their marvellous requests.

EPIPHANY : CHRISTOPHER

A few days later I was again walking by myself in the wood, but this time I went further on to a patch of water we referred to rather vaguely as the pond. It was a smaller pond by far than the Willow Loch and much less boggy, somewhat hidden in tall trees rather than in scruffy willows, much calmer because more secretive. Before the coming of the mains water this pond had provided the big house nearby with its water supply. Nowadays a general neglect had taken over and the old sluice was more or less collapsed so that when I walked round the far end, especially in the winter, I had to negotiate a small stream, though in summer when the water level fell there was nothing but a slightly squidgy mess to cross. At this time, the time I'm writing of, the surface of the water was almost clear and all the surrounding patterns of the trees with their interlacing branches were accurately, almost magically, reflected. In summer a thick growth of sedge spread all over the water leaving only a small space in the middle where odd shoots of horse-tail grew up and could give a mallard and her family some shelter. There'd been no rain lately to soften the autumn leaves which still carpeted the ground and rustled under my feet. I could see very little sign of spring. Then soon, in front of me, the trees opened out into a grassy space where the light came down to the ground all around me.

I was thinking about Christopher Lyall, our curate and about his having been made a deacon last year when he'd first come to us. His priesting was still to come, one day this next mid-summer, and I was wondering how different he would have been feeling now if he'd become a priest straightaway on his arrival here, as he would have wished, had it been possible, had it been the accepted thing. Before his coming we had been without a curate for over a year and he had been therefore warmly welcomed by all at St Andrew's and especially by Edward.

In lots of ways he was very different from Edward, and one of those most obvious was in his appearance. He was dark and short, whereas Edward was tall and fair. Also he was young and active, not that Edward was exactly old or lacking in energy, but for Christopher

51

nothing was too much trouble. He was fond of his bicycle and before he'd acquired his car, a grotty little brown 2CV, he cycled everywhere. Personalities are different, too, it's all a question of temperament. Not any one priest can do everything one hundred percent perfectly and enthusiastically: services and sermons, or home communions, or being good with the young as well as with the old, or with the dull as well as with the bright and intelligent.

Also, it makes life much more interesting in a parish to have a choice of knowledgeable clergy whom one can approach with all kinds of odd queries about the faith. Now we'd got Christopher as well as Edward, we did very well. Then there was Canon Harper, a retired priest, who was a dear, very gentle and kind, who came to help mainly on Sundays. He could tell you everything about the history of the church, about the several Scottish churches, especially our own Old Church, and the Anglican church all around the world, or about any of the other Christian churches. Each one of them was easy to talk to and they were willing to listen patiently to us and never appeared to think our questions trivial or absurd.

'Father Christopher, please. Tell me about the Jesus Prayer. I can't find it in any book of mine,' Or 'Please, Father Rankin, (only I wasn't usually so formal), where can I find out about the Angelus and the Hail Mary and the Rosary? In any book I've got they're either not mentioned or I'm expected to know already.' Any one of them would help me with my query however stupid it might sound to them, however much it might show up my ignorance.

I was thinking, as I walked along, that Strathlyon was a lovely place to come for a first job. And being with Edward, too. Christopher'd be sure to learn a lot, a lot of the right things. Nicholas and Duncan Forbes (our secretary) had hovered over him (but tactfully, not seeming to be interfering) and shown him some of the practical side of a parish. Nicholas had been saying only recently that he was progressing well. Of course he wasn't always tactful, especially with the old stagers like Duncan, who was perpetually knowledgeable and enjoyed telling people so; and of course with James Donaldson. All sacristans know everything and with Jamie this was especially so. It was difficult for Christopher, an enthusiast straight from college, who wanted to impart all the latest ideas to those who were already quite sure they knew best.

I'd loved Christopher from the very first. He soon made lots of young friends, so our care was hardly needed for long, except for a good lunch now and again. So long as he knew we were still around if he wanted us I could relax and not worry about him.

At this point in my brooding I stopped still, deep in thought. I tried to turn the silhouette of a blackbird, perched at the top of a tall tree, into a mistle thrush but without success, and then to turn a distant little noise into a woodpecker. Then I jumped. A woodcock flew up suddenly out of the old brown bracken from almost under my feet and flew off quickly into the trees with his wavering wing beats. He had got tired of waiting for me to move sooner than I had of standing still.

Five minutes or so later, as I climbed the gate out of the wood into the lane, the rather faint distant noise I'd heard had come nearer. It really was a woodpecker's little explosive chipping. After waiting a few minutes I saw him fly above me from one oak to another and climb up the trunk of this second one in jerks searching for insects in the lichen-covered bark. His black and white plumage with touches of red under his tail and on the top of his head were still dazzling, not yet rubbed and partly worn away with squeezing in and out of his nesting hole to feed his young.

A very good afternoon, I thought. I'd seen the woodcock, or anyway, *a* woodcock and also had a very successful view of a woodpecker.

So I returned home happy and ready for tea.

And everything turned out well for Christopher too in the end.

EPIPHANY: CREATION

On another day when Jane was over with me we were washing up after lunch. Well, not seriously washing up as most of the dishes went into the dishwasher. While we were doing this we could look out of the window at the birds feeding on the nuts and seed, the feeders being specially placed for this happy occupation.

'Let's go and stretch our legs now lunch is tidied up,' I suggested. "We'll just have a stroll along the lane. It'll be good for us and Tess needs a run I expect."

We hung up our tea-towels, changed our shoes, put on jackets, and walked up the short drive into the lane.

"I do think creation is marvellous, though," Jane said after we'd settled into our not very rapid but comfortable stride. "It's all so connected to itself and yet the variety is enormous, infinite it seems."

'It's a marvellous thing to think about. You could say everything is strangely strange, peculiarly peculiar. Think of all those funny different things like plankton in the sea or all those weird insects with their, to us, nasty habits."

"And the bower birds which are admired for what they do rather than for their looks. But the point is it all fits together into the world, into the whole system."

"That's true," I agreed. "If God wanted to create even one man he would have had to create the whole universe for him. All was ready for Adam before his creation, He and Eve needed the whole earth and the earth needs the whole galaxy and each galaxy needs all the others. I mean this is so, *really and truly*. And I mean Adam as the first true man in both his scientific and biblical aspects. There's no cut-off between ourselves and the seemingly infinite far away edge of creation."

"God could have created a man with a smaller supporting system."

"Well, of course, he could have but he didn't. Or is it 'of course?' I'm not sue we know the answer to that question."

Then I went on to mention a subject connected with all this but had not mentioned to Jane before.

"There's one thing which makes me certain that a good and truly creative mind made the round world. It's about water and ice, and the fact that, unlike most things (or is it unlike anything?), instead of shrinking as it solidifies, water enlarges itself. The result is that a certain volume of ice weighs less than the same volume of water and therefore floats, or, put the other way, the same weight of ice takes up more room than the equivalent weight of water. So we have ice forming on the top of ponds and lochs, and even on top of the sea. Just think how awful it would be if ice formed under its water, freezing all life on the bottom of the sea or on the bottom of ponds. There'd be no layer of ice on the surface of any water to make an insulating blanket to protect the fish in our fishponds or the plankton in the Arctic and Antarctic oceans, or any of the fish, or the whales, as there is now. It's hard to realize what a great difference it makes to the world that we have ice to walk or skate on, that there are floating icebergs and ice-sheets instead of their being down in the depths. Also, because water gets bigger as it freezes, the snowy or just plain wet tops of mountains are shattered by ice that gets bigger when the temperature drops to freezing and lower. So there are all those much admired dramatic spiky alpine peaks and their broken away rocks falling down the slopes to make scree as well as those menacing looking boulders fallen down all along the valley floor or transported miles across the country by glaciers. And so gradually, in geological time, mountain ranges become lower and are overcome by new mountains forced up by the continental plates squashing into each other. If ice didn't make mountains disintegrate the world would be much less habitable than it is now, there'd be no fertile plains or deltas. Of course, if water became smaller instead of larger as it froze into ice there'd be no burst pipes, which we might think a good idea, but what happens now in nature is so perfect for the world. Burst, frozen pipes are due only to our own carelessness, they don't have to happen. We know perfectly well outside non-insulated pipes will always freeze in frosty weather. It's all a marvellous example of the perfection of creation in its larger aspect."

"I worry though about what we're doing to creation all the same," Jane said, "for it's ourselves who are threatening to bring the whole earth to a stop, to a desert of nothingness. At the moment, we, all

55

people, (or do I mean all western people) seem to be surviving, more than sufficiently. We have caused many species of plants and animals to become extinct or, at any rate, much rarer. It might be that a point will be reached where a balance will be no longer possible between the fewer species that are left and so a catastrophe will occur. We'll all become extinct and the creation of life will have to begin all over again without us. And yet God loves us. We don't deserve his love. We are so horrible to his world."

"But of course we don't," I said. "No-one deserves his love. It's his gift, we can't earn it. That's what we're taught."

"Yes, of course, we can't. I'd forgotten. Every day we thank God for 'our creation, preservation and all the blessings of this life.' Yet we rush out in our selfishness and forget him and do our best to ruin his creation."

"We don't only ruin the plants and trees, and the animals and fishes, we don't protect the people who were or still are in tune with their surroundings, like aborigines or pygmies, or Red Indians, or Eskimos. It's fortunate we have a General Confession as well as a General Thanksgiving."

"Yes, that's true," Jane agreed. "All the time we follow too much the 'devices and desires of our own hearts'. We offend against God's holy laws as regards the earth, against his wonderful creation which we're charged to take care of."

"And yet, in spite of this, God still loves us."

"He loves us, so he has mercy on us, but he forgives us only when we acknowledge that there's no health in us and ask for his mercy and forgiveness. We are pitiable offenders in our feebleness, in our not being able to change the way we look after, or don't look after, the world. So far."

"It's those who are in power, in charge," I said, "who don't understand this, I think. So far as I can make out. It's not so much ourselves who offend in this way, on purpose or carelessly, but the money grabbers who are aiming to make their fortunes. For example in cutting down square miles of tropical forest without care about its future. Native people understand this and don't take so much out of their surroundings as to spoil the regeneration of trees and their food supplies."

56

"That's true, but we, those of us who understand should, could do more."

By this time we had walked along the long to the end of the wood and were half way back. The buzzards were soaring and displaying over the trees down towards Loch Spean, and above our heads a great tit gave a short little burst of his bell-ringing song.

"It's sad we have all those long winter months without any birds singing. It's quite late in the spring when we first hear them, later than in the south of the country. And they don't make up for this by singing any longer into the summer. I find there's not much to be heard after the end of June, except greenfinches. Though robins have their sweet autumn song, that's a great treat."

"Spring after winter is a bit like what St Paul says, there's no resurrection without the cross, no new wheat plant without the seed's first dying in the damp ground before germinating, or no spring and no birds singing without winter coming first with its long silent months."

"We certainly do appreciate everybody's song all the more after the long silence. If we heard birds singing all the year round we wouldn't find it such a great treat."

LENT: A SPRINGTIME PICNIC

Lent was with us, Ash Wednesday had come and gone with the ashes put on our foreheads and then surreptitiously and quickly wiped off. It would not do to be seen when doing our shopping in Strathlyon with funny dark smudges on our foreheads. Now too all our resolutions were at work, so far with enthusiasm and determination.

One morning a week or two later, Jane was on the phone for me. "Can you take today off?" she asked. "It's fine, so I thought we might go to Johnny Swann's. We need some new alpine plants for the garden here. And afterwards we could have a picnic by the river and then go for a walk."

I agreed at once. I'd no special, un-put-off-able plans for the day. So I left Nicholas busy, he was going to see what he could make of the St Andrew's half year figures. Later he would prune some of the unwieldy climbing roses where they'd fallen out of their supporting trees, and I'd catch either my hat or my hair in them whenever I walked that way. I was always complaining. "No, I'm not complaining, it's just an observation," I'd say in reply to Nicholas's defence of their neglect by him up till then.

Yesterday I'd been thinking, brooding away, not seriously thinking, just dreaming, how, at this time of year, it's hard to imagine what life will be like when it's summer again and there'd be roses in the garden. I'd noticed, in other years, they did come, after a bit, and after I'd welcomed their arrival, I'd begin to take them for granted. They were so many kinds of roses, even in those days, not just different species but totally different kinds. They flowered over a long time, over months it seemed, each overlapping the other all through the summer. I'd get used to their being, every day, all around us in the garden. I'd cease to be surprised and delighted. It was the same with swallows. They'd be back soon. Only another month perhaps. And when they first came I'd wonder how I ever did without them all through the winter. For a day or two after I'd seen my first, I'd exclaim and dash around remarking to all on their presence, but after a bit I found I was taking them for granted again. That was sad, and even when they disappeared in the autumn, I'd have to tell myself it was only natural. I made myself accept their going.

They couldn't possibly have stayed here anyway, not in this climate, there'd be no flying insects for them to catch and eat. But there'd be other birds in their place, fieldfares and redwings for instance. Still, in the winter it was hard to remember how much I'd loved their twittering and chattering as they flew back and forth over my head all the summer through. Swifts, too, I realised, would soon be screaming and dashing again excitedly round the old tall Strathlyon houses. It was difficult to choose between swifts and swallows for glamour. But there was no need, we could have both. Obviously, swallows were more approachable, or rather, they approach us more than swifts do. They don't fly so high in the air. That should make swifts more glamorous, for glamour, detachment and inaccessibility go together, I thought.

Shortly after I'd driven over to Jane's we set off with Tess and our picnic lunch. Jack didn't mind being left at home either. He always found lots to do around Drummore, in its old farm buildings or in the garden. After the fields were taken over by the neighbouring farm, a fair-sized piece of land remained around the house. Both Jane and Jack loved their garden. It was on fairly level ground, unlike our own, but high up with lovely views between the groups of pines which as I said before, protected it from the worst winds.

The weather that day was almost springlike and Jane remarked, "Normally here haven't you noticed, it's winter until June comes. And then suddenly it's summer and we're all taken by surprise. For a change, today is beautiful instead of blustery or raining. Quite unexpected."

I agreed. "One of the difficulties in this climate is knowing how well we need to be wrapped up for a whole day out. Luckily in these days of cars we can stack all we think we might want on the back seat with Tess."

We visited the nurseries and bought more than we'd intended. Jane chose her rockery plants plus one or two others she couldn't resist and I, who'd not intended to buy anything, had fallen for a little dwarf juniper. I knew exactly where I'd put it but was unsure about what Nicholas's comment would be.

We then drove down to a spot by the River Keldie we'd visited often before. It was a fairly level place so we were able to make ourselves comfortable on a rug, out of the wind and in the sun. It was warm there in a springlike way but, all the same, we needed to keep our jerseys on. The river flowed fast but smooth and deep. Jane, the artist of course, noted the strength of the flowing water as she watched little patches of bubbles, about the size of ten-pence pieces floating past her.

"It's fascinating, isn't it, how the river is both brown and blue. Have you noticed, Betty? The water is brown. I suppose with the peat dissolved in it, but the surface reflects the blue sky, though as a darker blue, as dark as the brown. It's difficult to analyze what your eye is actually seeing."

"It's like being fascinated," Jane went on, "by the colour of a field after the silage is cut and immediately carted away. I can't describe the green that's left behind, it must be luminous, a dayglo-green, if it is green, (or is it yellow?) but beautiful, not crude or vulgar."

"I've noticed that," I said, "It's pale, it looks as if were lit from inside. It must be impossible to paint, you'll know that."

Tess hunted round for a bit and then fell peacefully asleep at Jane's side. We were happy to be relaxed, lying back and staring into the blue sky, though dazzled if, by mistake, we looked at the sun.

And then after a pause I went on, "Have you decided yet to go to confession this Easter?"

Jane was secure in her beliefs and, I imagined, perfectly calm in her worship. For confession, she'd found the Prayer Book prayers or her own words perfectly sufficient. She'd told me that she felt quite well able, every week, to recall the moments when even her good kind nature had failed in one way or another. She knew though that I'd been to Edward and thought real confession, as I called it, was marvellous and I had recommended it to her.

On occasions such as this Jane let me talk about my new and still struggling enthusiasm for the faith. She recognised I was usually in need of encouragement rather than discouragement, though sometimes her calming influence was in fact needed.

"No, I haven't decided. It's difficult to decide," Jane replied.

"You really ought to. It's lovely. It's worth it. You feel so marvellous afterwards. Edward is super. He'll help you. He understands so well how people feel. And after all, he must feel awful too himself, when it's his turn, though 'awful' won't be the word he uses. He makes me feel relaxed and normal as soon as he begins to say the prayers that come at the beginning. The first time I was very nervous in anticipation, but not at all once I was there with him. Afterwards I felt marvellous, especially the next morning after the mind had had time to settle. It was lovely to wake up and feel myself with very much less weight pressing down on my hitherto overburdened head. It's not possible to describe that super feeling of lightness and warmth, of being in tune with God. It's worth that very short time of feeling awful."

Jane said, "It's hard to believe it can be like that. It's so different from anything I've ever done before."

"Last year I found three collects to help me. The first was in Lent, a year ago. I discovered on Ash Wednesday, in the one we say on that day and on every day from then until Easter, the words *'perfect remission and forgiveness.'* 'Of course,' I said at once, 'this is what I need. It's this perfect remission and forgiveness that's necessary and here it is promised me if I ask for it.' Here is a chance I can feel *perfectly* clean. And all through Lent I repeated those words every day, usually more than once in the day. But, all the same, I had to wait till after I'd been to confession at Easter for those words to begin to work seriously in me. You remember, in that collect we ask God to 'create and make in us new and contrite hearts, that we, worthily lamenting our sins, and acknowledging our wretchedness, may obtain of thee, the God of all mercy, *perfect remission and forgiveness.'*

"You see, if we worthily lament our sins and acknowledge our wretchedness, if we think of ourselves as we are and compare that with how God would like us to be, and if we are really sorry about this contrast, he will create and make in us new and contrite hearts. He is the God of all mercy, and so we *can* have perfect remission and forgiveness. And you see, it's not ourselves who have to do anything, we can't do any of the cleansing ourselves, but we must, first, repent and then, secondly, ask for forgiveness and then, thirdly, allow God to forgive us perfectly, and finally try to understand how, with God's help, we can be changed for the better. He will do the forgiving and the changing and we can help him but it won't be our own efforts only or mainly which can bring the change.

"And that word 'worthily' comes up again and so does 'perfectly' in another collect. It's in the Mass, the collect for purity, and therefore is very familiar to me, but it wasn't till just a few days before this last Christmas that its helpful and deep truth suddenly struck me as being what I specially needed.

"Cleanse the thoughts of our hearts by the inspiration of the Holy Spirit, that we may *perfectly* love God and *worthily* magnify his Holy Name. I'd never seriously thought about the real meaning of the words before, not in the way I was now understanding them. How could it be, I'd been thinking for ages, that I ever could do either of these things? Either perfectly love God or worthily magnify his holy name?

"But now I saw that *with God's help* I might begin to be able to do so. The Almighty Creator of the universe is powerful enough to make anything of me he wants to, if I will let him. Do you remember Thomas Merton's friend who said, 'don't you believe that God can make you a saint if you will let him?' So, in my mind, I knew that such a thing wasn't impossible, though I'd have to pray hard over a long time for it to come true. But now I knew, in my heart, the possibility had become real.

"Then a third collect came to my help about the same time as the last, also just before Christmas again, on the last Sunday in Advent. I was meditating on the problem of my being neither worthy nor perfect and deciding to tell God in my Christmas confession of my inability to sort things out. Then I picked up my Prayer Book and read, in the collect for that day.

"O Lord, raise up (we pray thee) thy power and come among us, and by thy great might succour us ... that ... thy bountiful grace and mercy may speedily save and deliver us.'

"Here, I could see now, was the power and great might I was looking for, which would be sufficient, as it was coming from God, to help me *perfectly* to love him and *worthily* to magnify his Holy Name. And, of course, *worthily* lament my sins and obtain *perfect* remission for them. We have to remember it's God and not ourselves who provides all the strength, the power and the grace we need. I once tried to confess to Edward that I'd not had enough strength to achieve something or other and he was quite cross, or cross for him, which isn't ever very, of course. He reminded me that all the strength we need comes from God and not ourselves, so I'd be able to achieve whatever it was if it were meant I should.

"So, this time in my confession, I had to explain to Edward about my wickedness in still having had these doubts about God's power and my penitence, and he was pleased at how much I'd discovered. He said the absolution, then I drove home. Later I went to bed and to sleep. When I woke up next morning I felt a completely different person. But I don't suppose you have these kinds of problems. You can sail along throughout the days smoothly and safely, trusting God and not worrying like I seem to have to do."

"Well, not altogether. I do have a problem even if they're not quite like the problems and confusions you're talking about. But I'm not conscious of a weight on me, nothing that makes me feel I need to go and tell anyone so that my burden may be taken away. And yet if it's like what you describe, it would be worth it. Edward is so un-alarming and I know he would understand what I was trying to say. And also he wouldn't himself be disapproving and would help me to pass everything over to God. That's what you're saying, isn't it?'

"Yes, it's like that." I wanted to be encouraging. 'of course there are horrid moments in confession. Once I said to Edward the day before we'd planned to meet in the church. 'I'll see you tomorrow, you know, that horrible thing, confession.' 'It's not horrible, it's lovely,' he said severely. Well, severely for him, which, of course, was not very. But it certainly looks horrible when you scribble a few words, your sins in headlines, on a small piece of paper and put it in your pocket so you won't forget anything when the moment comes. But he's right. It soon becomes lovely.

"Look, I know. I'll take you with me to the church at the appointed time. I'll hold your hand metaphorically. You wouldn't be tempted to change your mind and run away, would you - as you wouldn't be alone? I nearly did the first time. I nearly turned the car round when I got to the bridge, but fortunately the thought of Edward's face next time we met and his voice of sorrow or something like it kept me going straight on. The thought of hurting Edward was worse than my feeling horribly anxious about it all."

"I'll think about it," Jane agreed. "I'm sure you're right. I expect that once I've been I will really see it's the thing for me."

We got up and called to Tess who was already awake and anxious to be off, and began to walk downstream along the path. A dipper was searching in the rapid swirling water at the edge of the river where the stones were breaking the smoothness.

"They're so smart," said Jane. "Extraordinarily attractive. Very dark brown and very white. And their actions are fun to watch, they're so buoyant."

"And their song is so odd, well not odd, I can't describe it, not what I would have invented for them."

"But it's penetrating enough to be heard across a wide and noisy river, isn't it? And yet it's a sweet song, not raucous."

Then a moment later I saw something, and it took me two seconds or so to put words to it. "Look, a goosander, a drake, a real sign of spring."

"How marvellous. They're wonderfully beautiful birds at this time of year, all that contrasting and dazzling dark green and white, and the special pinkish tinge on the breast which comes in the spring. It shows well on this one."

"I love to watch them diving, all sawbills. It's so instantaneous, one moment the bird is there and the next there's no bird to be seen. If there's a flock of them to watch and I do, then suddenly they all disappear and there's not a bird on the surface, only some swirling water. But if I wait then they all come up again in twos and threes and I can see I wasn't imagining things."

Then after another short spell of walking a little further along the path it was time to call Tess, to turn round and go home.

LENT: ST BENEDICT

Nicholas and I were in the kitchen sorting out our week's purchases. That morning we'd collected our pensions from the cheerful old lady, well, slightly older than Nicholas anyway, who ran the local sub-post office, then we'd gone on into Strathlyon, to Sameways, the first supermarket to come to the town and still our favourite, where we'd stocked up with all we'd need for a week, we hoped. As soon as we'd sorted out freezer food from fridge food from cupboard food, fruit from vegetables, the edibles from the non-edibles such as tooth-paste or shoe-laces, I had then to dehead and degut the fish before putting them also in the fridge or freezer, depending on the day I'd planned we'd eat them. With the free part of my brain, (or was it my mind? I was never quite sure where the boundary comes, anyway the part which isn't needed for any totally practical task), I began to think about St Benedict whose Day was shortly approaching.

I knew I must go to Mass on whichever day it was, one day at the beginning of next week. I owed him so much. Since a few years ago, just after I'd read an excellent book about him, he'd been often in my mind, though just lately I had lost this habit, which was sad. He needed bringing back more into my life again. In this little book, I could remember well, I'd learned three important lessons from him.

The first was that life is more orderly and one's time more profitably used if, as he suggests, one's day is divided suitably into periods for prayer, study, physical work and recreation. This is a very practical idea of his, even, or especially, for those of us not living in monasteries. The trouble was, (and I find, to this day, it still is), a day is too short for all that I would like to do, and the strength for all this, and the ability to concentrate my mind on it, was insufficient. But, all the same, having a plan helped to keep the time spent on each occupation reasonably in proportion. It would have been lovely to have had more time for prayer and for study, though reading, which might be recreation, was often study, and much of it, too, was often closely related to prayer. My active work included household chores, cooking most often, as little housework as possible, and, I hoped, even less mending, preferably none.

Gardening was definitely active work. I enjoyed that in good weather, though I tried not to do any, as I've said before, when it was beastly outside. Going for a walk in the wood must be recreation rather than active work, as it was an activity which took up the time I would otherwise have given to gardening. Of course, walking often included meditation which was a helpful (if vague) sort of prayer. Listening to music was another recreation, though it, too, could often be thought of as a kind of meditation. Or is that wishful thinking?

What about letter writing? Though I didn't do as much even then, in those far away days I'm writing about. I'd almost given it up in favour of the telephone, which I enjoyed. I felt nearer a friend or one of the family on the phone, the whole process was achieved much more rapidly and more even-sidedly and more personally, the tone of both voices being heard on both ends of their line. (Let's not think of the extra cost - and I didn't!) But phoning couldn't classify itself very clearly into any of St Benedict's divisions, unless it was a recreation, though telephoning was often a serious business with serious often tedious subjects. One's words aren't often entirely flippant. I'd certainly never thought of them as such.

And even more than a phone call, I'd thought, driving in and out of Strathlyon seemed to fit into no category. It was an experience not experienced by St Benedict. It was possible, though, in the short spell of time spent in the drive, perhaps a quarter of an hour, to meditate on something simple. It depended on circumstances in the same way as such things are possible on a walk. There could be moments of calmness but they could be equally though unexpectedly interrupted on the way into town or on a walk through the wood. During a long run, as on the journey south to Westlake, things were different. Nicholas usually drove nearly all the way, so then I'd have plenty of time for meditation and be often helped by inspiration from the scenery.

Secondly, I had to thank St Benedict for teaching me that everything we do is holy. All our days and all the hours of the day are gifts from God and we must give them back to him. In consequence, all we do should be done well, as well as we can, as a form of prayer. Everything we use, he said, should be looked after with the same care as are all the holy objects on the altar. I was very impressed by this idea when I first read about it. I began at once to take great trouble carefully cleaning my trowel and spade and fork and secateurs when I put them away after working in the garden. I continued to do this and I still do, even after as short a moment of gardening as old age permits. That's the one time when I have continued to remember St Benedict. Though, I must say, at Whinside, our garage itself, where we stored all those objects, was fairly neglected. I knew I should never have made a good Benedictine for which I was sorry.

St Benedict's third bit of advice was about stability. I wished I had known about this when I was younger. I would have saved many hours of fretting. Wherever we are, says St Benedict, God is the same. There's nothing to be gained in the matter of finding him by changing our situation. We should stay where we are. Continue to do what we are doing. We can search for God as well where we are now as we could if we went away somewhere else. Similarly God can come to find us wherever we are now as well as he could if we changed our work place or our house or our friends. It doesn't do to keep chopping and changing. Of course, he says, we must all be open to God so we shall hear him when he does call us to change and go in a different direction. This message of change may come to us quietly, in slow steps, growing in its insistence as the days go past, or it may strike suddenly, unexpectedly, out of the blue, perhaps in the shape of a disaster which changes everything for us suddenly. In the first case, when the change comes slowly, we may hardly notice God's hand in what's happening and we may end up, in spite of this change, not feeling much nearer to him than we felt before. A few months may go past before we recognise God's part in all that's happened. But in the second case, in a disaster, we'd probably not be able to resist falling into his welcoming arms and would gladly allow him to support us with his love. Unless we revolted against what was happening and wanted to fight against it. But whatever has happened we must try to accept it, to find his love in it; certainly we mustn't give him up altogether, a loving God would never desert a loving child, however it may seem. Often we can't realize straightaway how he is going to change what looks like a disaster into a victory.

And of course there was St Benedict's ladder, I nearly forgot that. The ladder makes a very good illustration of our life on earth. The two sides of the ladder represent, on one side, our bodily and

67

intellectual, brainy life, and, on the other, there's our spiritual life, our prayer life. Twelve rungs join the two sides of the ladder together. On the bottom rung we start by learning about the fear of God which is the beginning of wisdom, and after we have climbed to the top rung we at last find that perfect love for God which casts out all fear.

Then, at last, after my awkward work with the knife on the fish was accomplished, I was putting the fillets into the fridge and freezer. (I'm at least three times slower at this fishy job than the experts are. Though later, long after the time of this story, there did appear behind the fish-counter, people willing to do it for me). After I'd finished this job, I began to wonder why the modern translation of the Bible had turned the old phrase about the loaves and fishes into the loaves and fish. It sounded odd. Well, certainly odd to me. Does it sound odd even to those young people who have never heard the old phrase? Do they automatically think of the Miracle of the Loaves and Fish and not of the Miracle of the Loaves and Fishes? Possibly it's happened that someone has spread the idea around that fish is a word like sheep or deer and has no separate plural form. I wonder.

As I worked I'd been practising saying to myself, 'I've been de-gutting the fish I bought', and I'd been hoping, this phrase could indicate there might be more than one fish on my chopping board. Sometimes it sounded in a way all right though at other times definitely not. The word fish can stand for one or more fishes as a collective idea. (How many fish in the sea? People are used to that), but I don't think that 'loaves and fish' as we meet these two words in the modern gospels sounds right. Especially as the actual numbers of fishes and loaves are quoted and the loaves themselves are given always a proper plural form. In present day language at the fish counter should I say, 'Please may I have two herring?' or 'Please may I have two herrings?' The first sounds very affected, as if I were a county person who would refer to the shooting of pheasant when he meant the shooting of many individual pheasants."*

---

* I've just learnt that in Africa animals are referred to in the singular however many these are, but the 'rains' is always used in the plural as a little rain never happens. Only great downpours.

68

As I washed my hands under the tap and was free to look out of the window, I admired the crocuses which, mostly, had opened out in the mid-day sunshine. Then just in front of me, in a corner of what was meant to be a polyanthus bed, though there was very little sign of this on that day, was a tightly packed clump of pale mauve crocuses not quite open. Suddenly a vole came running from under a little azalea bush, and he (or she) bit off one of the flowers and ran back again to the bush with the stalk in his mouth, the bud pointing forwards. In a few seconds he came again to bite off another flower and ran back again, and again he came, and again till I lost count of how many times. Soon almost half the flowers had been taken by the vole. Would it be to line his nest? Or was it her nest? How delicious, to be born a blind baby vole on a bed of crocus flowers.

At that moment Nicholas walked along in front of the house, the birds flew away from the bird feeder and the vole ceased for the moment to come for his/her baby bedding. Nicholas came in and I told him what I'd seen.

"It was so good," I said to him. "I've never seen anything like that before. I couldn't bring myself to run out to shoo him or her away, the crocuses are just as much theirs as ours, even though it was ourselves who planted the original bulbs. There are lots and lots of other crocuses for us to look at."

"It's time for lunch," said Nicholas.

"Yes, of course," I replied, bringing myself back with a great effort to the present moment. I made myself remember St Benedict.

"All work is holy, do all work as well as possible." I said to myself. "Don't panic, don't rush. Ten minutes more or less at the other end is neither here nor there. Don't be tense, relax your shoulders. Lift your ribs away from your pelvis as the egg out of an egg cup. Lift yourself up as if by the ears. Make your feet springy, move gently, don't stab at things."

I quite quickly had the vegetables in their pans on the stove and then I'd only to get out the cold chicken and stewed brambles and apples all of which were ready and waiting in the fridge.

'The yoghurt has just come home with us," I encouraged myself. "The coffee can make itself while we eat. I would have some sherry if it were not Lent, so I must not. I feel reasonably calm, cool and collected, how marvellous! Perhaps I don't feel quite as conscious as I usually do of the fact that I don't enjoy cooking. I'm not interested in it. But that's not true. I'm interested in producing well-prepared food, not overdone or underdone. I like it to be nourishing, digestible, enjoyable and not junk food. It's the actual job of cooking I find tedious. It takes me away from the things I'd much rather be doing. All the same I appreciate my blessings, the good health of both of us, a happy home and lots of work most of which I do enjoy very much indeed."

LENT: AT PHILIP'S

In a week or two the day came for us to set off by car to spend ten or twelve days with our elder boy Philip and his wife Joyce in Marvin, a village not all that far from our old home at Westlake. It was within easy reach too of Philip's job at Riverton (a little nearer than Seaborough), and we could easily drive to see most of our friends and relations who were still living in those parts. This annual visit of ours took place usually in March, a fairly calm month for Nicholas and the St Andrew's accounts. It was a time, too, usually uncomplicated by the arrival of Easter and also the spring was hardly ever so advanced that Nicholas needed to begin any serious gardening at Whinside. Also, by then the days were lengthening out quite a lot which helped our return trips back to Marvin after evenings spent with friends who lived some distance away.

We had a good trip and arrived in good time at Roundwood, the family home. Nicholas hooted the horn gently and at once Joyce opened an upstairs window.

"Go away," she called laughingly. "Go away! I'm not ready for you. Your beds aren't made yet."

"Well, yes, it's true," Nicholas called back. He'd got out of the car by then. "We've arrived a whole hour earlier than usual, than we meant to. We are sorry."

"It's the roads," I said as I, too, got out of the car. "Every time we come there's a new length of road been opened. It's remarkable what a difference even a short bit makes. We forget about this, of course, and leave home early with a great effort just like we used to, instead of taking things easily and not rushing to get away."

"Come in all the same, we'll soon be sorted out. I'll put the kettle on."

Our two grandsons, Michael and Robert, were at home too, also Lucy, another black labrador. Mike was in his second year at a comprehensive school, a short bus ride away, and Bob was half way up the local village school.

Marvin was on the whole a picturesque and historic old village which over the years had been enlarged and developed as such places

71

are these days with various areas of modern housing built in the gardens of demolished grand Victorian residences. A noble copper beech grew on the green at the heart of the village, around it some fascinating old sandstone and black and white houses of different shapes, sizes and ages stood. At Christmas time there were coloured lights strung on the branches and on one evening many people gathered to sing carols. In spring, the time when we were usually there a grand display of crocuses in yellow, white and deep purple cheered up the ground under the tree, and celebrated another happy season.

From the green, twisting old lanes led to groups of houses of various periods. Many of these so called roads were unadopted and so, as a result of their intentional neglect, could be full of potholes to discourage inessential traffic, and this was achieved even more so in wet weather when the hollows in the rough surface became deep puddles.

Only a short walk away from here in a pleasant leafy road, Philip and Joyce's small white house, Roundwood, stood surrounded by its garden. Throughout the village, as here, there were many groups of tall old trees as well as newer and quite adventurous kinds which were set in grassy areas and along the verges of the roads.

I enjoyed staying at Joyce's. I felt as welcome there as I did when I went to Jane's house at Easter Kilcoy. Nicholas too was always very happy there. He could talk in his own idiosyncratic way without offending anyone. He could relax and not have to plan overmuch what he was going to say before he said it.

"Here you can ask what time the next meal will be and get an informed answer," he said to Philip. "Not like at your brother John's. Christine is a bit vague about time."

"That's putting it mildly," said Philip.

"But she's very organised for places," I put in. Poor Christine often needed defending against the family's masculine element. "I mean in her house everything does have a place, though it's true nothing much has a time."

"I suppose you've got lots of friends and relations to see," said Joyce.

"Well, yes. Of course we're going to see John and Christine as soon as possible."

72

"And we'll ask them over here for a meal next weekend."

"Oh, that would be lovely," I said. "Nicholas has to go to see his sister and brother-in-law, and I need to visit my cousins on their hill in Wales."

"Will you come with me to the Mothers Union on Thursday evening?" Joyce asked me.

"I'd love to. I always enjoy it. Though I'm just waiting for the courage to ask why, at your meetings, you don't say a prayer for the most wonderful Mother of all, but I wouldn't want to get you into trouble."

"Oh, don't worry. I'm usually in disgrace anyway so a bit more wouldn't matter. I'm always putting my foot in it at the PCC too. I get sticky about things and won't always say 'Yes, Vicar', as we're expected to and most people do."

"After I got back home last year I was thinking about Mary the greatest Mother we have. I was thinking perhaps it would be a good idea if the Mothers Union said the Angelus at the beginning or end of their meetings. Only you needn't call it that, they might be nervous. After all, they'll know the words, they're more or less directly from the New Testament and the collect at the end of the prayer is the normal one for the Annunciation, so no one should take offence. It's in your Prayer Book as well as in ours. You know:

'... as we have known the incarnation of thy Son Jesus Christ by the message of an angel, so by his cross and passion...'
and

'The Angel of the Lord brought tidings to Mary: and she conceived by the Holy Ghost.' '...Behold the handmaid of the Lord; be it unto me according to thy word.'
and all the rest."

"Don't be too imaginative, Betty," said Nicholas. "Anyway, we'll not worry about getting in touch with any of our friends or relations tonight. Tomorrow morning will be quite soon enough and we'll have by then regained some energy, with luck, enough for telephoning and coping generally."

"If it's all right with you," I said, having suddenly remembered my poor friend. "I want to go off for a night to visit Ruth. It would be too much for Nicholas, a night at Much Milford. He couldn't stand it.

But I seem to be able to bear up without too much trouble, in fact I enjoy being there."

"I suppose it's because she's always lived by herself," said Joyce, "that she's developed her own peculiar ways and anyone else's ways upset her."

"But you get used to it. A lot of her strangeness is due to her back trouble and because of this she has, all over the house, lots of long flexes in loops and knots leading to all her electrical gadgets, radio and TV and heaters and so on, so they're always handy for her to switch on and off. For the same reason, in the kitchen, the electric kettle and suchlike things are propped up on trays or on odd bits of wood at just the right height for her to reach. To an ordinary outsider everything looks precariously balanced if not perhaps actually dangerous, but to Nicholas it's all definitely alarming. I get used to everything and in a strange way feel at home there in a very short space of time."

"When do you want to go?"

"Will it be all right if I go by train on Monday? And then Nicholas can come on Tuesday by car, stay for lunch, and then bring me home. I expect he'll have to do some odd jobs for Ruth and look at some of her dangerous electrical arrangements, or maybe move some of the furniture around."

"How's your father, Joyce?" asked Nicholas suddenly.

"He's fine. Better than he was last year. He enjoys going up to the club, playing snooker or just talking. He's looking forward to bowls again in the summer. I'll ask him in for a meal one evening."

"Yes, do," I said. "And we'll pop round in a day or two to say Hello. But, Joyce, you exaggerate about people annoying you in the PCC. Nicholas and I are always so impressed by how many friends you have here, both of you."

Joyce's father lived just round the corner. Her mother had died a few years before which had naturally meant a great change in her father's life. He'd given up his old house in Westlake to come to live near her and had had to make new friends which had not been easy for him. However this last year he'd begun to feel himself much more part of his 'new' village where Philip and Joyce played a very active part in what was going on.

LENT: SUNDAY AND SERMONS

It was Sunday. I had woken early and was beginning to contemplate getting up to make a pot of tea for Nicholas and myself. Philip was already up, he wasn't a lie-in-bed type of person. The boys felt restless when they heard their father moving around and so were pleased to get up too. Joyce tried to relax in bed for a little while more but she soon joined them and so, as usual, the whole family were not much later sitting down to breakfast than on a weekday. Philip was good in the kitchen, he usually organised Sunday's breakfast as well as, often, Sunday's lunch.

I got up and made our tea and then went back to bed to enjoy it and wait till Philip had finished with the cooker and toaster. I lay in bed thinking about the day that was to come. Nicholas and I had planned to go to the morning service, (the Mass, only it wouldn't do to use that word in Marvin), in the parish church. Bob was going to Sunday School in the church hall accompanied by his mother who was on duty that Sunday. Philip and Mike were staying at home. Philip liked to assert his independence at times and often enjoyed a quiet Sunday morning at home on his own or with just his elder son. Mike used to sing in the choir, and he had been confirmed, but nowadays he often chose to stay at home with his father.

On Sundays at Ardness we went whenever possible to the Mass (where the word was regarded as normal), to St Andrew's and also to Evensong, and we often went once or twice in the week to the midday service. When we were away from home we always hoped to go on the Sunday to Communion if we could do so without putting our relatives to any trouble, which was certainly the case at Marvin.

Then my mind wandered in the way it usually does in the early mornings. I began to think about the possibility of my ever having time to go to Mass every day, and would that be a good idea? Not that it was likely to be a real possibility.

If I could, if only I did have the time, it might keep me facing in the right direction and I wouldn't feel so lost before the next time came round. But that's an 'If only' question and Edward often warns us that it's not a good thing to go through life saying, 'If only..' and here I am doing just that. Silly of me though this kind of 'If only', if one thinks about it, can't be really wrong. I do agree with him, though, its an awful waste of energy to spend time, as some people do fretting about what didn't happen in the past, or that things could be different now. When I say 'If only I had more time for prayer in my life', I'm expressing a very natural feeling. I'm not seriously moaning. It's a wish that might lead to something better. And then I began to think about nuns and how I was obviously unlikely to become one. I'd never get on in a nunnery anyway, I didn't think.

"You could be the abbess," Father Christopher had once suggested when we'd been discussing such problems some time ago.

"That would be hopeless for everyone," I'd remonstrated rather promptly. "It takes me all my energy to organize myself. I'd never have any left for organizing a conventful of nuns. And from what I've read, they don't sound the easiest of people to manage."

But all the same I knew it would indeed be a benefit to have enough time for all the daily prayers I would like to say. If I were in the right place to put me always in the right mood then I'd love it. I'd feel safe then, as if I could never set off in the wrong direction.

Then, soon enough, it was time for me to get up and make breakfast for the two of us. And shortly four people, grandparents, daughter-in-law and one grandson, set off to walk up to the church.

"It would be silly to pressurize Mike to come to church, or either of them for that matter," said Joyce as we walked along.

"I agree," I replied. "Though I don't see anyone ever bothering to try to pressurise Philip, not into anything."

We soon got up to the green with its beech tree and bright display of crocuses. Then, only a short distance beyond, was the ancient sandstone pre-Reformation church of All Saints. It was a beautiful building with many interesting details of different periods, outside and in. There were gargoyles with hideous mossy faces to let the rain off the roof, gothic style windows on the north side with lovely colourful glass, and unusual classical ones with small panes of plain glass on the south. There was a beautiful carved oak screen in front of the Lady Chapel, carved pew-ends of varied designs in the choir, an elegant chandelier of brass, its original candles replaced by not too obviously electric lights, and a plaque with a bullet hole in it, a reminder of the

Civil War. I never could remember the real purpose of this plaque, my whole attention each time I looked at it being taken up by the bullet hole. I need hardly tell you either that, though it was an old church with a history from deep in the past, it was not therefore secure from modern liturgies. We were to have Rite B.

"No need to fuss," I said to myself. "It's almost all similar to what we're used to. It's just that little bit different in a few places, enough to trip me up." So I settled myself down for a short prayer of hope, and, in the end, I enjoyed all the service except the sermon.

The subject was taken from the Gospel set for that Sunday in Lent in the ASB, the Transfiguration. I was used to this event being celebrated in August, but I told myself again not to fuss. There are good reasons for its inclusion in Lent, for it must foreshadow the cross and the resurrection.

However it turned out to be one of the strangest sermons I had ever heard. I was upset in a way I'd never been upset before. It was altogether contrary to any idea I had of what a sermon should be. It should be, hopefully, I thought, a call to deepen our understanding of the gospel and therefore of our faith and to increase our love for God.

The preacher that morning was not the vicar of Joyce's parish, for he had gone to preach elsewhere. It was a retired clergyman who had kindly come from a neighbouring town to take the service in his place. At first he spoke quite encouragingly about the symbolism of the event, the change in the appearance of Jesus, the nearness of God, and the words: 'This is my Son, my chosen, listen to him,' and the fear of Peter, James and John. But then he went on to say that none of this really happened. I was very indignant at the time though of course I had to keep my feelings bottled up inside me. Afterwards in my account of it to Philip and Joyce over lunch I was able to explode and let off steam.

I told them the preacher had said we need not strain our imagination to visualize anything out of the ordinary. (Really he did say this. I wasn't making it up!) The disciples, he went on, sensed that Jesus was moved by an inward experience, 'as if' God were there and had spoken to him. There was no need to think Jesus was really changed in his physical appearance at all. It was only just that - as you would say of someone who has had a lovely surprise - 'His face lit up.'

All that lovely bit about his face really shining as the sun (certainly not only 'as if' so doing), and his garments becoming white and dazzling, white as the light, such as no fuller on earth could whiten them, those words weren't meant to be taken literally, not as truly descriptive. It was awful, for those words are so memorable and seem truly to be describing an actual happening. I'd never worried about their perhaps not being true and I wasn't going to begin now. Anyway unless we see the supernatural side of Jesus' connection with his Father the story seems very pointless and flat and certainly in no way increases our faith.

I couldn't stop in my telling the others about this, the words were coming quickly from my heart. "How can it be that a clergyman of all people should take the magic out of the Bible? I don't mean magic in its literal sense, but in the sense of the strong glorious mystery - just what we turn to the Bible to find. It's monstrous. I'd wanted to jump up in the pew and shout that of course it was all true, every word of it, that it was truly a very much out of the ordinary and infinitely significant happening. It's true the Transfiguration is a kind of forewarning of Easter Sunday morning: Christ glorified. I do wonder though what that clergyman preaches when he comes to Easter and the resurrection. Does he say, 'Don't stretch your imagination, it didn't really happen?' Does he say, "Christ didn't rise from the dead, the tomb wasn't empty, he's not risen or ascended or glorified?' Does he think it's only something made up afterwards to make us feel good? Is that what he'd say? What does his congregation think?"

"I thought I was going to have great trouble restraining your Mother," said Nicholas to Philip.

"I couldn't even complain to the preacher afterwards, for he was deep in conversation with some one at the door. Though perhaps that was just as well. If it had been your own vicar who always remembers us, or pretends to in a charming sort of way, it would have been different, I would certainly have stopped to remonstrate. Though normally there's no trouble with him. He usually preaches helpfully if a bit dryly. Perhaps it was just as well I'd no opportunity. I might have got heated and ratty which might have done more harm than good and got the Dashwoods a bad name. I might have involved your happy respectability for no good reason."

After the roast lamb was cleared away and the fruit salad and ice cream had been brought it, and there was a gap in the conversation, I began again.

"It reminds me of when we were still going to St Margaret's at Dunmarkie. Here again it was a visiting preacher. He was on holiday, staying in the rectory while our own rector was on holiday. The subject that time was Lazarus and Martha, with Jesus saying, 'I am the Resurrection and the life' and Martha's suddenly understanding, and then Jesus at the door of the tomb saying 'Lazarus come forth'. It's all so dramatic, isn't it? And so out of this world, no one could possibly have made it up. "He stinketh'. it must be true. * And here again it leads up to the real resurrection of Easter which defeats death altogether.

"And again the preacher went on to say we needn't stretch our imagination to believe it. He said Lazarus wasn't really dead, not physically, only spiritually dead. He'd lost interest in his religion and gone off into the wicked world on a spending spree and all sorts of bad people had had an evil effect on him. So Jesus came and talked to him about the spirit of God and he repented, and for some reason this made Martha believe Jesus was the Christ, truly the Son of the living God. It could hardly be his just getting Lazarus to be sorry for his spiritual weaknesses that would provide the right opportunity for Christ to say, 'I am the resurrection and the life' nor set a seal on Martha's understanding. I couldn't believe my ears. I was less worried at that time than I would be today, for that was still in my doubting period. Though I never doubted Jesus's miracles. I've always been sure about their happening, just as it's written about them."

"I remember all that very well," said Nicholas "Your mother got all fidgety and wanted to start arguing but she knew it was impossible. And in those days she felt too shy to go and talk to the clergyman about it afterwards. Just as well."

"I was amazed at what I'd heard," I went on. "As it stands in the Bible it all makes sense and is completely convincing. Thank goodness for Edward and Christopher who preach the faith as it has

---

* One of the modern NT translations uses the words 'bad odour' instead. Oh dear!

79

always been. And Canon Harper too, they are all so good. They never preach anything except the faith and the Gospel and how it all affects the way we live, its effect on our hearts and minds. We are lucky, fortunate, at St Andrew's."

Joyce said, "Our own vicar is good, his sermons are very reliable. I nearly always enjoy listening to him, though, as you say, he's a bit dry, not very exciting, not likely to convert anyone."

We all agreed with these opinions, though with different degrees of enthusiasm. And then, although the conversation went off in other directions, my thoughts stayed with Sundays in general and with this present one in particular. Then I began to wonder how they all were in Strathlyon and what kind of sermon I'd missed there. Whoever had been in the pulpit it would have been a sermon infinitely more worthwhile listening to than today's at Marvin. I wished I'd been there. If only ... Oh, that won't do at all. It would be awful to have even the slightest attack of homesickness at this stage when we're really having such a good time here.

LENT: AT RUTH'S

To get to Ruth's from Marvin, I had to be driven by Nicholas to Riverton and from there catch a not very grand train to Much Milford. This chugged its way peacefully and unhurriedly through the calm countryside of the Welsh borders. I always enjoyed, though it was a rare pleasure, looking out at passing landscapes from a train. This sideways view of the world is much more restful than the usual one from the front seat of a car. That's more like being blasted. Often when driving along with Nicholas there's a rather frightening view of fast approaching traffic, or alternatively, there's the alarm of being suddenly overtaken by something enormous from behind. Fortunately motorways are a great improvement after busy single roads. There I can often detach myself altogether from at least the on-coming cars even if not from those overtaking us. But, of course, on motorways, at busy times we can be almost totally surrounded by movement and noise so we feel then there's not been much improvement.

On this day, happily, the carriage windows were cleaner than usual, so once we were out of the town I could clearly see the sunshine on the distant Welsh hills. This cheered me up, which was a good thing for I had been worrying a little about how I would find Ruth. During the first half hour the line ran across an open plain, later the scenery became more hilly and we wound our way through little wooded valleys each with its own little meandering tree-lined stream. I was enchanted here by everything, this scenery was much leafier and more friendly than our own at home, where we are surrounded mostly by mountains and wild open moorlands. Cosiness is charming for a change, I thought, though I knew I'd love Ardness when I got back there.

I thought about Ruth, and how, when she'd first gone to live in Much Milford, she'd still had time and some energy to spare. Before she moved she talked about looking forward to going to services in the beautiful ancient church there. She'd imagined herself being totally wrapped up in a reverently conducted service with the well-loved traditional words, those she'd known in childhood and which she hoped would bring her comfort and the confidence that, after all, she

81

would grow back into the faith she had so sadly grown away from while at work in London.

Well, I think that's what she hoped for. She'd certainly hoped the vicar would be like her father, educated, kindly, understanding. Instead he was modern and brash and evangelical. He had swept away the old Prayer Book and his services were strange and unpredictable. Those anchors which she'd expected to be forever there in the church had been taken away. Visits from the vicar and his wife didn't help her either: instead of listening to her problems and difficulties and then encouraging her, they never hid their disapproval of her doubts. Both of them seemed to share the parish visiting and they both appeared rather to despise her as she was not one of *them*. They knew of her reservations about the incarnation and other basics of Christianity, but had no idea how to help her. Ruth had tried to discuss the subject quietly with the vicar only, but this had turned out to be an impossibility.

I found the situation very confusing, I must say. Ruth seemed to want the comfort of the old traditional services, but how did that fit in with her lack of belief which she often expressed, of Christ not being truly the Son of God? How was I going to help?

The train eventually came into Much Milford station and I got out. Ruth was there to meet me with her wicker shopping basket on wheels. On the top of this we rather precariously balanced my case, and then walked together up the tree-lined main street of the town. We called at several shops for some last minute purchases and then took a short cut to her house through the churchyard. This was a fairly large and attractive area of well-kept grass round the church overhung with old trees which naturally so early in the spring were still in their winter bareness. There were some interesting old tombstones, though I noticed many were flaking, shedding large pieces, their elegant inscriptions sadly sliding to the ground. Then going through the gate on the farther side we found ourselves opposite Ruth's house, one of an attractive terrace, black and white above, red brick below, with a few feet of garden in front of each. The back garden however, as I saw from my bedroom window, was springlike with early daffodils and bright polyanthus primroses.

"I noticed the garden was all looking very cared for," I said, as we sat down for a cup of tea.

"It's not bad at the moment but I've no longer much energy for looking after it as it ought to be. I can't read much now either for it strains my eyes."

"I'm sorry then to have bombarded you with my letter about St Paul. You probably weren't in the mood for anything like that as you're not feeling up to so much these days."

"Well, I find I'm quite happy just to be myself, not to worry about believing or not believing. So long as I'm not a nuisance to anyone, so long as I keep well and am friends with my neighbours, I'm content. And I've really had to give up hoping the church, or rather the vicar, will help me."

"Can't the church come to you, I mean bring you communion. I mean Edward says that's one of his really important jobs, communion for everybody. It's what the church is all about."

'I'm not fussed. I've got used to not having it. I don't think I'm meant to be a religious person. I just carry on trying to do a little good now and again, and trying to do as little bad as possible, trying to earn a place in heaven."

"You can't earn a place in heaven," I remonstrated. "Heaven's a pure gift from God. God loves you for what you are, not for what you do. Though, of course, if you are good, you will do good anyway. It shows all the time you do love him because you are so good to people, even to the annoying ones."

"I don't really feel a need for the Mass, as you call it. I don't believe in anything supernatural. It just doesn't appeal to me."

"You mean the earth is where we are now and is as we know it, and God's in heaven and we came from there when we were born and we hope to go back there when we die."

"Yes, that's about it. It seems to work. It's very plain and simple and it keeps enough hope and courage alive in me. But all the same I would love to go to a traditional service. It would comfort me, it really would, and would be worth the effort of getting there. It's such a pity in this town where there are so many retired people, old people, that we don't have a traditional kind of church with a traditional kind of vicar. Some people drive ten miles on Sundays to Little Milford. I was given a lift there a few times by friends, but then I had a patch of not being well and after that it didn't seem worth the effort to start again."

"You must think I'm a bit odd then," I said, "because I'm one of those who like to bring a bit of heaven down to earth while I'm still living here, and I feel the need to be lifted out of this earthly dimension into the realm of the spirit . Christ came to tell us we can do just this, and left for us the Mass where he comes into the Bread and Wine as we offer it to him and where we give ourselves to him at the same time as we receive him into ourselves."

"Oh, you make it sound too involved and complicated. I couldn't think of it like that. I used to go to communion regularly but I felt no different a person then from how I feel now when I don't go. As I've said to you often before, almost all church services worry me because I find the creed a great stumbling block. I don't like having to say I believe so many things which either I don't believe or I'm not certain about. The creed does sound as if it must be a list of certainties, and I know I must be honest or it's worse than useless. I don't believe that Jesus was conceived by the Holy Ghost nor born of the Virgin Mary, and so I suppose I can't be a believer in the Holy Catholic Church."

I admired Ruth's insistence on sincerity, but I was getting worried about what I should say next. I began again, "It's certainly true insincerity is pointless, for God sees all of each of us all the time. As you know, I used to feel just like you do, so much was unbelievable and so I thought I ought not to count myself a real Christian. But I've found over the last two years, (that's since I discovered that Jesus has to be Christ the Son of God and has been so from the beginning). I've gradually come to understand all these seemingly impossible facts must be true.

"Perhaps if I could explain it in my kind of simple words it would help you," I went on. "If Jesus is man from being Mary's child, and he is also God from being God's Son, he must be conceived by the Holy Spirit. So Mary must be a virgin. There is no other way. And I was always able to accept in my mind that there must have been a real resurrection. It seems to me that if God is powerful enough to create the universe and ourselves he is powerful enough to raise Christ from the dead. Not just his spirit but his body as well. Also it's theologically necessary for the resurrection to have happened, not only for the big reason that Christ, as God's Son, has to ascend to his Father in heaven with all that's implied in that, but for the lesser reason that as he, Christ, is both God and man, only his human part could die in the way that we die, the God part couldn't start to moulder away in the earth when buried; his whole body and spirit had to burst out, and it did. So the tomb must be empty, has to have been empty. He couldn't half rise from the tomb leaving his human half here on earth. All of him rose and went back to his Father which is why we are now joined to the Father too, in a way we never were before. I now think all those bishops who once helped me so much with their doubts are absolutely and totally wrong about all these things. They seem to imagine they are being very advanced in their views, but in fact they are leading themselves and lots of other people backwards.

"Beginning with Christ as God ... you don't mind my going on saying this do you?"

"No, no. I love it, it's fascinating, but it won't change me."

"If I say this to you aloud it helps me too. It sorts my ideas out for me. Because I'm not used to expressing them, my explanations can sound confused, even when I understand the problems in my mind. I need to begin with the belief that Christ is God, everything holds together from that in a solid cube of faith. You can know that Christ is God because the love which he demands from us or draws from us is a totally different kind of love from even the greatest love we give to human beings, even our best loved ones. The love he gives us is on a different level altogether from any love that humans can feel for each other. If we begin to chip away at the edges of our cube of faith, saying that such and such a detail of belief is unimportant, then the cube becomes like a collapsing tower block and the whole of our faith falls. If there were no virgin conception or no real resurrection, then Christ is not God and if that's so you must throw out all John, all Paul, most of Luke and Matthew and Mark, really all the New Testament and lots of the Old. In fact you destroy the heart of Christianity."

"You make it sound very convincing, but the day after you've gone I'll be back again where I am now. To believe for sure and on my own there would need to be something inside me which I've not got. It's not just faith which is missing, but a desire for faith. I'm content to be as I am."

I couldn't do more. Except that I made a resolution for more prayers for Ruth. I felt, all the same, that she was robbing herself of much happiness and contentment.

During the evening Ruth needed to watch one of her favourite TV programmes so I got out my book: Charles Morgan: *Sparkenbroke.* I thought this must be his best book. I was enjoying it very much. I was glad I could read through almost any noise and I still can. Of course it's got to be a good book, and the noise mustn't be too loud a noise. I've got too old to want to watch TV plays about other people's problems and romances. I've had so many of my own (I mean problems, not romances) in my long life. I've not got the necessary energy any more to be bothered listening to imaginary people's imaginary worries. I suppose real literature raises stories onto another plane so that our reactions are more - would it be - heavenly or rarefied? Beyond ourselves, anyway. I'm not sure. The telly's excellent for Ruth, though. It's like a good book for her. It's just the thing to pass the time now that she can't read much.

Nicholas arrived as arranged in the middle of the next morning. Ruth gave him some odd jobs to do. She had bought two time-switches to be fitted to electric fires which could therefore come on before she got up in the morning, one would be upstairs and the other in the kitchen. This is probably a better idea than her leaving a gas burner burning all night on the cooker as she used to do, though I couldn't have produced a very well-founded reason as to why this should be so. Then there were a few other patches and replacements to be achieved, including the moving around of the two heavy chairs in the sitting room.

After lunch after we'd said our farewells to Ruth Nicholas and I set off for our return journey back to Marvin.

"But poor old Ruth," I said to Nicholas as we drove along. "She's still in a muddle, but that won't surprise you. She'd love to go to a traditional church service with all the comforting old traditional words (as well as the Comfortable Words, of course), but she jibs at most of the creed. But that doesn't seem to worry her. So I mustn't let it worry me, I suppose. I shall just pray for her. And be terribly nice to her. But quite a few of her neighbours are very good and hover over her somewhat. And she's grateful and in return takes trouble with them."

"I sometimes think," I remarked about half an hour later, "one of Ruth's troubles is that life when she was younger, in the large family in her rectory home, was hardly connected to what her father preached on Sundays in church, the love of God and Christ as a trusted friend. I remember her saying how formal life was and in a way restricted. Her father was usually in his study or out visiting his flock and not easily approachable. He came in for meals but they were eaten almost in silence, all very staid. It's so different from the cheerful disorder we associate with family meals these days, eaten in the kitchen with everyone talking at once, or even how things were when our boys were young."

In another half hour I spoke again. I'd been thinking about modern services and hymns with catchy tunes and people's being keen on 'singing a new song'. I mentioned this to Nicholas.

"Well," he said. "It all depends on the new song. If we are to enjoy taking into our personal collection of well loved hymns some new song, it must be better than or at least as good as the best of those we already find a place for. It's not use trying to fit in some feeble verses where the words just happen to scan and rhyme but don't do you any good or there are repetitions enough to be boring; enough to make them easy to learn but not the sort to make us want to hang onto for ever.   And hymns need to praise God, they're not just to make ourselves feel good. We aren't in church for our own benefit but to worship God and thank him for our blessings."

"Yes, that's true. And my idea of good hymns are 424 and 425. In case you don't remember which those are I'll tell you. They're 'King of glory, King of peace' and 'Lead, kindly Light, amid the encircling gloom.' They're good and permanently memorable not only because they *are* good in themselves but all the more surely because so because they were written by poets, George Herbert and Cardinal Newman. And I can tell you too, following on from those, 426 is 'Lead us Heavenly Father, lead us o'er the world's tempestuous sea." though I can't remember who wrote it except he's from a long time ago, and 427 which is George Herbert again: 'Let all the world in every corner sing, My God and King!' A new song needs to be very worthwhile indeed to earn a place in my collection."

Then, a bit later, it was Nicholas's turn to break the silence: "Is it Joyce's night for Guides?"

"No. Tomorrow's her Guide night. Tonight's not even Mike's judo either. That was last night and it's also on Thursdays. But there's so much going on in that household I don't try to remember it all."

"There's Joyce's Rangers on Mondays and Mike's Cadets on Fridays."

"And you never know when the Residents' Association will need Philip to go and take the minutes."

"And just when I'm beginning to learn about all their activities, it's the day for us to go home and I've got it all to learn over again next year. For it will - much of it - have changed by our next visit.

Then we were nearly back in Marvin and we'd only to look for the right gateway and drive in and we'd be there with lots of friendly cries of welcome greeting our return. How super!

LENT: DREAMS

We were safely back at Roundwood, both of us glad to be again gathered into a sane household. Later in the evening, when we were all sitting round the dining-room table after finishing the evening meal, each one of us unconsciously loath to be the first to move and break up the pleasant moment of relaxation, an interesting conversation began.

Mike was telling us that, a night or so ago, he'd had a dream. "I was sitting in a train going along, I don't know where to now, though in the dream I did, when, suddenly, instead of going straight on, as I'd expected, we began to take a left hand turn onto a side line. I knew this was wrong for me but could do nothing about it. We went on a bit further and naturally came to quite the wrong station from the one I'd intended. We all got out, and, though everyone else seemed to have got to where they wanted to, I didn't know where to go to nor what to do. Then I woke up before anything could happen about trying to come back to where I'd wanted to get to.'

"If you have a dream about being in a train," said Nicholas. "I think it means you don't really know where you want to be going in your real life and are letting someone else drive you along so to speak. But that might be not unnatural in a young person, such as yourself, though not good for an adult."

"That's right," said Philip, "and if you dream you're driving a car you are guiding your own life. You're still guiding your own life even if you find you're going the wrong way and you're getting lost. You might in your dream find yourself in a suburban area where there were no sign posts because everyone is meant to know his own way, or you are in the country where the signs point to places you can't find on the map. This shows you're unclear about your life. If you're the passenger in a car in a dream and know who the driver is, it's he who's influencing your real life too much. In a train, you don't know the driver, so you are not aware of who or what is influencing you though somebody must be. I've had all these kinds of dream, but thank goodness, I've grown out of them. They were very frustrating. Even being in a car driving myself in a dream seemed unsatisfactory for

89

nothing ever went right. I still got lost in one-way streets in towns and ended up in the wrong street and outside the wrong building."

"I used to dream about trains too," I added. "It was awful. I would try to pack for a journey but I never was able to finish the job because I kept losing what I needed, or nothing fitted into the case properly and then I couldn't get it shut, and so I never got to the station in time for my train. Even now I feel awful about real stations and I get depressed even when I've gone to meet someone I'm looking forward to meeting. Jung says the dreamer of that kind of dream is too ambitious and is, as it were, pushing himself to catch a train he's not intended to travel on. The dreamer's straining to live a life that's too hard on his nervous system. It might be an ambition to get on well socially in society, or to do well at work, or want to climb up in business beyond one's natural capacity. But with myself I decided that, being only mediumly good at lots of different things, I was trying to be very good at too many things, including being a good mother for which I'm certainly not well equipped at all.

" I managed to persuade myself not to try for perfection in every direction, not to attempt too many jobs in a day, to have fewer hobbies, to accept there should be some things left undone or not begun at all, and also to realize it didn't matter if I did waste some time of each day doing things which weren't obviously productive, to relax in fact, to stop the struggling which had become a habit. Then the train in a station dream went away.

"It was hard to change myself into a more easy-going person, it took me a long time, but after a bit I did get the hang of it and then I felt a lot better and more cheerful. It's important to give up being an ambitious person or a perfectionist. Of course there are some people who need to be more ambitious or less slapdash or their train would never leave the station at all and they'd be sorry later."

"I had a strange dream the other night which I can't make head nor tail of," said Joyce. "In my dream I'd gone round to Dad's to do some odd jobs and was going to get him some lunch ready and stay to eat it with him. He'd put some things out on the bed for me to see to, mending and such like. Then he went out into the garden to do a bit of digging or something. I sat on the bed and began to work but soon fell asleep - this was all in my dream - with my head on the pillow. When I woke, still in my dream, it was just about one o'clock and not only had I done hardly any mending but I'd done nothing about lunch. Almost at once I heard my father come in through the back door and I thought, 'Oh, good, here's Dad. He'll tell me (as he certainly would in real life) not to worry, that he's not cross with me, that all the jobs can be done another time, that we'll soon find something to eat'. But it wasn't like that at all. He came along to the bedroom and began talking to me in a strange declaiming kind of voice. He spoke fairly loudly and slowly but all the same I couldn't understand what he said. His words were going over my head and splitting up in a jumble into their separate syllables. I was upset and puzzled. Then Dad just walked away. And that was the end of the dream and I was left, when I really woke up, in the real morning, with a feeling of failure, of insufficiency, as if I'd failed my father in not understanding him, as well as by falling asleep, of course."

"Well," said Nicholas. "that's very interesting. I'll suggest part of an explanation. We'll suppose your father is God, which is probable, as we often call God, Father. He's given you some jobs to do and you went to sleep over them."

"But I was very penitent about falling asleep and my father who represented God perhaps, as you say, should have been forgiving but he wasn't. And although I didn't understand what he was saying, I could tell the words weren't meant to be comforting."

"There's probably something in what you said about the words going over your head," suggested Philip, "more than in their bursting apart. Perhaps God's words were too difficult for you to understand. They in fact *were* going over your head as we say."

"I could actually see them going over my head before bursting. Of course that's a very dreamlike thing to see, to visualize a phrase that's normally just a series of words rather than a pictorial description. One often says 'went over my head' without thinking about one's actual head."

"It's all very puzzling," I said. "It sounds an important dream although its meaning isn't obvious. Perhaps we'll see the answer, or one of us will, later, when we're thinking about something different. The message of a dream often takes some time to come to us."

And then I thought it was my turn: "I had a really good dream just before Christmas. We were having some kind of a parish meal, at a long table. And my father came in. Well, you know it's years and years since he died and my memory of what he looked like is no longer at all clear. But there he was aged about 40 or 50, in 3D, not just as if I was seeing him in a photograph. I'd forgotten he'd ever looked like that, he looked so real and true, convincing, exactly him as he used to be. I was so surprised to be reminded of him so clearly. He had a folded bit of newspaper or a page of a magazine in his hand. When he first came in he took no notice of me at all but walked up the far side of the table talking to different people. This worried me. I wondered why he was behaving as if I weren't there. But in the end he came back, handed me the piece of paper, and at last smiled at me. Printed on this were advertisements of several rather grand houses for sale with photographs of each, as if it were a page out of the first bit of Country Life. That was all, he didn't talk to me or explain anything.

"When I woke I thought: 'Yes, I see. I think my father is God. His walking up the length of the table while taking no notice of me is like things had been in my real life, when God seemed to be keeping away from me although I was looking for him. Then at last when he turned to me and handed me this piece of paper, I couldn't think what it signified, what the country mansions for sale could mean. I'd not been thinking of any subject remotely of that kind. Then it was time for me to get out of bed, and I went into the bathroom and began cleaning my teeth, brooding on the dream and staring into the hand-basin. I was trying to make my mind concentrate on the house shown in the bottom right-hand corner of the page which fortunately I could still remember pretty clearly. It was illustrated, not with a photograph as all the rest were but by a line drawing. It was special. It was a Georgian or Queen Anne mansion, my favourite kind of house, with a great cedar on the front lawn. Then I understood. Of course, a cedar of Lebanon, of Libanus, as in the Psalms, and the lovely mansion. So I decided without hesitation that the message from God for me was that I will be welcome in his kingdom and he has my mansion waiting for me there, one of the promised many mansions. It was such a marvellous feeling, of relief partly, but also of satisfaction. The meaning felt right. It was like when you solve a crossword clue and you realize there can be no other answer. Only this was a much stronger and happier feeling than the crossword kind of solution usually gives."

"That's very clear," said Nicholas. "though I must say my own dreams are rather too rubbishy to be worth remembering. I certainly never do, for long."

"It's funny though," said Philip, "that God should send us these puzzles instead of making things clear for us straightaway."

"I think we are meant to be very hesitant about anything too straightforward," said Nicholas. "Some religions have everything clearly disclosed to the founder, every detail written clearly down for all to see, and this can lead to some very strange and rigid beliefs and behaviour. But we have our marvellous Bible in which there are so many problems and puzzles and alternatives among all the certainties that even the brainiest and most devout people are kept occupied in their Bible studies for whole lifetimes. This depth of hidden meanings seems to us more real and reliable that anything simple and clear. If anything is too clear we are suspicious. We are intended to ponder on what we read."

"And dreams," said Philip, "have always been puzzled over and their interpretations studied. Think of Joseph and Daniel, famous and valued as interpreters of dreams."

"Which is why it would be nice to help Joyce with hers."

"I did have a dream once," said Joyce, "which came back every night for about a fortnight, until I found the answer and then it went away. It was about my feeling naked and vulnerable when I was having a bath, which one doesn't normally do. Normally in a bath one feels comfy and cosy in the hot water and one's so used to this sensation that one doesn't notice one's nakedness and in fact any garment would spoil the jolly effect of the hot water. But here in my dream the bathroom had a large glass dome high up in the ceiling, and outside the glass people were walking round this dome, I suppose, on a raised-up sort of pavement. I was nervous they'd see me if they looked inside and downwards. This was a few summers ago, in August, when we were on holiday. I went to the local church each Sunday and after about two weeks, as I said, I heard the necessary answer in the Epistle. 'But put ye on the Lord Jesus Christ' - it was so simple. I just prayed and told myself to put Christ on as a garment and

I never felt naked again in a dream about having a bath. This new dream of mine didn't make me feel naked as such really but, rather, insufficient or inefficient, as I said. Though it did make me remember the old dream."

"What were the words of the Epistle which helped you last time?"

"It was about love as well as about putting on the Lord Jesus Christ. You'll know all the famous phrases as well as I do.

'Owe no man anything but to love one another ... love worketh no ill to his neighbour ... and it is high time to awake out of sleep ... the night is far spent, the day is at hand ... let us put on the armour of light.'

And then Paul adds:

'but put ye on the Lord Jesus Christ.'

"So I told myself to put on the Lord Jesus Christ and my dream stopped happening, I'm glad to say."

"Maybe this time we need to look in another Epistle or in one of the Gospels," suggested Nicholas.

"That's possible. Perhaps Joyce, in your dream you couldn't understand your father's words, because the Spirit of Christ wasn't in you, isn't in you, or not sufficiently or not yet. You need to take the Spirit more definitely into you.

"That's a good idea, isn't it?" said Philip. "And hopeful for you. Will we be able to find the place and in which Epistle?"

"Come on, Bob," cried Joyce, "it's long past your bedtime." Bob anyway had some time ago taken himself off to the playroom and was quite happily occupied with the radio car he'd got for his birthday. Mike too had gone upstairs to read his newest book, a thriller.

Later, when Bob was safely in bed Joyce and I got out our Bibles.

"I'm sure I was reading just what we're looking for not long ago," I said, "about the Spirit of God being in us. It must be in one of the daily lessons. Let's find the list in the prayer book. Let's see. Let's try 1 Corinthians, it seems about the right length of time ago. Look, here we are! Yes, this is it in the second week after Epiphany, in chapter 2.

" 'Eye hath not seen, nor ear heard, neither have entered into the heart of man, the things which God hath prepared for them that love him. But God hath revealed them unto us by his Spirit: for the Spirit searcheth all things, yea, the deep things of God.' "

"Yes, that sounds hopeful," and Joyce read on from her own Bible.

"'For who among men know the thoughts of man except the man's spirit within him? In the same way no one knows the thoughts of God except the Spirit of God.'

Then I went on to read the next passage:

"'Now we have received, not the spirit of the world, but the Spirit which is of God: that we might know the things that are freely given to us of God.'"

Then Joyce read.

"'This is what we speak, not in words taught us by human wisdom, but in words taught by the Spirit, expressing spiritual truths in spiritual words.'"

Then it was my turn again.

"'But the natural man receiveth not the things of the Spirit of God: for they are foolishness unto him: neither can he know them, because they are spiritually discerned only."

"All of which means, I think, that we each need to grow into a spiritual dimension and that is what you in your dream hadn't got so the words went over your head. It's all reasonably plain really, in comparison with some of Paul. He can often seem very abstruse and involved."

Joyce then added her version of the problem: "Those who have the Spirit of God in them will understand the truths taught by the Spirit, but ordinary men who don't have the Spirit of God in them, like I was still, in my dream, can't understand the thoughts and words of God: they can understand only thoughts and words of men. So my dream showed me the necessity of having the Spirit of God come into me. When this happens the words of the Spirit will no longer go over my head and break up into meaningless fragments but enter into my heart. That's really clear now, isn't it?"

"It's marvellous," I said, "you had such a good dream and we have so well discovered its meaning. Perhaps it is good we have to struggle a bit to find things out, what we are meant to do on our pilgrimage. Then we value the help we are given all the more."

"Let's go down and tell the others."

Later, as I lay in bed waiting for the sleep which was almost upon me, I suddenly thought of those peculiar sermons we'd been talking about on Sunday. It seemed as clear as anything to me now. Those preachers, both of them, had removed from the Bible stories all the words of the Spirit as they were written and which express so well the spiritual happenings involved in the stories and had replaced them with human words, words of the human spirit only, and then had hoped that this remaining human wisdom would satisfy their listeners, their congregation. One presumes *they* were supposed to have no spiritual dimension and their clergy had seen no need to help them find any. Which is what you and I would suppose was the purpose of going to church and listening to sermons. It's so unlike Edward who not only well understands the difference between a man's spirit and the Spirit of God and has told us often of the difference between the heart and the brain.

And I saw too, that that was what was the matter with Ruth. She actually wanted - it wasn't unconsciously she was doing it - to throw away the supernatural. Perhaps though it's not quite like the baby and the bathwater - but I wonder.

LENT: TO JOHN'S

It was still early in the week when Nicholas and I drove over to see our other son, John, his wife Christine, and their children, Simon and Anne. Often in other years we'd stayed with them at Westlake, but this time his shifts at Quince weren't convenient as he'd been working nights and needed to sleep quietly during the following mornings. Today however that spell of shifts was just over and he was enjoying a whole day at home. The children were close together in age, both of them younger than Mike but older than Bob.

Their house was similar in size to Philip's and equally comfortable. The decor inside was perhaps a bit more glamorous but the outside was definitely less so. Its situation was certainly different as there were almost no leafy areas in Westlake and the house was in a very windy though jolly spot just off the sea front with nothing taller in the road than privet or euonymus hedges and occasionally a dwindling sycamore or two.

"It's very advantageous not to be right on the front, especially on those days of terrible gales," said Christine, "though really, in my heart, I would have loved to have a house looking over the sea, to be able to watch the tide coming in and all the marvellous summer sunsets."

We had arrived in time for lunch and Christine had made a great effort to have it ready at the expected moment. We were enjoying a great exchange of news with John when we were summoned into the dining room. Our meal was ready.

After lunch we had our coffee in the sunny sitting room looking out at the small neat front garden.

"Look at your jasmine, it's much better that ours," I said. "Your rosemary looks happy too, ours almost always dies in a hard winter, wherever in the garden I put it."

Then we went a walk along the prom. This seaside road was never called the promenade, not being actually grand enough, I suppose, for such an elongated name, though its actual street signs proclaimed it The Parade, (though that name was never used either). The tide, a spring tide, had not long turned so there was water and just a bit of sand showing at the bottom of the sea wall below us.

"High water springs!" I exclaimed. "What a treat! It's usually neap tides when we're here with you and when we come out after lunch there's hardly any sea within sight."

The waves were turning over each other peacefully as we walked along, though all the time more and more smooth wet sand was being exposed by the ebb tide. Dunlins and sanderlings were running along the water's edge looking for food. They gave me a lot of pleasure, for I could remember how much I'd loved the sea all the long years we'd lived here. It was the one thing I'd really missed at Ardness, though there were, of course, many other excitements all around with mountains and moors and rocky coasts.

Suddenly some oystercatchers and curlews came flying past in small flocks low over the water, I was thrilled. Quite like old times, I thought.

"I'm enjoying this," I said to Christine, "At least you can be sure of showing good birds to your visitors, except perhaps in the summer when they've all gone away to their breeding grounds. When people come to stay with us they want to see eagles but it's not so easy. We can hardly ever find one."

John pointed out one of the many oil cans floating on the tide. This was where he would shortly, when the sailing season began again, be fixing a proper mooring buoy. He was not a Swift owner any longer but had a more substantial boat, one of the Seabird class named Kittiwake, which he kept in the winter on a piece of flat ground at the sailing club. His shift work gave him the chance to have lots of weekday mornings, afternoons and even whole days free, when he could take the boat out. He especially enjoyed sailing single-handed, though at weekends or in the summer holidays he usually took one or both of the children with him. Simon was a keen sailor, and he and his father spent many happy hours at sea, returning home full of fresh breezes and sunshine. The Westlake scenery itself was not romantic: the land behind the sea wall was flat and uneventful, but above the boat and all around were sky and sea. There were many opportunities to learn about the wind and the tides. On the flood tide the water came rushing in over the sand at great speed taking the unwary by surprise.

Conversely on the ebb it disappeared with a rapidity beyond expectation, threatening to leave oneself and one's boat high and dry on a sand bank before there'd been any chance of reaching one's mooring. Fortunately it was always possible at this stage to climb out of the boat, make the anchor secure and walk home across the sand. Then one could walk out when the tide was making again (though preferably not in the middle of the night) and sail the stranded boat to safety.

We got back from our walk just as Anne arrived from school followed shortly by Simon. It was lovely to see them, how much they'd grown, both in height and perhaps width and certainly in grown-up-ness. There was more talk again, of course. Anne was going to Brownies shortly, Simon has no special event to take him out that evening, but two difficult lots of homework which would need much concentration. As usual with all Dashwoods it was languages which gave the most trouble.

"Simon is still hopeless at spelling too," said Christine, "and Mrs. Banks is always grumbling about Anne's writing as well as about her spelling. Fortunately arithmetic comes easily to both."

"My own writing is awful," I said quickly to encourage Anne, "and it still looks messy and unformed, as if I were still only halfway to being grown up. They've probably inherited my handicap. I don't like *writing* as opposed to *lettering* which I do love. I mean I can't write nowadays even as well as I was expected to do at school, certainly not well enough for what's meant to be a respectable letter. But *lettering* as I need to do when I have to create a notice for the church, I don't find difficult, though I have to concentrate on what I'm doing. I do sympathize with Anne."

"I hear you're all coming over for a meal at the weekend," said Nicholas.

"Rather," said Simon.

Family reunions aren't always totally delightful I began to warn myself. It's not possible when several strong characters get together for all to go smoothly. But Joyce and I, the non-Dashwoods, would see things through. Christine's a non-Dashwood too, of course, but she didn't seem to notice the aggro that went on. However there'd certainly be more laughter than cross moments when we did all meet.

And fortunately children are not a problem in this respect, they're much easier than parents.

After an uncomplicated cup of tea with a few edibles out of tins and a lot more talking it was time for us to leave. There were many best wishes for all and for when we'd soon meet again, and then we drove off back to Philip's.

"It was lovely to see them," said Nicholas as we drove back. "They seem well and happy. It would be good though if the church were more a part of their lives."

"There's not much point worrying too much about that just now," I said, remembering my own earlier life. "At least they do go sometimes - at special times. For instance, Christmas doesn't just mean for them presents and eating and drinking. They do believe they're celebrating Christ's birthday. And Christine did mention Simon and confirmation to me last time we were here. John works hard and he so much looks forward to his sailing. He knows the sea and the fresh air are God's and being out in the boat is doing him good, even if he doesn't at present realize the goodness is spiritual as well as physical and mental. I mean it's not only his body and mind that are benefiting from being out on the sea, but his soul too."

"Yes, that's all true, and I expect his working often on Sundays and over some of the shifts at Christmas makes him feel it is only natural to go sailing even on Sundays when he's off work."

"And they're very keen on helping with local things like raising money for the lifeboat and John helps with running the sailing club. Christine's keen on the school and the PTA. They do join in doing helpful things."

When we were stopped at some traffic lights further on Nicholas said suddenly. "In a week's time we'll be really on our way home."

"I do look forward to that. Although I enjoy coming away to see everybody, I love the moment when we turn northwards onto the motorway. With the sun behind us and the blue sky ahead we begin to unwind the miles to home, or eat them up or whatever a car does. And I love that journey home just the same even when the sky's grey. It's lovely."

EASTER: IN THE GLEN

Easter was already over. Life flew past. However one afternoon in the following week I drove over to see Jane.

It was a lovely sunny day and I arrived to find Jane had been painting. A vase of spring flowers was on the table by the window, her new painting was propped up on a chair in a good light and her painting things were still on the table waiting to be put away.

"Oh, look, how super." I was very thrilled to see such a new and lovely thing. "You've got iris stylosa, (Oh, bother, it's iris something else now. It's so annoying, stylosa was such a stylish name. It had to belong to a lovely flower), and pussy willow, winter jasmine, Christmas roses, and primulas. Christmas roses are certainly not for Christmas in these northern climes."

"No," said Jane, "but it's lovely to have them now. Every year I collect nearly always the same kinds of flower, though more of some and less of others, depending on what I can find, and the vase may be a different one, but I never get bored with painting them. They arrange themselves differently every time. Every year the spring and its flowers has to be rejoiced over. I look forward to this day."

"You're right. Your painting is a celebration of spring. I couldn't ever get tired of looking at it, and obviously you haven't with painting it. The paint is so deliciously wet-looking, the colours are transparent and clear and bright. I love it."

"Things look beautiful when spring comes round again and the light begins to illuminate things rather than just enabling them to be feebly visible. I don't enjoy those awful gloomy mid-winter days, having to get up in the pitch dark for weeks on end."

"What about our going for a walk? Do you think it would be a good idea?"

"What about taking the car along to the beginning of Glen Donan and going for a walk from there?"

"Let's do that. We've not been for ages. Come on, Tess."

So we drove for a few miles till we came to a junction with a narrow untarred road which lead us into a little glen. As soon as we could, we parked the car and set out on foot with Tess running on ahead. For a few minutes we walked through a young birch wood and then came out where we had a loch on our right. On the left a hillside ran steeply up with a sparse covering of shattered birches clinging rather feebly to life amongst their many dead but not yet altogether rotted-away companions. (The result of overgrazing by the sheep which replaced the native population of the glens, those who were 'cleared' away to the coast or to America).

"I thought we had a very super Easter, didn't you?" said Jane.

"Oh, yes, I do. It was lovely. Or I thought it was. Or it was for me anyway."

"We are fortunate in having really special and lovely Holy Week services, it's all so different from the rest of the year. It's a great event, *the* great event."

"The road to Easter seems to begin on Ash Wednesday," I went on, thinking back to the weeks just past. "It's a road that brings us through Lent and then into Holy Week, with Maundy Thursday and Good Friday and Easter Eve, and then to Easter Day. The Saturday evening Mass was lovely. Especially it was so this year, I thought. The church was so quiet and beautiful when we first went into it, unlit except for the lights from the street outside shining through the coloured windows. Then for a short while our candles flickered and sparkled, and then all the church lights came on. I'm usually sorry when this moment comes, when the church returns to normal. It all seems rather disappointing. I feel it's not true it can be really Easter yet at that moment. Though the daffodils and other Easter flowers are all there, freshly arranged, a lovely change after a Lent with no flowers. I find it's hard to believe that Christ will be risen before we go home. In some way the church still seems too normal. I feel it's still Saturday, it's not yet Sunday, not Easter Day. Christ will rise on Sunday and not before. It's not like things are at Christmas where his coming takes places definitely after midnight, at the beginning of a long dark winter's day. At Christmas we've come to church long after our normal bedtime, we can feel it's Christmas morning. I never feel Easter is truly come till I wake up next day, on Easter Sunday morning, hopefully in the bright sunshine."

"I feel a lot of that too," said Jane, "though I hadn't put it to myself in so many words. I was thinking, though, to go back to Holy

102

Week itself. I always enjoy most of all the Seven Words from the Cross, the Three Hour Service on Good Friday. I love the quietness of everything in the church. There are people coming in and out all the time, but so silently, not disturbingly but creeping gently to their places. Everyone is kneeling devotedly, listening or praying, or standing to sing a hymn, all through that long period of time. The actual individuals are changing but they leave an impression on me of a really great and quiet crowd. Even if we're not all there at the same time there's an impression from every soul left on the atmosphere. We're all peacefully and totally absorbed, though what we are contemplating isn't peaceful: the immensity of Christ's redeeming us in his agony on the cross. But his words are full of hope, he is doing his Father's will which is his own will also, he and the Father are one, he is in control of events, even if at times we are doubtful this might be truly so. The weight of our sins is being lifted from us, we carry the hope of Easter Sunday in our hearts. On this Friday we kneel quietly, absorbing as much of this great mystery as our human nature will let us. It's after this service we can see Christ's saving grace, the day Christ is laid in the tomb and the work of his resurrection is begun."

"Edward always reminds us," I said, "that we are acting a story, the words of which are already written. We know about Easter Sunday before Holy Week begins. Every year we come to church to say and hear the same words, to increase our understanding, as well as celebrating a memorial. Every year we make the story more a part of ourselves. We learn we can't have Easter Sunday without Good Friday, there can be no resurrection without the cross."

"The story of Holy Week," Jane went on, "makes all our life make sense. Once I begin to join in the worship and the drama, the enacting of the story of Easter, I find myself carried along and I feel I mustn't miss any part of it. Many people seem afraid to come to church during Holy Week. Maybe this is because it's not something they've done habitually all their lives, and so they can't see clearly what to expect and so they stay at home safely. Is it safely?"

"Easter is deep and complicated. That's one of the marvellous things about Christianity. However brainy and intelligent anyone may be he will never get to the bottom of all the mysteries of faith. There will be always be more depths for him to explore and meditate on though it's a heart that's needed really."

"I think it may be that many people don't join in the worship of Holy Week because they're afraid of being swept into their religion more than they want to be. They like to keep their feet on what they consider to be the firm and dry ground of reality, what seems to them to be normal, that's to say, real life at the river's edge. They're not daring to let themselves be swept along in the stream. I love to feel the excitement of being in the stream of faith, especially in Holy Week."

"I remember once at Westlake taking a friend to a mid-week communion, she'd been in hospital and was still very unsure of herself and so was keen to come. But she wouldn't come more than once. She was a bit nervous, she said, she might develop religious mania. I'd never thought of that. Perhaps that's what I do have. But if it is I'm quite happy about it. After all, God doesn't want only part of us, only part of our time, only part of our hearts or heads, or even only part of our money, part of our wealth however small. He wants all of us and all we have. But that doesn't mean he wants us to give up everything, to go to be missionaries around the world, or to go about penniless or without real homes. It's more that God wants us to die to the world so he can replace that dead us with his own live, living us."

"I've read that, it's C.S. Lewis, isn't it? It's one of the things that needs remembering, that the whole of us belongs to God, we don't own any of ourselves. That's all quite true, and we shouldn't be able to forget it, for every Sunday in the Mass we say,

'For all that is in the heaven and in the earth is thine ... all things come of thee and of thine own do we give unto thee.'

And that means everything in the world belongs to God, even those things we consider to be our own. When we give anything to God, that thing is already his."

"On Sundays when we're saying those words," I joined in. "I want to jump up from where I'm standing and fly over all the congregation as if I were an angel and wave my wings above the stingy or thoughtless people, those who are holding themselves back, and call to them, 'Do you hear? Do you understand? Why don't you give all your life to God and all you have? Not just a measly bit of money and an hour or two of your time on Sundays and a few thoughts now and again during the week.' It's not as if God wanted to take all our possessions away from us. He wants us to put them to his service, then he will tell us how to use them. We are to give him our whole self, our whole life, and he will tell us how we are to act so we can bring his kingdom to more people. And this not necessarily in an obvious way, it might be very quietly: he will lead us into a new life, though not an impossible one. There's no doubt about that. We will have no regrets when we have given him everything."

"We really would become much happier and more carefree than we'd ever been before. All this is connected to Easter. The dying of ourselves, of our life lived for ourselves, for an earthly goal, and being born again as sons of God."

We were enjoying our walk and our talk. Then I said to Jane,

"How did you get on with your confession? It was sensible of you to go home without waiting for me."

"I felt I needed to go home straight away. I needed to be by myself, to concentrate on what had been happening to me. You were quite right. It was super. And it worked in a quite unexpected way. Edward was very helpful, just like you said he would be. He made it so easy. His being there helped my thoughts to be made into words. It seems to me when one confesses to God either in church, where are all saying one of the general confessions, which after all is what they are and why they're called general, or conversely, when one's on one's own, saying one's private prayers, one doesn't need actually to put one's bad deeds or thoughts into simple plain words. We usually only think about them, or visualize them wordlessly or even rather vaguely. We might think we've told God all about our sins but we haven't really. When I found myself with only one other person, and he was the one who was going to help me, I had to make everything sound real and true by using whole sentences made of solid words, and that was something quite new for me and different and powerful."

"That's what I found. It's the actual words one uses which seems to be extraordinarily cleansing, and there's no need to mince them either. The stronger or plainer the words the better the confession will be."

"The absolution sentences are very healing, I thought, though I can't remember what they are. Anyway I'm very glad I went."

105

"When I hear those forgiving words pouring over me like spring rain I feel a marvellously new person - for a bit, at any rate. What was your penance? I'm sure it will have been as simple and super as the one I've been given."

"To say the Lord's Prayer very slowly as a meditation."

"I had to read the first verse of Hymn 470, Praise, my soul, the King of heaven, especially concentrating on the line.

'Ransomed, healed, restored, forgiven.'

Which of course it is, though it's hard to realize this sometimes."

We'd come to the end of the loch by then and very shortly turned back. We were able to give the water more attention now. On the whole there was not much to see but suddenly I exclaimed, "Look, there's a pair of golden-eyes over there, and a diver too beyond them. Do you think they'll nest here?"

"They might, but it'll be most probably on the other loch further up the glen where there's an island. That's safer for them."

"I do hope they will."

We got back to the car and then were soon at Drummore and shortly it was time for me to drive home to Ardness.

EASTER:
THE ROAD TO EMMAUS

It was after lunch on the Sunday after Easter, Low Sunday, (which name, I remembered, doesn't mean necessarily there'd be very little money in the collection plate, even though, after the generosity of Easter, there might be very little indeed, but derives from the verb *laud* meaning praise), so I've been told. And I was day dreaming, I was looking out of the window at the sunlight on distant Cairn Dhu, not dhu or black at all that day, as one might suppose from its name, but still snow-covered from the winter. I was due to read the second lesson at Evensong.

The Road to Emmaus. It's one of my favourite bits in the Bible. There's so much to it, not only what's obvious but what's hidden. I could never imagine why it's set to be read at Evensong only one year out of three, though I see it comes every year on the day after Easter Sunday in the Mass. (Though I don't think there will ever be many worshippers at that service, on Bank Holiday). When you think of what we do have read to us on some Sundays at other times of year, for example, all those kings of Judah or Israel who did evil in the sight of the Lord, and there seem to have been a great many of them. I never could see that their life histories helped our faith. It's quite an effort for the reader or listener to make the scapegoat or the stiff-necked people come to life, and in the modern translations even those instantly recognisable words have disappeared.

One of the two disciples in my lesson is Clopas the brother of one of the Mary's who stood by the cross when Jesus died, but the other is unnamed, and it always seems so strange to me that, although they were disciples (though not Apostles) and there was much sorrow amongst them all, they don't stay in Jerusalem with their friends but set off for Emmaus, a walk of about seven or eight miles. As they walk along and they are talking together of all these sad happenings a Stranger (whom *we* are told is Jesus) comes up with them and joins in the conversation. The two don't recognise him, they are both so convinced Jesus is dead, so for them he is just a Stranger and he seems to know nothing about all that's been happening in Jerusalem. They tell him of all that's being said there, about all these sad events, how they'd trusted it would be Jesus who would redeem Israel. But their rulers and chief priests delivered him to be condemned to death and crucified. This is now the third day since his death and the disciples were astonished when some friends, some women, didn't find his body in the tomb when they went to anoint it, but angels who told them he was alive, 'And certain of them which were with us went to the sepulchre and found it even so as the women said.'

'O foolish men,' the Stranger says to the two: 'and slow of heart to believe all the prophets have spoken.' And he explains to them about Christ's having to suffer and tells them of what's said in the Scriptures about it. I can imagine all three walking along, looking at the ground, two of them listening intently to the third.

When they arrive at Emmaus the two ask the Stranger to stop and eat with them (he seems to have been going on further). And it came to pass as they sat at the meal that he took Bread and blessed it and broke it and gave it them. And at that moment their eyes were opened and they knew the Stranger was Jesus. Then he vanished out of their sight.

It's the action of the breaking of the Bread which makes them recognize Jesus. So it seems they must have known the Eleven well and heard about the Supper on the Thursday night in the Upper Room. They must have known what Jesus had said and did the evening before his death, his breaking the Bread and afterwards passing round the cup of Wine and about the significance of what he was doing.

As soon as he is recognised, Jesus vanishes. They are alone again. It's dramatic and the Gospel words accentuate the drama.

The two of them then begin to feel a little foolish: why hadn't they guessed sooner who it was who had walked and talked so earnestly with them? 'Did not our hearts burn within us? and still we didn't see.'

And it's strange too how they can decide then to turn back to Jerusalem? Whatever the reason was for their going to Emmaus in the first place hasn't prevented their changing their minds. Their meeting with Jesus is now the most important news in the world. They must rush back to Jerusalem to tell their friends of all that has happened as soon as they can.

They arrive back to find the Apostles still in the Upper Room, and they, who have already heard that Simon has seen Jesus, listen while our two recount their story.

It was with the Emmaus two as it is now with us, still, today. It's the breaking of the Bread which opens our eyes to Christ's presence at the meal. His body broken on the cross for us is in the Bread. This Bread opens our hearts to him, and so we are certain he is still here for us in the world today.

But I knew in the lesson, in the passage I was going to read that evening, that the last important words about the Bread are tucked away in the last half of the last sentence. And because of this it's very easy to rush too quickly at the last moment. Then the point of the story is lost, the lesson will have come to an end before the reader has made certain his listeners have understood everything he's telling them. By then of course, if they've not understood, it's too late. It's not possible, in the middle of a service, to go back and reread the last sentence with the proper pauses and emphasis. I knew I must remember to go carefully and pause in the right places, to slow down and say carefully 'and how he was known of them', and then pause again and then add 'in breaking of Bread'. Not long pauses, that would be absurd, only slight hesitations.

It's a marvellous story. I love to visualize all the disciples as being as uncertain about the future as it's possible to be, and not only uncertain but cast down, heartbroken. After Friday it must have been hard to risk any hope, and yet not possible to let hope die altogether. And then the incredible, joyful end to the third day. It's in the second half of the chapter which isn't read that evening that certainty overcomes uncertainty. Christ comes through the closed door into the room with them, he eats broiled fish and part of an honeycomb, to show that he is really alive and not a spirit only. (Though the honeycomb has disappeared in the modern translations. A pity).

In the Authorised Version the translation is wonderfully readable. The words come gradually and perfectly, one following after the other disclosing its meaning.

'But we trusted that it had been he which should have redeemed Israel ... O fools, and slow of heart to believe, ... Did not our heart burn within us?'

The whole lesson is a joy to read aloud. It goes smoothly forward all the way from beginning to end. And the word 'And' is used many times. People don't realize until they come to read aloud in church how many 'Ands' can help them. In these twenty-three verses I've counted forty-five 'Ands', (although I got a slightly different total every time I counted). And sixteen of the verses begin with 'And'. So the listener as well as the reader can feel the inevitability of the story, one sentence following another as if destined to do so by an unseen hand (as indeed it is).

When Evensong came I read my so very carefully prepared lesson.

"You were good," Nicholas said later, "And I could hear every word at the back."

"That's fine. That's what I aim for, to be heard by all the people in the back row. I'm improving a bit with practice. All the same, when I get back to my place, my legs often feel very odd and wobbly. It's silly. I'm sure they ought not to by now. And some lessons are lovely to read because we can put our hearts into them, so my legs ought not to react so stupidly."

"It seems important," Nicholas was thinking aloud, "to remember we are separated from God by mystery and so it's natural there should be mystery in this story which is about God's communicating with us. We are created by God, not begotten of him. We are his created beings, and so there is no human reason why we should be able to communicate with him, our Creator, at all, nor he with us. We begat our children and are able to communicate with them, but we can't communicate with our own creations. They have no life of their own and no understanding of us. But in fact, as we saw in your lesson, God does communicate with us. Sometimes he sends angels with a message, sometimes he speaks in a cloud or in a burning bush, but in the end he communicates with us by his Son. Because Jesus is truly God, begotten by God the Holy Spirit, he can speak to his Father with perfect understanding. Because he is truly man through his Mother Mary he can speak to us similarly with perfect confidence that we'll understand him. Though communication with God is still full of mystery, it's a reality."

"And when you think about it," I added, "communicating with God through his Son is the most important thing we do in our whole lives."

EASTER: TO DERVA COTTAGE

"It's about time we made a determined effort to go over to see that sister of yours," Nicholas was saying one evening when we'd just switched off the News.

"Oh, yes, let's. The days are longer now, and already some are springlike and cheerful. I would love that. We've been working so hard here lately. I'll ring her up, not this evening, it's too late, but tomorrow perhaps, if we remember."

So one day in the following week, Nicholas and I set off on our great day out to see my sister, Angela, and her husband, Peter. They, the MacQuarrie's, lived in the west, on the Isle of Olva, just off the mainland of Lorne. It's a wild romantic island but the inhabitants are, fortunately, in contrast to the landscape, very friendly indeed. Peter had said in one of his more pompous moments, 'We felt at home at once, we felt part of the Olva scene almost as soon as we arrived.' But Angela made many a true friend in her first year there, just for their own sakes, with no idea of any social scene in her mind.

The weather promised to be kind that day There was still not much holiday traffic so the miles swept past easily. I settled into a pleasantly relaxed state while Nicholas drove, one half of my mind on the countryside and the other brooding happily on my latest contemplations.

Gradually, as we travelled further westward the scenery became more and more interesting. The west of Scotland is so much more excitingly beautiful than the east, or even than that around Strathlyon. There are grander mountains and lochs and many more islands making much lovely scenery, especially on a calm sunny day like we had that day. There were fantastically pure reflections in the still water and lovely soft colours all around us. The distance was beautifully hazy, certainly not so clear we should fear any rain before we got home that evening.

At last we arrived at the slipway where the ferry left for Olva.

"I shall get out of the car and look for birds," I said to Nicholas. Soon I saw a sandpiper flying over the seaweedy stones, its wings held in a slight downward curve, uttering its little trilling song. Then it stood on a rock and bobbed its tail up and down.

"Our first for the year," I said as I went back to the car. On the way across the sound I wandered around the boat, squeezing myself through the narrow spaces between the cars, to view our surroundings, to look carefully at the water all around. There was a wind, of course, but only that made by our own progress. I saw a seal swimming quite close to the boat. I was struck how extraordinarily human the animal seemed with its round head, very like our own, and its two big dark eyes. These looked at me as if it were just about to say something intelligent but sad, and I thought, if it were to moan, it would make just the noise I imagine I would make, or would want to make, if I were moaning.

I could see too, some distance away in the sunshine, a flock of terns diving like white arrows into the smooth water. They seemed like international beauties, they had style and elegance and a controlled energy. They were obviously not just local country bumpkins, they were international. Each year they fly from the far north of the world to the far south and back again. They don't ever know winter. They're a real jet set. At both ends of their journeys they live through the longest days of summer. With those lovely swallow tails, gleaming white and pale grey bodies, and shining black heads they are prize-winners for beauty.

After we'd arrived at the Olva slipway we were soon heading westwards along the edge of Loch na Ronich. At the seaward end of this loch we would reach our destination, Angela and Peter's house, Derva Cottage.

"It must often seem tedious to have this long drive from civilisation to one's home," said Nicholas as we drove calmly along. "Can you imagine our having to drive up and down this narrow road in the carefree way we drive from Ardness to Strathlyon and back?"

"But we wouldn't," I said. "There's hardly anywhere to drive to on Olva. There would be no need. I often think it would be lovely to feel you couldn't get to your house without driving the whole length of this loch. It would be marvellous to come along here every week of the year and see all the changes of the seasons. It's so wild and beautiful and romantic. And look at the mergansers on the calm water, and that's probably a red-throated diver further out and lots of oystercatchers are nesting on the stones near us. I especially love the way the yellow flags grow where the little fresh water streams come down to the sea. They appreciate the dampest though not salty ground. They're very west coast flowers, we don't see them at all around Strathlyon. They're lovely. Imagine having all these excitements along what you would think of as your own road. This beautiful loch and its islands and the mountains opposite would all become part of you."

After a few further miles of delight, with the view and the birds, we came within sight of the house and then a few yards beyond we turned back and suddenly down onto a rough track with many potholes. This led through a thicket of hazel and then across a rushy field to the garden gate from where a short path brought us to the front door of Derva Cottage.

It was still a very modest house. The old part, the fisherman's cottage was of stone, the newer additions were of Scottish brick harled (that is roughcast) as ours is with marble chips.

For many years Angela and Peter had lived in London, they'd both had university jobs. Peter'd been some kind of professor and Angela had helped him in research in ways I'd not ever totally understood. Now they'd come to live on Olva, something they'd been planning for years, they were completely and happily occupied, never overtaxed and certainly not regretting their move. When they'd first discussed their move I'd been a bit worried they would never be able to settle, never mind transform the old croft they'd bought into a comfortable home. But now, each time I'd come and seen their latest improvements, I was more and more certain they were not only very happy but comfortable. They'd chosen to live in surroundings which fitted in with both of their temperaments admirably. Peter went on writing his erudite scientific books, the remoteness of the place suiting his temperament, and Angela helped him by typing and she enjoyed the general island life.

Angela, like myself, from childhood, had always preferred the country to the town. Pavements and continuous rows of houses were surroundings to be escaped from. What are art galleries, theatres and cinemas compared with mountains, lochs or the sea?

113

Nicholas tooted gently on the car horn to announce our arrival, and at once our hosts came out to greet us, accompanied by their two spaniels. We were all soon indoors and exchanging news about our families and friends.

Their house, Derva Cottage, was in a lovely position, it faced south-west across the loch towards the high mountains, the highest being Ben More Olva. The original croft consisted downstairs of a kitchen and bathroom, and upstairs two bedrooms. The wonderful new extension consisted of Angela and Peter's bedroom over the lovely new sittingroom built onto the end of the house. The last time we'd been there the extension work had been well under way but not yet ready to be shown off, but this time we could be taken straightaway to see these marvellous and now completed improvements.

I need hardly say, though, that life in Derva Cottage did have some disadvantages. For instance the water was brought from the hill behind by a burn which dried up almost every summer, and its feed-in pipe froze whenever the weather was exceptionally cold and wintry. In very wet weather the drains weren't quite sure what to do with the superfluous water. After very heavy rain several other little burns formed and came cascading down from the hill and, joining forces, came hurrying almost straight into the back porch. This bogginess, however, was a great asset in summer for plants, especially thirsty vegetables, were able to go on growing, unlike, in ordinary circumstances, as in our own garden, where a drought could bring all to a standstill. It was lovely water to drink, and a great treat for those like ourselves who normally had to choose between chlorine-treated town tap water and bottled Scottish water.

"But this happens to everybody on Olva, it's just life," said Angela. And it was true, I'd decided this some time before, that no disadvantages yet discovered weren't shared by all other nearby Olva residents, and thereby cancelled out their tiresomeness. Anyway inconvenience was easily outweighed by Angela and Peter's continued enjoyment of this beautiful place.

With the house facing south-westward, catching almost all the sunshine, it wasn't a cold house, though on days of gales and rain there was no possibility of any of the old windows keeping the water out. Not that our own windows were one hundred percent rainproof.

Of course each time we came over to Olva I was struck with envy by Angela's view from the kitchen sink.

"Your high mountains," I said, "rise so dramatically, straight out of the loch and it's all so near to you. Our main view is not from the kitchen, as you know, but from the sitting-room. It's a very beautiful view but our mountains are much more distant than yours, much less exciting. And our kitchen outlook is, as you'll remember, almost straight across our road and into the daffodil wood, though it's a lot better than looking out at a street of all boringly similar houses. So I'd never dream of complaining."

EASTER: WITH ANGELA

After lunch the men went to inspect the garden, they were also to discuss the best type of car for Peter to buy to replace his old Landrover. (The answer was another Landrover, preferably second-hand). Then they were to climb the bracken-covered hill at the back of the house to choose a site and, if possible, erect an aerial of their own on top of the hill, this hill cutting off all signals from their nearest repeater mast.

Angela and I, with the dogs, decided to walk across the expanse of wild lumpy grass down towards the loch. Cuckoos were calling that day from all directions, which was a treat for me, for I'd hardly heard them at Ardness. All the time little wrens were singing too and popping in and out of the stony places imagining they were St Kilda wrens, though I'm afraid they weren't.

The two of us, Angela and myself, were pretty alike, enough for us to be seen to be sisters. She was brainier than myself too, which fact, I couldn't help feeling, was an attribute rather wasted on the desert air of Olva, though in opposition to these feelings, I knew well that brains anywhere are an asset to anybody. And after all, Angela did help Peter with his scientific writing. She typed professionally, not like myself who had to concentrate totally on my fingers if ever I tried to type. But I consoled myself by realizing that typing is a knack once the skill's learned, not necessarily requiring brain.

In fact, I knew in everything I was medium: medium height, medium weight, medium in looks, medium in brain, medium in the general practical equipment needed for life. Fortunately, therefore, only medium accomplishments were expected either by others or myself. This was quite advantageous as there was less likelihood of disappointment either in my own heart or in other people's, no need to strive for perfection or dazzling achievements. Though it took me some years to learn this, as I've related to you already, I'd discovered it wasn't necessarily a good thing to strive harder than is natural to any one of us.

"It's striking here, around where you live," I said, as we approached the water's edge, "how there are so few houses and only one road with hardly any cars on it. That must be why it's so marvellously quiet. In the old days it must have been similarly quiet everywhere in the countryside. Horse traffic and people and barking dogs would have made the most noise, and the wind and the waves on a rough day. There would have been no tractors with ploughs, nor power saws, nor lorries revving noisy engineers when changing gear, nor any low-flying aircraft."

"As well as being silent," Angela added, "it's very dark here at night. When there's no moon, I mean, or when it's overcast. On a clear night the stars shine very brightly."

"That must be lovely, and interesting too. On cloudy nights at home there's a great orange glow in the sky from Strathlyon, and even when the sky's clear the town lights themselves are very dazzling. We can see only the brightest stars and the nearest planets, except towards the north. I feel sad about the stars. I feel God built the universe and all the stars and I'm letting him down by not learning about them. I *ought* to know. I feel it's a kind of insult to him not to know which is Aldebaran or which Capella. I did know once, when we were living at Westlake. I learned the names of some of the easiest stars, and though I think I can still find Castor and Pollux, and of course the Pole Star and the Dog Star and Orion's Belt, I've mostly forgotten all the rest."

We paddled in the tide for a short while watching the different seaweeds moving rhythmically in the little waves, the very clear calm water never threatening to wash over our welly boot tops.

"I was thinking about the stars the other day," I began again after we'd turned to wander back towards the house, "and I was wondering if they'd been put there in this wonderful and intriguing way especially by God, just to show us his greatness, the greatness of his creation. An endless source of marvels for scientists of many kinds, not only for astronomers, so they can go on discovering more and more of everything. So that we, too, the non-scientists, (although you must be partly one of them), can learn more and more about his greatness."

'I'm not sure about anything like that," Angela replied. "Not being very much in with God at present. Though I find myself pondering about him. Sometimes I like to imagine I've been put here on this island by chance, or maybe it *is* by God, and I'm here to get on with my own life, looking after Peter and not worrying about anything or anyone else, except, of course, keeping in touch with the children and a few of my special friends. I find it difficult to think about our all being dependent on each other. I suppose we are, especially these days, and God might help in that. It's lovely, living on a not very big island, it makes me disagree with the idea that thinking of myself as an island is necessarily a thing to be disapproved of. It seems to me an excellent idea. But then, when I consider the whole world I can begin to see I might be being selfish. I find it awfully hard to feel an interest in people who are quite different from myself. There is a great difference between sorts of people from different countries around the world. The world's growing smaller, one hears it said, but it hasn't made us more alike each other, or I don't feel it has."

"But basically we are hardly at all different from foreign people. When we are born we are babies with parents and when we grow up we become parents with babies, and we all have similar basic instincts and have the same basic needs."

"That's true. Peter doesn't worry at all about that kind of thing. He's always thinking about knowledge rather than people, saying we are so marvellous and intelligent, there are no problems we'll not be able to solve in the end, nothing that won't in the end be discovered. The secrets of the universe will be unlocked, even the secrets of life, he says. And we'll see clearly what to do and how to do it. We'll be able to go on living here on this earth quite normally for ever. That's what he thinks, or at least at the moment it is."

"Our discovering more secrets of the universe will show us about the power and love of God, I think." I suggested. "And we shall see our spirits to be stronger than our bodies, But Peter doesn't believe in the life of the spirit, that the spirit works in us, does he? Those things play an important part in how we react to life. I should think you could hardly live here amongst all the beauty and not discover in yourself another dimension to life, the spiritual dimension. Though a spiritual outlook doesn't necessarily include a religion with the idea of God as our Father. There've always been people poetically aware of beauty who didn't believe in God at all."

"That's true. I do feel things here which are hardly explained by any scientific attitude. They seem to be beyond even the latest modern ideas of what the unconscious mind is or does or can be."

"You are a very good person naturally," I was able to say easily and with no hesitation. "You're so good at being friendly with people, though you don't recognize this. But if you compared yourself to some spiky person who was always trying to score off other people, to make them feel uncomfortable on purpose, you would see the difference between yourself and them, if you see what I mean. And this goodness represents the spirit in you."

"I'm not sure about that, though I always want to make people feel better or happier when I meet them, than they did before. So it's not totally true what I said about feeling myself to be a separate island. I never feel detached or uncaring about my neighbours and I'm always hoping they're getting on well. It's more, I suppose, that I feel the need to cut out the demands and pressure of the faraway world."

"I think that's very natural," I said. "Especially if we remember that no long ago no one country's inhabitants knew very much about any other country's inhabitants. It would be hardly surprising if we were to need a hundred years or so to adapt ourselves to absorbing easily all that comes to us on the telly and radio, the telly with its *pictures* too. Pictures pierce the brain, and the soul too, much more fiercely that words only. Also, if you think about it, in the old days everything that happened, say in a war abroad, happened long before it was ever heard about by ordinary people here in this country. By the time things were known here, known generally, events had already lost their immediacy. Battles and suchlike events would, by the time they were generally known be only news and not NEWS, with immediate capital letters at nine o'clock. There were no telegrams then, or telephones, no radio, no TV. Only people on horseback carrying the good news from Ghent to Aix.

'I sprang to the stirrup, and Joris, and he;
I galloped, Dirck galloped, we galloped all three.'
Or there were bonfires."

Angela came in here.
"'Till Skiddaw saw the fire that burned on Gaunt's embattled
pile.'
(that's to say Lancaster Castle, in case you've forgotten)."

Then myself:
"'and the red glow on Skiddaw roused the burghers of Carlisle.'"

"And even not so long ago," I went on, "we were arranging for church bells to warn us of an Invasion, but fortunately we never had to hear them."

On the way back to the house we talked about our children. Angela's Frank and Isabel and Michael and my two boys. Then, by the time we arrived we just had time for a good refreshing drink of tea and a few biscuits before Nicholas and I had to leave to be in time for the ferry, but not the last one. That would be too risky. We said our many thanks and farewells, got into our car and then drove slowly along the potholed track, across the rushy field and between the hazel bushes, and turned up onto the narrow island road. Then back up the loch, which looked even lovelier in the late afternoon sunlight than it had in the morning, and at last we took our place successfully in the queue for the ferry. Then we were soon away from Olva, and over the water, then driving smoothly and speedily homeward along the comparatively wide (well, two-way) mainland main road. We soon began to relax and to think about our day.

"I'm glad they're so happy," I said. "When they first came to Derva I was afraid the tiny uncomfy house and the remoteness from everywhere, after London, would be so strange for them and would cause too many problems. But they've done so much to improve everything, the house is really jolly and bright and cosy now. It's just not exactly convenient for going anywhere, but if they don't mind, it's not a problem for them and therefore not for me to worry about."

"I think in a way the remoteness suits Peter, he doesn't like being sociable."

"And it suits Angela because there are so few people around and everybody can be a friend and she's naturally friendly, she knows how to be a good one."

"It's a pity," Nicholas said, "that neither of them wants to belong to the church there. You know that I think there are two basic things: a firm belief in God keeps one going steadily in the right direction, and also it's good to meet and do things, to co-operate a bit, with church people."

"With some exceptions, I would say," I replied. "I hear you grumbling often enough about certain people in our church. But the Olva Old Church looks a dear little building, all among the pines. I suppose there's a service there once or twice a month. I expect it's locked up all the rest of the time. What a pity. Just imagine how super it would be to walk up that little path through the trees every day, open the heavy wooden door with its large circular handle, and go into the dark quietness. There'd be a lovely smell of wood, and do you think there might be a slight smell of old incense? Perhaps there's already someone caring for the old place, so even if I came to live here, the job wouldn't be for me. All the same I could creep in and there'd be a light burning over the reserved sacrament and I would kneel down and find it easy to pray."

"Betty," said Nicholas, severely, though not very, just in his semi sarcastic voice, "as usual you're letting your imagination run away with you." Then he went on "I suppose Peter's non-believing attitude is due to his having been a scientist, a professor, and the son of another professor, and it was generally supposed, in his day, that science had all the answers, or would shortly find them, and God wasn't necessary."

"Angela could go off to church on her own if she wanted," I said. "Peter is much too kind to object or cast aspersions or anything. But she doesn't feel any need."

"I'm glad we went to see them, all the same, and in spite of the distance. It was a good day. I enjoyed my afternoon with Peter. He really is not at all a bad stick. And he's quite easy to talk to. He's fine for a short while, while we could keep to general observations."

"I do envy them having that real wildness so near to their home. But we have so much more fun. One can't easily imagine a life without St Andrew's and all the ramifications of the Parish, the Diocese and the Bishop and the Province and the General Office in Eaglesburgh."

"Well, Peter and Angela too, could have all those ramifications. What they haven't got is the desire to take a first step into their own St Ninian's or into a church like our own St Andrew's."

"Island life is something completely different from anything we know," I said. "All the Olva people must feel bonded together because they're on an island, attached to the wide world only by the ferry boats and their crews, a very tenuous life line, likely to go on strike any moment, or be held up by gales or fog. Though there's a helicopter now for emergencies it relies on good weather even more than ferry boats do. Perhaps it's because of this bond Peter and Angela have firm friends enough already and they don't feel the need of a church to bind them all the more together. We aren't bonded in the same way. We can take off for anywhere at any time almost without telling anyone, so we are more conscious of the need to be bonded to God and so we belong to St Andrew's and that binds us to everyone, even to those who don't go there, nor to any church."

After a few miles I said, "It's true that Angela's a bit dotty about life on Olva. Olva colours so many of her reactions, especially to adversity. When the water rushes down the hill into the porch and through the house, she doesn't worry about it because it happens to everybody on Olva, or all the people she knows anyway. It's the same when she gets a cold. Even if she's feeling lousy, she's comforted by the knowledge it's an Olva cold and many of her friends are similarly afflicted."

"Your sister has some very strange ideas, as I've remarked before."

I agreed about this to myself, but Nicholas's words touched some part of me too strongly and I sprang to my sister's defence: "It's part of the island bond, isn't it? And you can see it does nothing but good for her. It helps her through life. It's just that we find some of its manifestations somewhat amusing."

Later in the month, on the last day in fact, I read in one of the Psalms set for that day,

'He telleth the number of the stars and calleth them by their names.'

(Telleth means counteth, think of the tellers in the bank, they *count* our money). But the stars are important, important to God. It probably is important I should learn more about them.

'Great is our Lord, and great is his power, yea, and his wisdom is infinite.'

122

EASTER: THE SLOE LANE

During this time Jane and Jack had been away to the States, to California, to Monterey, where Jack had some not very closely related cousins, with whom perhaps for that very reason they always got on very well. They'd come over for lunch to tell us all their adventures and also to learn how we'd been getting on.

They had some more hopeful news of Prue too.

"Oh, yes. It's interesting," said Jane. "We saw David in London on our way back. We spent the night after we'd flown in from California in a hotel near his flat. He's full of hope. He says he often talks to her on the phone now. She had been seeming less cheerful than before but now she often mentions someone called Colin, though I don't know how or where she's met him. David had been a bit worried that Martin wasn't being very nice to her and that this might by why she's been more upset that usual. But if this is so then she will all the more easily make up her mind as to what she wants to do. Jack and I had originally thought of going over and taking her and Martin out to lunch but, after hearing David's news, we thought it might be better just to ring up and have a long chat on the phone to her about things other than Martin. It would be embarrassing over lunch to have to suppose all was well with them when in fact it wasn't. Prue would hardly know how much she should pretend to us."

"On the phone she sounded very normal," said Jack, "But we talked mostly about our holiday. She didn't mind our not going to see them. They live far enough away from David's place that it would be an effort for us all to meet, although possible if necessary. We vaguely discussed their having a week or two in the summer up here with us, but of course it would be lovely if it were Prue on her own or with the new Colin. David himself will probably meet Prue soon and will report to us."

"Let's walk down to the loch," I suggested to Jane when the meal was over. "I've not been for quite a while. It should be lovely today."

Nicholas and Jack made excuses, as I'd expected. Jack needed to catch up on the St Andrew's news anyway, and there'd be sure to be other subjects on their minds.. So they went and sat on the patio, taking the folding chairs out of the garage for the first time that year, shaking the spiders out and knocking off the loose bird-droppings, before they could sit down on them. It was really the first decent day we'd had this summer (or was it still spring?) which was happy for them.

Then Jane and I set off with Tess. First we walked down through the wood. It *was* lovely. The trees were almost at their spring best. No fierce gales had come yet to tear at the delicate new green leaves. Curled crooks of fens were unrolling, and the bracken reached only up to our knees, not yet threatening to engulf us shoulder high in a deep sea of green. Though it was no longer morning the chaffinches were singing gaily and the newly arrived willow warblers were joining in with their sweet tumbling song. Blackbirds and song thrushes uttered their louder clearer notes from high in the trees.

After we'd gone down the hill a bit and we'd come out of the wood we walked though the steading belonging to the big house, past some young beasties eating, as well as treading on, the straw and their own muck.

"Don't you think it's fantastic," I said to Jane, "how they can eat their bed, and what they don't eat they turn into lovely muck to spread on the fields for cereals and turnips to provide more food for themselves for next year. And then we can eat *them* too. It's admirable. A marvellously productive and conserving piece of creation. We humans are great entropy wasters in comparison. I mean by the time we die we shall have taken a great deal of goodness, of energy, out of the earth and put almost nothing back."

"A lot of that could be put right. Our modern sewage systems are very wasteful. Think of country people in the old days with earth closets. They spread their waste goodness back onto their gardens and then dug it in, instead of letting it, as we do, be swept away somewhere else into rivers or out to sea. Even if it's treated first and transformed, it's not for home use."

"And when we die we are either burnt away to steam, smoke and ashes, using irreplaceable fuel, or we're tightly boxed up in a coffin so our no-longer-wanted bodies are unavailable for worms to turn into nourishment for the soil, or not for a very long time. It all seems a strange way of doing things. Not very pro-God."

We turned into the drive which led past the big house and followed it down to the loch. We saw some tree sparrows in the oaks and admired their smart plumage. How cheerful and neat they looked in comparison with their cousins, the house sparrows, which I think always look rather scruffy even in the clean country.

"I was pondering," I said, "'the other day, about a more common bird. We were driving slowly home along the lane near our house when a skylark dropped suddenly down from the sky in its usual and wonderful rapid parachute fall to the ground. He landed in a field just by our car. I thought of the song he had stopped singing, though being in the car I hadn't heard it, and how it couldn't possibly be that such a lovely thing as that song should have evolved in the impersonal system we are meant to believe in. It can't be just to do with the survival of the fittest skylarks, or to do with survival at all. It may be the best singing skylarks who find the most fertile females, but that doesn't explain the first developments of the lovely song. Some birds survive very well with awful voices, though those are often the kinds of birds which are very beautiful to look at. Like peacocks!"

"I read the other day that the sight of a peacock's tail feather made Darwin feel sick, for he could see clearly that it worked against what he was proposing about survival. This fan of glorious feathers the male carries on his back doesn't help him flee from danger, nor fight successfully against his enemy, nor hide himself, but only makes him more attractive to peahens and maybe also encourages him to see himself as rather swish and successful. Our creator must be a God with infinitely inventive powers, a God who is a Person, and who created all the beautiful things in the universe with love."

"But it's difficult to fit the world's ugly or menacing creatures into God's love though, isn't it?"

"Yes, it is. I often worry a lot about nasty insects or funny or not so funny sea creatures, with their unattractive habits. Or parasites or deadly bacteria or viruses. It must be God who created them I used to think, because we were taught that God versus the Devil was a dualist thought and therefore not right. I used to wonder if God meant those unpleasantly odd things as a challenge to our love. But last week I read, in a commentary on Mark's Gospel, that Christ saw the Devil in people's illnesses, especially in illnesses of the personality, and he exorcised them. The Devil is made to come out of the stricken person, the afflicted one is cured. The author wrote something like 'the overthrow of demons should be seen as part of Jesus' proclamation of God's kingdom'. I found this an intriguing and helpful idea."

"That's interesting. I've always found it difficult to say about God that he hated nothing that he had made, as we do in the Lent collect. It would make some of the terrible things that do happen to people a lot clearer if we could say they were not from God, but from the Devil."

By now we'd come to the loch, the water was calm and reflected the delicate spring green of the sunlit birch woods on the far side.

"Let's turn to the right here and come back by the sloe lane," I said. "I wonder if there will be any sloes this year. Last year was hopeless.

"There are some very interesting points I love to brood about, about creation," continued Jane. "I don't know what you think, but I think it's a ridiculous idea about there being no trees in the quad if there's nobody there to look at it."

"So do I. I don't think you can believe all creation was made for only humans to enjoy," I said. "That's a very old-fashioned idea."

"I can see God provides us with plants and animals for food, but often I think about sunsets, for instance, or rainbows. We see the beauty of creation in the beauty of sunsets, and the variety, never two alike even from the same place, but there must have been sunsets before the creation of man. Dinosaurs must have had sunsets to look at, though I don't suppose they took any more notice of them than Tess does of our present day ones. All those past sunsets had to exist as the earth was developing enough for us to inhabit it."

"Of course, God may enjoy his sunsets, I think he must enjoy thunderstorms. They make me frightened in away which reminds me of his greatness and wrath, especially his wrath. Dogs notice thunder, even if they don't notice sunsets, but maybe that's different. My mother had a Pekinese who hid under the bed in thunderstorms, and also in air raids. I don't think she, Ming, could tell the difference between them."

"Well I can sympathize with that."

We had turned into the sloe lane by then.

"It's too soon to tell about the sloes, don't you think?' Jane went on. "I mean there's a lot of blossom which is hopeful, but they've not yet changed from blackthorns into sloe bushes."

"That's true. But it's not ourselves who need them, it's Mary-next-door who makes sloe gin, I'm glad to say. Gin not being in my line."

Then we turned right again and were facing towards home.

"Personally, to go back to the tree in the quad, I need to think that all things exist even when I'm not there to look at them. When we are too busy to get over to the West Coast, or up to the North, or down to the Southwest, or if we have decided to go to one of them and have to choose between them. it's only the fact that I know all those lovely places are still existing which consoles me. After all, when I'm dead they'll have to get on without me."

"It's possible to feel homesick for a place which isn't home, isn't it?" said Jane. "I've found that. It's possible to be in love with a place so much it hurts. It's often a lovely spot one knew as a child, perhaps a holiday place, not necessarily home. Home is often of necessity rather ugly or shabby, or the environment is unattractive, even if life was happy there . For happiness depends more on people than on surroundings."

"That's true."

And then we were back at Whinside again. Nicholas and Jack had been only a little stroll into the lower wood nearby after they'd finished discussing church subjects. Then it was cups of tea for all and after some more desultory talk the Morlands drove home.

Later, after a rest, out of curiosity, I looked up in the Book of Quotations the verses about the tree in the quad.

> 'There was once a man who said 'God
> Must think it exceedingly odd
> If he finds that this tree
> Continues to be
> When there's no one about in the Quad'.

In a different part of the book altogether, (because the two verses were written by different authors, one by Anon and the other by Ronald Knox). I found the answer,

> 'Dear Sir, Your astonishment's odd:
> *I* am always about in the Quad.
> And that's why the tree
> Will continue to be,
> Since observed by, Yours faithfully, God'!

"That's more or less what we decided."

WHITSUNTIDE: CATASTROPHE

We had a lovely service on Whit Sunday. The church, in the early summer sunshine, had looked its best. It was beautifully decorated, even more so than usual, many people were full of praise for the flower-arranging ladies, in spite of anything Nicholas would have said about it if he had thought of expressing himself aloud on that subject at all. He much preferred a church without distracting flowers, as in Lent.

One afternoon later in the week, after Nicholas and I had been working in our garden, weeding rows of promising seedling vegetables, grumbling at the energetic, flourishing and vigorous chickweed, we'd come in to enjoy a peaceful cup of tea. We'd been relaxing for only a few minutes when the phone rang. It was Sandy Grant, the St Andrew's organist, in a great state of agitation. He had gone during the afternoon, into the church to practise. He had so often walked up the aisle with his mind on his organ, he'd not noticed anything unusual. It was only on his way out that his eye was caught by a long piece of stone, like a narrow pillar, lying at an angle on some of the pews by the font, to the left of the West Door. The ceiling plaster had been torn into a great hole and pieces of wood from the roof were dislodged and broken. He'd then gone to look outside at the aisle roof and could again see the jagged hole where many slates were missing or broken, fallen to the ground. He had tried to contact Duncan Forbes, the secretary, but unsuccessfully, so he was now ringing Nicholas. I could hear only half the conversation but was able to gather most of the story from Nicholas's questions.

After Sandy had rung off Nicholas said, "It must be that piece of stone pillar which divides one of the tower windows. Christopher told me about its being out of place. It's not a real pillar but a rounded length of stone, normally fixed onto the front of a square section that's the true supporting pillar. It divides the two lancet windows which are fairly high up and not well within our view, unless we look up purposely. It had been leaning slightly to one side and Christopher, with his young eagle eye, had seen it and had reported it to Duncan, who told him it was under control. He'd told me about it too. I'd better get on to Edward, I suppose. Oh, dear! And he will expect it all to be covered by insurance, he always does."

"And it hardly ever is. I remember when St Andrew fell off his plinth and got broken beyond repair, he wasn't insured. That was sad and the monks took so long to make a new one for us."

"I suppose the noise of the crash wasn't heard by anyone because it happened on the side of the church away from the street."

"Anyway it's a very busy and noisy street. Lots of vans and lorries are passing all the time."

"That's just about it. I must ring Christopher too. He'll be very upset, after the good fortune of his spotting the trouble and then the damage being done all the same. It must have happened after everything had been tidied away after the half past twelve service and everyone had gone home."

"It's strange about Duncan. What can he possibly have been thinking about? Why didn't he do something? Where is he now?" I was puzzled. Though I was used to finding, at St Andrew's, happenings often didn't make sense.

Edward had the same story. Christopher had told him Duncan had it all in his care. When Christopher, himself, heard about the disaster he was indeed very upset. It had been pouring with rain and blowing a gale when he had been trying to describe to Duncan which window and whereabouts on the tower this stone pseudo pillar was that he'd noticed as being out of place. They'd been standing in the porch and Christopher'd been able only to wave his hand in a not very exact direction, but he'd never thought Duncan had misunderstood him.

"Anyway, Duncan had only to go and look to see which was the pillar in danger of falling," said Christopher very down-heartedly.

A little later Nicholas was able to get hold of Duncan. He'd been out all day fishing and had only just returned. He was very shocked, very upset, at first not believing such a thing could have happened to his beloved church. He had understood Christopher to be talking about the lower windows in the tower where some small bits of dividing woodwork had been out of place for some time. A carpenter had been expected to begin work there very shortly, so Duncan had not seen any need for any further inspection. He would now go immediately to see the damage and then contact the builder and the architect. It was unlikely to rain tonight, nor the wind blow overmuch, so all action could be left till first thing the next morning.

Of course, it was clear to me there would be recriminations all round. They're one of the easiest arrived at and most tiresome manifestations of any trouble caused by mistaken messages or warnings.

But I was sorry, sorry for Duncan, especially. It wasn't like him at all to make such a mistake. I remembered, then, how Nicholas had been worried about him some time before. He'd seemed rather distracted and not his usual competent self. He was normally such a good secretary and he loved the church too much not to look after it as well as he could.

The next morning Nicholas drove into Strathlyon to meet Duncan with the builder and the architect. Edward would be there too, and I thought I'd better go to see exactly what it was everybody would soon be talking about. But I didn't need to stay to hear all the experts expounding their favourite theories of what they thought had happened or what had best be done about it. After I'd seen enough and had expressed my sympathy, I walked up into the High Street to buy a few things I'd not had time to get the week before.

Normally, I met only one or two of the St Andrew's congregation when I was in the town, but this morning, of course, I encountered at least six. All had heard of the disaster. I was correct in my forecast of recriminations. It was all Duncan's fault, he's getting beyond it. It was Edward's fault for not making sure Duncan had understood. It was Christopher's fault for not making himself explicit enough. And most of all, of course, everything was Nicholas's fault, especially the fact there'd probably be no insurance. Nicholas said to me quietly later, after I'd come back to the church. "There's not much hope we'll be covered. A connecting iron bar was rusted through and that will be due to faulty maintenance or normal wear and tear. That's why the pillar fell. It was because of a simple misunderstanding that there was a delay in attending to it and one can't insure against misunderstandings. We might get a grant from the office in Eaglesburgh, though, to help with the repair. Or a loan, but loans have to be repaid. I'll do my best."

We stayed for the Mass. Nicholas spoke to Jamie, the sacristan, who assured him all had been as usual at one o'clock the previous day. He too knew about Christopher's observation and thought Duncan was meant to be arranging for something to be done. He was very upset about the whole thing.

I was glad we could be at the service. I could look forward to the lovely familiar words, they would have such a calming influence on me. And at the end I felt strengthened, though I still wasn't totally at ease.

I heard Edward read from the Gospel:

'And the sheep hear his voice, and he calleth his own sheep by name, and leadeth them out. And then he putteth forth his own sheep, he goeth before them: for they know his voice... I am the door; by me if any man enter in he shall be saved, and shall go in and out, and find pasture.'

'And find pasture,' I said to myself. That's what so often I'm hungry for - for holy pasture, for spiritual food, and here it is in the Mass. Now we can put the disaster and the recriminations in their proper perspective. Some of the shepherd's sheep are distressed, but the shepherd has called us by name and he will comfort us. The Comforter, that's what this week is all about. What was it in the Whit Sunday Gospel?

'I will not leave you desolate: I will come to you... we will come unto him and make our abode with him.'

That's ourselves who love Christ, and whom the Father loves.

'Let not your heart be troubled, neither let it be afraid.'

Driving home with Nicholas, along the river, I found my thoughts and prayers being swept away from myself, as if by an outside force. I didn't seem able to concentrate on my surroundings or on Nicholas, my prayers kept drifting away as if someone else were in charge.

Perhaps it was the Holy Spirit praying in me, like I've read that he sometimes does. It felt as if it were for good, as if it were doing good, but there were no words. That wasn't necessarily a bad thing. I was thinking about words the other day and deciding it's the feelings that belong to the words that count, that work in us, and it was certainly feelings and not words which were working in me at that moment. Though this isn't to say that often the power of good words, in the right place, can be incomparable. It was very wonderful, I did hope the Spirit would help everybody feel better about each other again. I felt very bruised in my mind because people were saying awful things about each other.

The feeling of the Holy Spirit praying in me didn't last very long. As soon as we got home there was lunch to prepare, and this, of course, brought my mind down to practicalities. However the memory of the morning came back the moment I had time to myself.

The Spirit in me needed nourishment. I felt as if I was nothing and the Spirit was everything, but it could, would die in me without some nourishing prayer. This was a real Whitsun happening. I asked the Blessed Spirit to stay with me.

'Lord, take not this Holy Spirit from me.' How sad that this good thing, the Spirit, which had come into me, came from a disaster. But good can come from bad. With prayer and God's love, evil can be turned to good.

WHITSUNTIDE:
THE SPIRIT IN ACTION

That same afternoon I decided to go up on the hill. It was a lovely afternoon, but the real reason I wanted to go was to sort things out in my mind. I decided to walk through the wood rather than along the lane, enjoying the company of the grand oaks.

Then I climbed up to the edge of the wood, scrambled rather inelegantly over a wire fence and then immediately over a ditch, crossed the lane and took a narrow sheep track up through the heather to the top of the hill. I sat down there in the sunshine and leaned my back against the white concrete pillar of the trig point. There was a lovely soft breeze from the west which gently blew my feeble hair about. The gorse flowers were fading now but the broom was at its best.

Gorse can be more dazzling than broom, I was thinking. The flowers are more tightly packed together, but broom is more elegant, falling in fronds and sprays, and its yellows are more varied. I suppose broom is the more beautiful, but gorse the more welcome, as the flowers come earlier in the spring and last over a much longer period of time. 'Kissing is out of tune when gorse is out of bloom' - that's meant to be never, but this notion must apply only further south, for in most years there are certainly here one or two months when there are no gorse flowers at all.

I needed as soon as possible to make quite sure about the Holy Spirit. One Sunday Edward had said, 'Remember the other name for the Holy Spirit is Holy Ghost. This name has at present gone somewhat out of fashion. The word ghost means a gust, like a gust of wind which comes unexpectedly in time and direction. When we are not expecting it the Spirit's gust or breath comes to us and enters into our hearts.' I can remember this morning those not very nice recriminations, and as we drove home along the river, how I discovered the Holy Spirit. I was certainly not expecting him. He's not only the Spirit who joins the Father to the Son with love, but is also the living force which brings that love into us.

I could feel everything was changing for me, already things *had* changed, and they were going to change more. I felt that maybe, even probably, I'd have no more of the old despondency; or rather, the despondency, when it came, would be different. I would be different. Perhaps I wouldn't need any longer my faithful brooding stone at the bottom of the garden, where I sat and felt useless, staring out at the hills and the sky, feeling out of tune with them. How marvellous. Now there'd be no more searching for Christ, nor for God the Father, nor for the Holy Spirit. I am thankful, grateful, blessed, beyond any words.

A party of linnets flew up the hill towards me, twittering sweetly. One cock bird settled amongst the bright yellow flowers at the top of a gorse bush, his read head and breast glowing resplendent in the sunshine. He sang a little gentle varied tune which fitted the lovely day and my now happier mood. Though there were still shadows across my mind from the events at St Andrews, gratitude for my discovery or the Holy Spirit was uppermost in my mind. The power of his prayer in me was strong at that moment.

After a short time of realization and thankfulness, of seeing things more clearly, of recognising a little what had been happening to me, I got up and walked happily down and home across a still pale green silage field, shorn not long ago of its crop of grass. I was hopeful of the future, what it would bring. I hoped I'd not be disappointed.

The next day I was discussing the problem of the Holy Spirit with Jane, who'd come over from Drummore. She was always helpful with basic religious problems, always a great help to me in her very quiet and patient way. She'd been so very well taught about some of the most important points of the faith, that exchanging views with her was usually very helpful to me.

We were down at the bottom of the Whinside garden, I was sitting on my perhaps not much longer to be needed brooding stone and Jane on a similar one at my side. We were looking across the field where, at that time, turnip seedling were growing rapidly, destined to nourish many sheep and cattle next winter. Beyond the field and the loch the mountains were wrapped in wet-looking clouds though we ourselves were still enjoying the sunshine. This lower part of our garden was very steep and stony, hardly less wild than when we first arrived here. Every autumn Nicholas slashed and trimmed the whins back as much as possible, but each summer they always took over again.

"Wherever I look there's gorse!" I was saying to Jane. "I have to remember it's called whins here. - in the plural. It certainly is in the plural, isn't it? It seeds everywhere and spreads in all directions. It's very strong and full of vigour, not easily defeated, very tough and spiky. I can't imagine how ponies can chew it and then swallow it, but in the winter, when there's very little else, they do. I've often watched them in astonishment."

Then I spoke yet again to Jane about her puzzlement that my beliefs should have taken almost a whole lifetime to come to me.

"When at last," I said. "I began to understand about God and his Son. I suddenly found life to be perpetually absorbing. Since then I've felt so much recovered from my almost permanent lowness of spirits. Though I don't think the lowness showed itself to other people all that much, I hope not. But often I used to sit here on this stone and look out at the marvellous view and think my life had been so very much wasted. I thought things had turned out badly for me which, in fact, seems to have been the very reverse of the truth. I remember getting in a muddle between 'thoughts that do lie too deep for tears' which is Wordsworth, and 'sighs that do lie too deep for words' which St Paul wrote about and which belongs in a quite different and more hopeful context. He says the Spirit helps our infirmities, and that, when we don't know how we should pray as we ought, he prays in us, making intercessions for us with groanings that cannot be uttered. And now I've found the Holy Spirit in me, I feel altogether a better more cheerful person. It's clear to me the Spirit really can and does choose for us what we ought to pray for. So long as we listen to the Spirit we don't have to worry. Or we may not always even have to listen, he may pray in us while we're dreaming of nothing in particular, which is, I suppose, what happened to me yesterday when we were driving along by the river."

Jane said, "St Paul is often very good and helpful. He says though sometimes it's very difficult for us to believe this.

'...that in everything God works for the good of those who love him, who are called by him for his purposes.'"

And I added: "Though we're not sure what his purposes are going to be. And it's best, I suppose, that we don't know. Or even try to guess."

Later that evening I was reading a book by Thomas Merton, whose work I really enjoy. He writes simply, in sentences which, on the whole, I can understand. I came across some words he was quoting written by Father Monchanin, a French priest. In a way it hardly suited my ideas of the greatness of the Holy Spirit, but on the other hand it showed that even work of seemingly little importance can be what we are intended to do for God with love, and therefore not of less value to him. It was about the ant and work. I used sometimes to get a bit depressed about how much more other people were able to do for St Andrews's than I could, more important work with a name to it. But my filling in the unobvious interstices is the kind of work I prefer to do, it's perfect for my temperament, it's varied, interesting, different every day, and it's what I enjoy. Though, all the same, I'd often wondered whether there was really much value in what I did. Just because my jobs were hidden there would be very little noticeable difference if they didn't get done. That's why there'd been interstices in the first place. Who would notice? Only Nicholas and Edward. However, here was a helpful idea which put my work in a better light. Father Monchanin says:

'Let it be good enough to know ourselves to be in the place God wants for us, and carry on our work, even though it be no more than the work of an ant, infinitesimally small, and with unforeseeable results.'

Quite suddenly, as I read these words, I saw a reason to be more cheerful. I read them over several times. I'm an ant of St Andrew's. But I'm an ant of the Holy Spirit too. And after all. it's not the ant as a mindless insect which is being referred to here but the ant as a small quiet worker who works without saying all the time. 'Look what I've done!" I would be like that. And the unforeseen part was good too, for we are not to know beforehand what the effect of our work will be or to know what will happen to ourselves.

WHITSUNTIDE:
THE SPIRIT IN THE
SCRIPTURES

I'd borrowed a book from the library. It was about the trial of Jesus. It was a very factual book, very interesting and clearly written, not difficult to follow. The author uses historically proven facts to comment on the trial. He described how, at the time of the writing of the Gospels, Christians in various parts of the Roman world were thinking about themselves and their faith. This led to some differences, he said, and biased the writers in the telling of their stories. At first I enjoyed these analyses, but when I came to the story of Peter's denial, I began to feel uneasy.

The author separated the telling of this story about Peter from the account of the Sanhedrin proceedings, though, in Marks' Gospel, the two are interwoven. This is a natural arrangement for both are happening simultaneously. He suggested this story of Peter had been added to the original account of the trial by Mark in Rome, in order to denigrate the church in Jerusalem where Peter was working.

As I read on through the book, my uneasy feelings got stronger. I began to feel confused and threatened. It began to be too much for my poor mind. I was afraid if we went on in this way there'd be no Gospel left. Each chapter was examined closely and I imagined the author digging cobble stones out of a pathway, looking closely at each with a strong magnifying glass, and, in the end, finding the path had become a strip of dry concrete dust with the stones lying in a disorganised pile on the verge.

Then I suddenly understood what was being done here in this book, and also I presumed in hundreds or other books. It was the undoing of God's truth as shown in the Gospels, in the way they've come down to us, as we see them today in the Bible.

In taking the Gospels apart in this way, people are undoing the Holy Spirit's bonding of the scriptures. God's revelation is being allowed to fly away, to be lost. It's as if we had Bibles with no binding and the pages have become detached and scattered on the wind, allowing the true message of God to be lost perhaps for ever. Far from helping us the better to understand what is written for our learning and inspiration, this kind of criticism disorientates us. In order to encourage us, to enable us to learn about our faith, God, through his Holy Spirit, has taken diverse elements of history, facts, writings, traditions, even misconceptions and biases, and has welded them together so, as they are now, however puzzling and contradictory, they contain for us the true revelation of his Word. This bonding of the Word by the Holy Spirit shows us a world which is deeper, wider and higher than anything we could imagine for ourselves. In the Gospels there's everything we need, the unsearchable riches of Christ. Some people may enjoy modern methods of analysis, but this one made me feel unhappy and confused, even lost. It would be less upsetting, if, as he went along, and he could have done so, the author had taken care to keep God's truth in our minds, but he didn't.

It's like pulling down your house to see how the builders did their work, and then finding you have destroyed your home. It's like dissecting a frog in a biology class, and the further the dissection proceeds the less and less the frog can be seen as resembling itself, displaying its frogness, let alone functioning as one.

The world of the Spirit is like the Great Barrier Reef. On the surface of the sea the waves are rolling in from the Pacific Ocean. The sunlight sparkles on the water. A man in a small boat would be able to see this surface with its two colours only, as Jane, the artist, would, the colour of the sea itself and the reflection of the bright sky, and the whole decorated with patches of white foam from the breaking wave crests.

But, for those who know to dive below the surface, a whole new world is opened; a world of wonder unfolding before their goggles, lit by their torches, as they swim down towards the fishes and the corals and the sea floor. However often they dive, however long they spend in this deep underwater world, they never come to the end of the wonder of seeing, of learning, of the endless discovery of all the marvellous things that are to be found in the depths.

So it is with the world of the Spirit. However deeply we enter into its depths we can always go further down, exploring its wonders, finding more and more love, joy and peace, the fruit of the Spirit. This world of the Spirit is the world to which we really belong: it's where we came from, where we should be during our lives but may not find that possible, or hardly so, and where we are going to return, where we shall find the reality of the power of God and his love.

On and off during the next few days I kept going back in my mind to my discovery that the world of the Spirit is the real lasting world, as opposed to the world of the senses that's full of short delights and sad deceptions.

Of course other people have discovered this too. We are learning about it all the time, but the realization doesn't always sink in to our understanding, or, if it does, it's not for long. Mostly people go through each day with their minds caught in a world of jobs and food and houses and amusements till Sunday comes round, and the Spirit returns to their remembrance once more. Whereas the Spirit needs to be with us always, and we, equally, need the Spirit in our wide-awake consciousness for ever.

The Spirit lives in the Bible: as we read and learn we can hear his voice making everything gradually clear, bringing the truth out of the words for us. After we've had some practice, we begin to find he's reading aloud to us and explaining everything as we go along, rather than we ourselves having to use our own eyes to take in the words, and our own minds to be wondering whether we are understanding aright.

It's not only in the Bible, of course, as I said, we find the Spirit, but in all our life. The Spirit in our life and our life in the Spirit is the foundation which supports us always. We are here at the present moment on this earth, so we have to think about jobs and food and houses and keeping warm, but we can show our love for God by doing our best for the world, by helping our neighbour, bringing the Spirit into the world of every day life.

I looked back to Ascension Day and Whit Sunday and the wonder of Christ's being received into a cloud, taken up into Heaven where he is glorified and for ever redeeming us. He has taken up his humanity and ours to the Father, so we are now living in another dimension from what we were before, now as sons of God by adoption. We are, because of this, members of Christ's mystical body which is the Church. Or we can look at it another way, the Church is his body. Christ is the head and we are his members, as if we were his arms or legs or eyes or ears or mouth or, as St Paul says, even his nose. Or again, we can think of the Kingdom of heaven as Christ's being in us, and our taking him with us wherever on earth we may be, every day of our lives.

This change in our human nature is a wonderful thing, wrought for us by Christ in his death, by his mighty resurrection and glorious ascension. This truth is necessary for us. We have to believe in Christ's promises for our salvation. Christ redeemed the world, or we might, as Paul says, as well give up altogether. It's unhelpful for scholars to suggest the Easter and Whitsun messages can be watered down, saying there might not have been an empty tomb, or Christ in his body might not have truly ascended to heaven. (We don't have to accept a materialistic description of his ascension, we cannot still imagine that heaven is in a place just above the stars and not all that far away from earth. Mysteries can multiply as new things are discovered about the universe).

In the end each learned scholar will discover that, in looking for the literal and literary truth, he is missing God's living truth. It's like discussing the shape of the letters on a page instead of reading the words with understanding. The real truth is missed. It will become harder to find, though some people are pleased to discover that a faith made of the remnants is 'easier', or 'more reasonable', a faith they can believe in with their intelligence, involving nothing supernatural. (Remember Ruth!) I used to be like that. Some people will remain with this modernized faith throughout their lives, for it makes sense to modern minds. But others, such as myself, will be drawn by God to step over the door sill and into the church. I'm thinking of the kind of church doorway, where, as one enters, there's a step down onto a cool dark stone floor, lower than the street level outside. A doorway that gives pilgrims a sense of entering and surrendering themselves into a church of great peace. God's peace which brings also strength. There they find themselves, over the days and weeks that follow, feeling more and more at home. Their hearts take over and what seemed 'hard' beliefs become no longer hard but necessary.

Anyway, I'm glad to say I never finished that book. I didn't want to finish it after I'd learned that the Scriptures were written as they are with the Holy Spirit's guidance, written for our learning. We can study them without worrying about the opinions of learned scholars. I was very glad and relieved the day I took the book back to the library and exchanged it for something more able to help me grow in the Spirit rather than shrink.

TRINITY SUNDAY

After lunch on the following Sunday, Trinity Sunday, I was sitting on the patio having a welcome mug of coffee and reading about the arts and books in my favourite Sunday Review.

I'd never thought, after all the rain last summer, it would ever again be sunny enough to have the garden table out and its umbrella up. But this afternoon the light was dazzling, and the sun shone down on me through a lovely refreshing breeze, so that, strange to say, for once, I was neither too cold nor too hot. I thought, hopefully, perhaps the sunshine will kindly persevere and beam down on us throughout the summer months, or at any rate revisit us fairly frequently.

I'd enjoyed the service that morning at St Andrew's, but it would be a sad day if I hadn't. I went on thinking about that morning's service. On Whit Sunday we'd heard about the tongues of fire and the mighty rushing wind bringing the Holy Spirit down onto the disciples. Now today, on Trinity Sunday, we'd heard words about God's love which constantly flows from one Person of the Trinity to the other from eternity.

Edward had said in his sermon that since God is love and he is Father of all, he needs a Son to love, and similarly for the same reason the Son needs a Father. It's the Holy Spirit who is the love which binds the two together and to us, all this continually. We can see ourselves bound into the Trinity because we know we have, from the resurrection, become sons by adoption. I could see this Trinity Sunday had come at just the right time for me, bringing together in my mind the ideas which had been taking shape there those last few weeks.

It's not surprising, I was thinking, that Edward should say Trinity Sunday is more important than Whit Sunday (which is now called Pentecost by some). Trinity Sunday should be three times more important to us than Whit, for we are celebrating not only the Spirit, but the Father and the Son, all three bound together in love. The Trinity is the great distinguishing foundation stone of Christianity.

That afternoon I was contemplating, as I sat under the red umbrella, what else was involved in Trinity Sunday. I knew we'd come to the beginning of what I think of as the long haul down through

142

Trinity to Advent. (Can one have a long haul down? Probably not, though I can't clearly see why not). All the same I love the long progression of Sundays after Trinity. It's a time of peaceful growth. It's not at all boring, in fact so much happens I often think it's not peaceful enough. We proceed quietly from Sunday to Sunday and the whole fabric of these weeks becomes a lovely wallpaper, a calm and helpful background to our lives, and a great contrast to all those dazzling stained glass windows of events which lit up our lives from Christmas through to Easter and then to Whit and then to this day, Trinity Sunday.

But in fact, I knew there'd be a great deal of important happenings between this Sunday and Christmas. There'd be Corpus Christi on Thursday, then this year there'd be Christopher's priesting, then the days of the Visitation, the Transfiguration, St Mary Magdalene, the Assumption, St Michael and All Angels, All Saints. All Souls and then at last we'd come to Advent and St Andrew's Day and so to Christmas. I do hope Heaven will provide us with a life equally full of similarly lovely and eventful days. I'm sure it's wrong to imagine Heaven as a place where bliss continues on one level only without valleys of calm and summits of cheerful and interesting happenings and happiness.

Sunday afternoon was usually spent restfully with my paper or a book for later, after Evensong, it was one of my jobs to help Nicholas sort out all the week's cash from the church, getting it balanced with his books and ready in bags to take to pay into the bank next morning.

And that day I'd begun to think that although my ideas had been somewhat changed, my habits had not, or not all that much. In a way, I'd thought about all this before. I knew it was no good trying to rush God. I began, that day, seriously to try to change myself from being a solitary person into a friendly one, to be interested in my neighbours rather than pretending I didn't have any: to ask God to help me change. Up till then, in those days, as soon as the morning service was over, while Nicholas talked to those who had problems or queries about their giving, or other subjects to do with money. I used, rather than talk with anyone, gradually getting to know them, to go and sit in the car all by myself and read the Sunday paper. I much preferred my own company to that of even the nicest people. It was safer, I thought.

But now my own company and the newspaper was perhaps beginning to feel a bit insufficient, even dangerous. Perhaps, I'd begun to wonder, there might be something missing. That day I'd seen there might be people around me who needed friendliness and I could learn how to give it them; perhaps I was hiding from people who needed me. Perhaps I should try at first just to look as if I were glad to see them, then I might grow to be really glad to see them and so learn really how to cheer people up,

I saw there was a lot in this. I was finding it very hard to change myself. I used to be a very detached spectator and I was finding it very hard to become part of the congregation. Before Edward came and made me feel differently about things I used to kneel there in that same pew Sunday after Sunday feeling rather lost, almost as if I shouldn't have been there, except that I came with Nicholas. I'd go up to the altar rails because it was easier to go than not, then I'd listen to everyone else's footsteps going up there and back and regret my detachment, and then wonder at my empty heart. I knew only vaguely those worshippers I watched, they were faces with bodies but they hardly had names. They seemed entirely wrapped up in what they were doing, they could understand its necessity for them. How marvellously different things have become. Even now I could feel God still changing me. And although the change became especially identified in my mind with Trinity Sunday it took really a long time for the wonderful ideas to sink all the way into myself, to become an unconscious part of me. I expect the best changes happen in that way, slowly and surely.

Then, unexpectedly, as I was enjoying my relax under the large umbrella (we ought to call it a sunshade), there was the noise of a car arriving. A family had arrived to see us, father, mother and two young boys, a family we'd met a few years before. We'd all been on a sailing holiday with our boys and many other families, joining together in races and picnics or just simply sailing. They were on holiday again. They were coming through Strathlyon and had decided to turn off the main road and come to Ardness to call on us. Oh, dear! I realized God was rushing me. I was hardly halfway through sorting out all my ideas about the new things I was discovering. I must jump up, put down my paper and leave my brooding thoughts, full of great interest to me, drop all my plans for a quiet afternoon, and smile in a welcoming way. I remembered my half-made prayers and resolutions. "How lovely to see you,' I said. By acting my pleasure, I found myself soon really and truly enjoying the afternoon and the unexpected tea party as much as everyone else was.

I was surprised and pleased at my success over my natural disinclination though it was God's success not mine. He'd rushed me all right. If there'd been only Nicholas and myself together in the garden all afternoon I might have forgotten my new decisions about friendliness. The unexpected invasion put a seal on my beginning to learn about neighbours, even, or especially, those who'd come without warning from afar.

Later that evening, at Evensong, I much enjoyed the music. I enjoyed the prayers too of course. I was learning. But the music helped me very much, often dominating everything else.

It was Jack to read the first lesson, from Jeremiah, I heard him say:

"'...Their idols are like scarecrows in a cucumber field ... Be not afraid of them for they cannot do evil, neither is it in them to do good. They are made of beaten silver and gold. But the God of Jacob is he who formed all things. He made the earth by his power, he established the world by his wisdom, by his understanding he stretched out the heavens, he makes the mist rise from the ends of the earth and lightnings for the rain.'"

"That was good," I thought. But then Jack always reads well.

Duncan Forbes read the second lesson, from Ephesians. He gave a little introduction or summary before he began on the lesson itself. He always did this and it made me feel uncomfortable, though I wasn't sure why. We always referred to this little speech as Duncan's mini-sermon but we forbore to tease him about it. For us, the qualities of a faithful churchman excused his harmless eccentricities.

He really was so good a person we had to let him have his funny little ways undisturbed. Though I've a feeling that, if a lesson is clearly read, it shouldn't need an introduction, especially as normally the words are already familiar to us. I did hope Nicholas was wrong about Duncan's being unwell. But, .. and then my mind went off at a tangent temporarily. I was thinking that some people did have funny ideas about reading lessons. There was Jeremy Fisher who got everything wrong. He couldn't ever have read the rubrics, those words in the Prayer Book that used to be printed in red letters. He would introduce the passage by saying, 'This evening' as if it could possibly be the morning or last Sunday or next week, and 'taken from' when in the prayer book it's clearly stated we should say 'written in'. I remembered too, at Dunmarkie, at St Margaret's, there was a very nice friendly lady who had such a strange way of reading, she made even the most serious and dramatic subjects, such as Thomas's doubting or Peter's denial, sound like the Tale of Mrs Tiggywinkle. Here at St Andrew's, too, we had Mr Todd who was odd to say the least, and not only in his way of reading which was very didactic and dry and abrupt. He came only to Evensong, very disapproving of the Mass. He would definitely have preferred Matins but they were not to be found at any church in Strathlyon. All through every hymn he stood, his arms tightly folded in front of him, his mouth tightly shut, all solely to show to everyone his objection to what he considered the slow pace of the hymns. Though I failed to see how he could possibly achieve any speeding up by so doing, and anyway I've heard hymns played even more slowly and drearily than at St Andrew's as well as so uncomfortably fast, I lost my breath trying to keep up. I wondered if any responsible person in the church would ever notice his actions, or, if anyone did, would they respond in the required way? People are funny, I mean peculiar. And Edward was much too kind-hearted and patient to remark on people's oddness to their faces.

However that evening Duncan's lesson was short and simple so he said beforehand only:

"Here Paul is pleading for unity amongst Christ's followers."

He then read about the people, the new Christians, of Ephesus, (though they were probably not known as Christians at that time, I forget), called to live a life of patience and meekness, forbearing one another in love, maintaining the unity of the Spirit and the bond of peace. Paul explains that, though they are each called to different work as members of Christ's body, all should aim for the unity of the faith and the knowledge of the Son of God. By doing this they will no longer be like children, tossed to and fro by every wind of vain doctrine; instead they will be joined and knit together at every joint, each part working together, so making bodily growth themselves and also building Christ's body, the Church itself, in love.

The anthem was lovely and marvellously well sung: Schubert's Holy, Holy, Holy, in celebration of the Trinity. The young voices of the trebles went soaring up to the roof beams and down again. Then Canon Harper's sermon was good, livelier than usual. He spoke of the Holy Spirit and that we must allow him to enter into us so he can involve us in our church, to be involved in all that's happening in the services. Many people, he said, come to the church to be spectators only and leave again at the end, their hearts untouched. They don't feel themselves bound to other Christians in the congregation or to those in the world outside; they don't feel they are firm members of either St Andrew's or of the Church in general, they are as yet not part of Christ's body and so don't understand this wonderfully encouraging and helpful idea of Christ the Head and ourselves as limbs.

I'd thought about much of this before. I knew it was no good trying to rush God. And yet he had earlier that day rushed me, and he still quite often does. After our invasion that afternoon, I'd even more seen the need to change myself from being a solitary person into a friendly one, to be interested in my neighbours rather than pretending I didn't have any.

TRINITY: CORPUS CHRISTI

Jane rang just a day or two after the festival of Corpus Christi (the day we celebrate Christ's giving us the Holy Communion at the Last Supper when he and the Apostles were together before the Crucifixion): a day of celebration during the summer while our minds are somewhat freer than in the sadness of Good Friday.

"Do you think it would be a good idea," she said, "if we took a day off and went over to the West Coast? I feel like a change." The weather had been quite pleasantly encouraging for the last few days and one could imagine without too great a strain that it would continue in similar manner for a few days yet. "Do you think," she added, "we could possibly leave the men behind?'

"Or we could all go over, have a picnic lunch at Inverbroom looking over the bay, and afterwards we'd persuade them to visit the Gardens, and we could drive round to the point and look at the birds."

So it was arranged. We were fortunate with the weather, the day continuing the fine spell, a lovely mid-summer day. We quickly organized ourselves and left home with lots of daylight hours still ahead of us. There was no need to rush over any part of the trip.

We got to Inverbroom in time for an early picnic lunch. It was warm enough to enjoy eating our food sitting on rugs on the sloping grassy bank that stretched around the bay between the road and the wet seaweedy rocks. We watched the sparkling light on the incoming tide slowly and unthreateningly approaching our feet. (We knew from experience it wouldn't reach them). Afterwards we separated, Nicholas and Jack walking the short distance to the famous Gardens to enjoy the rhododendrons and azaleas which should be at their best, as well as many other treasures, while Jane and I drove the few miles further on to the point. There, after we'd parked the car on a relatively flat piece of ground at the end of the road, we climbed up to the old gun emplacements which faced, of course, out to sea, and there made ourselves as comfortable as we could, leaning against a concrete wall. We chose as much as possible a spot with maximum sun and minimum wind and there relaxed in the expectation of watching many kinds of different birds from those we saw at home. At first Tess gambolled about playfully but finally came and lay down beside us and quietly slept away the afternoon.

The first bird I saw wasn't an exciting seabird but a pied wagtail. He was quite close by, catching the flies sunning themselves on the warm rocks. He caught a few and then flew off to his nest in a hole not far away between some stones. After a pause to feed his young, he came back again to look for more. Meadow pipits and skylarks were singing high over the grassy slopes behind us, and well below us, at sea level, oystercatchers were flying around piping or sitting on rocks. Shags and cormorants were criss-crossing over the calm water in ones or twos. I searched in vain for any gannets, but they must have been all far away, busy in their distant nesting colonies.

I picked a tormentil flower from the short grass at my side and began to examine it carefully, noticing especially its delicate construction. I remembered that, according to my dictionary, its roots are astringent; perhaps it would torment those who ate too much of it.

I think it's a lovely little flower. It stands up bravely to close examination, a four pointed yellow star, well, not sharply pointed, the petals are more rounded. They shine so brightly out from the close cropped grass they remind me of stars shining out of the night sky. Wherever they're found, they spread out in all directions for ever and ever. They made me think how strange it is that such a common flower seems by its very familiarity to appeal to us so much. I knew I loved them all the more because all over the Highlands wherever one looked there'd be millions of them. It's like the stars in the Milky Way, if there were only a few specks of starlight up in the black sky, we wouldn't be specially interested, not as amazed as we are now by the great display of billions.

Then I began to think about the Thanksgiving for the Institution of Holy Communion, Corpus Christi, and I mentioned this to Jane.

"It's difficult to imagine life without Holy Communion, without the Mass."

And as I said this, I was reminded of a strange but funny episode of a year ago. And I told Jane how Trefor Pari-Jones, one of our more self-important (and obviously not Scottish) Vestry members, had spoken very scathingly to me. We had been standing after Evensong at the west end of the church examining the noticeboard, when he remarked to me how much he disapproved of my writing 'Corpus Christi' in the notice announcing the evening Mass to be held later that week. I don't remember exactly what I'd been able to say in reply to his jibe, except that I told him I preferred writing the short Latin phrase rather than 'Thanksgiving for the Institution of Holy Communion' which had several disadvantages for a scribe. Not only were the words Thanksgiving and Institution and Communion difficult to fit on an A4 page and yet be large and clear enough to be legible, but Communion has those double M Ms which either won't fit in well or look badly written. I'm very slow-witted with people like Trefor. It's a pity, for later I thought I should have asked him if, instead of the Latin word 'Magnificat' for the Evensong canticle he'd just been singing, he'd prefer to refer to it as the 'Song of the Blessed Virgin Mary', its English title. I was certain he'd not prefer anything of the kind, knowing how firmly (and often furiously) anti-Roman he was in outlook. Though perhaps he could have been only teasing, but I doubt it.

Then Jane returned to our intended subject: "Before Christ came everyone lived without the Mass. That was natural. It's obvious but it's also hard to realize the reality of it. In comparative, I mean in comparison with all the centuries of ancient history that went before, it isn't all that long ago Christ was alive here on earth and walking among other not so dissimilar people. And only at the end of his life did he show people what to do with the Bread and Wine and tell us that as often as we ate and drank them we should do so in remembrance of him. And it's more than a memorial."

"It's the most important THING in our lives," I said. "I'm reading Eric Mascall at the moment, about the Mass. He's a wonderful teacher, he says the same things over and over again in different words and without ever being boring, so that even I, in the end, can understand what he's writing about and more or less remember his points. Let me see if I can remember what I read yesterday. He's so sound, as well as convincing. He's very worthwhile concentrating on. I'll try to tell you what he says and if I get stuck we'll look it up tonight, when we get back, or tomorrow. I'll look it up anyway, he uses better words than I shall remember.

"First of all he says worship is not something we do on Sundays in order to live better lives during the week. Nor do we worship God because he loves us and looks after us. We worship him for what he is not for what he does. He is perfection, the source of perfection, he deserves our perfect worship. All through time men have felt they must offer to their god or gods a sacrifice which is as perfect as possible, but they have realized that, however hard they try, even the beast without blemish is never going to be perfect enough. This imperfection is unavoidable because man is imperfect, flawed, because of the Fall. He cannot offer anything perfect of his own however hard he tries.

"Next, Christ has three bodies, only not really." I went on. "I mean they are called modes, there are three modes of his body. There is first his natural body which grew in Mary's womb, which suffered on the cross and which ascended with him into heaven where it's glorified in the presence of God the Father. Because of this we too can be seen to be taken out of the realm of sin into the realm of Christ as members of his mystical body which is the second mode. Christ is the perfect head of the mystical body and we are its very imperfect members. Thirdly, there's his sacramental body which comes down and is present in the Bread and Wine in the Mass. This body is perfect too. All three bodies are present in the Mass, each in its different way.

"So, as Christ offered the perfection of his natural body on the cross, and comes down in his sacramental body into the Bread and Wine, it has become possible for imperfect man to offer up for the first time a 'full, perfect and sufficient sacrifice'. His perfect sacramental body comes down through the priest's words and actions into the Bread and Wine which we then offer back to God. The Bread, Christ's body, the perfect sacrifice, is broken on the altar. We also offer our imperfect selves, as members of Christ's mystical body, to the perfect Head to be ourselves in him and he in us. Because of our imperfections we need to be brought into contact with this perfect Head for healing and growth.

"All this can happen," I was pleased with my being able to remember so much so clearly so far, "only because of the incarnation, of Christ's being both God and man. Without this our offering could not be perfect. As God only is perfect, Christ can have no perfection unless he is God too; and, if he were not God, he would not have a sacramental body in which to come down into the Mass. You can see, too, the important part which the priest plays in what is happening in that service. This special spiritual grace he uses has been handed down to him from the Apostles through bishop after bishop from all that long time ago.

"As well as the Incarnation being necessary, so also is the Trinity. Perhaps I should have explained about the Trinity first. If there had been no Son of God, to offer himself for us on the cross and to be taken up into heaven where, in his glorified body, he gives eternal praise and love to the Father, and where we are taken up with him as members of his mystical body, there could be no Eucharist. And you can see the Holy Spirit too must be included in all this. He's the Spirit who goes from the Father to the Son and from the Son to the Father continually, and is present over us all and in us all, through all the service of the Mass and beyond.

"I'm nearly through, so don't be anxious," I said hopefully. "You can see from this that what the priest does in the Mass is something very special indeed. He's not *representing* Christ. He can't do that because Christ comes himself and needs no representing. In some way he calls Christ down into the Bread and Wine and he becomes Christ's figure for us, standing there at the altar. This is why some of us think a priest must be a man. A woman at this point would be not right theologically. We feel too, that images of a woman on the cross are false, though for many this feeling has been overcome.

"It was funny, last year, well, odd and unexpected." I changed the subject slightly because I remembered something that seemed important. "I remember waking up one morning realizing I'd become a Catholic, though still Anglican of course. This was when I was in hospital with my womb, or rather not with my womb, but celebrating its departure, and I suppose, I had lots of time for thinking. There was plenty of time there, in the ward, for meditating, which I did, but I was surprised to discover what had happened to me, what had been going on in my mind without my realizing it. Edward came that morning with my Communion and I told him what I'd discovered and he laughed at me but was pleased all the same. I mean, *he'd* known already that I was changed, and he was just waiting for me to notice what had been happening.

"But to get back to where we were," I went on. "Dr Mascall also says the Mass is the *cause* of unity in the church. He says we don't need to come to the Mass to express our unity, it is the Mass itself that unites us all in Christ's mystical body. The Mass is the verb which does the uniting. Unity is not something we need to search for, to work for. All baptised people are members of Christ's mystical body. From the Mass we all go out into the world bound together by the grace of Christ. Dr Mascall says we are wasting a lot of time and energy having meetings and conferences about unity. Diversity of forms of worship is not necessarily bad. In Strathlyon Episcopalians can choose between the Cathedral, St Andrew's and St Columba's churches, all of which are remarkably diverse in their services. And think of all the many other churches. But we are all Christians. If we questioned people in St Andrew's, in just one church, we'd be surprised, to put it mildly, at the great variety of beliefs they'd express. Or else they'd admit to being permanently confused. This is like myself. I mean, in one person there can be a whole range of certainties and uncertainties according to the passage of time. As you know, one year I believed very little but by the next I believed nearly everything, or almost, and I was still the same person."

"I expect," said Jane. "it's very good we can choose which church we go to. Ordinary people aren't fussy about dogmas and all that, so long as they like the atmosphere and the minister or priest. We've all got different temperaments which need different ways for best expressing our love for God."

"Edward often says it's harder to learn to love our neighbour and to practise this consistently than to have yet another ecumenical conference which will achieve probably very little."

"We need to work with all members of God's church for the growth of his Kingdom. It's a bit like what a coalition government does in wartime, all parties working together for the country. We're all working for Christianity."

"I wonder how far, or near, the others have got in all this time," said Jane, beginning to sit up and collect her things and look around her. And then she said suddenly, "Betty, look to your right. Do you see? Below us a bit and over the water."

I looked to where Jane was pointing and saw at once a great brown bird floating on the air, coming towards us but keeping parallel to the cliff top. It was perhaps a hundred yards out. We could perfectly clearly, through our binoculars, see the long square-ended wings with the primary feather tips separated like fingers, these wings unmoving, as the bird drifted on the up-draught.

"Look carefully, Jane," I said urgently, "at everything you can notice. Is it an eagle? Yes, surely. It must be a sea eagle. It's got a white tail."

"I do wish I was more expert at recognising raptors. We must remember enough details so we can look in our books later."

"How exciting it would be if we were really certain."

"I think we can be certain. How exciting. We've neither of us seen one before."

I wonder if Jack and Nicholas will have seen it."

The bird had now glided past us on its way towards the point which was round out of sight to the left. It had risen a little now and appeared only as a long almost straight line silhouetted against the sunny sky. We watched it out of sight, then called to Tess and began to collect our belongings.

"That was marvellous, wasn't it, and so unexpected," said Jane. "There are really quite a lot of them about now. I do wonder. Can we be really certain?"

When we really had collected our things, after all the excitement, we walked back to the car and began to retrace our way towards Inverbroom, expecting any moment to meet Jack and Nicholas. This we did about half way back. They had thoroughly enjoyed their afternoon, both the visit to the Gardens and their walk along to meet us. They reported the rhodies and azaleas to be mostly still beautifully in flower and there were also some grand magnolias. They were each carrying a carrier bag though both were Nicholas's. There'd been some good ground cover plants for sale which had inspired him to buy some for us at home. They'd had a good browse round the shop too where Nicholas had found me a wooden chopping board in the shape of a pig, in oak, very thick and strong. I was thrilled, partly to have something useful as well as jolly and partly to have such a good memorial of our great day out.

"Just what I need. I really do mean that. Our old one is very shabby, not very respectable any longer."

Jack had bought Jane a tea towel with rows of puffins printed on it, in pairs, kissing. "It was the only birdie thing I could find," he said, "that was also useful."

"It's lovely and amusing too, thank you very much," she replied. "And it's a hundred percent linen, how advantageous."

"I'm sorry your chopping board isn't a birdie one, but there was no choice." apologized Nicholas.

"That's all right," I said. "I'm very fond of pigs so long as I'm not in charge of them. And anyway with birdy objects there's the permanent problem of their very thin legs and feet and what to do with them, unless they're made invisible by being put under the water as with a swimming duck or whatever, or under a sitting-down bird."

154

The men had seen mergansers and an undisclosed kind of diver in the bay, also a raft of drake eiders looking very handsome and dazzling, black and white in the sunshine. On their way along the road there had been wheatears and a stonechat, chat-chatting in its own way, among the boulders.

"And we heard a raven which made a nice change, but we didn't see him," said Jack.

Then we told them about our marvellous eagle and why we had decided it might be one of the new sea eagles, rather than a golden one.

We decided to stop for a meal at a pub on the way home, which made a very pleasant change for us all, but of course it was past our bedtime by the time we got back. So I decided to put off looking up the eagle in a bird book and for Dr Mascall's explaining words until next morning.

And next morning, as soon as there was a pause in the jobs that had to be done, I opened, first of all, one of my helpful bird books. There all the eagles were all quite clearly illustrated. Just as Jane and I had decided the day before: definitely a sea eagle.

Then I turned to Dr Mascall's book to see how much I had missed out from my explanations to Jane, Dr Mascall's words were more expressive than my own, of course, which I had known they would be.

'In the Eucharist," he had written, 'Christ offers us as members of his Body.' And he quotes from St Augustine, 'The mystery of yourselves is laid upon the table of the Lord.'

All the same, all he'd written about the three bodies I still found very confusing. So I was glad to read in a footnote. 'It is not what the Christian feels is taking place at the Eucharist, but what *is* taking place that matters.' So, it seems, we can enjoy the feeling of mystery which fills all the gaps in our understanding. I can be happy about that.

'The Christian,' continues Dr Mascall, 'is then the liturgical man whose whole life is set in the context of the perpetual prayer which Christ for ever offers in heaven ... Our whole life as members of the Christian Church is an act of worship ... Our whole life is liturgical.'

TRINITY:
CHRISTOPHER'S PRIESTING

It was the day of Christopher's priesting. Happily the weather had improved towards the weekend from what it had been a few days earlier. So when the Saturday dawned all was wrapped in a light mist which soon cleared to reveal a beautiful summer's day. The ceremony was to take place in the Cathedral, St Mary's, that morning.

It would be solemn *and* festive, I was thinking. And I went on to realize that almost always festivity without some solemnity was empty, though there are occasions which are sad and solemn when there can be no festivity. That day, I knew, would be solemn and festive in turns. But then not even all funerals are totally sad; there's often an element of celebration and thanksgiving for a good life well lived and therefore some good festive food and drink afterwards are very much in place.

Christopher, I was thinking, had chosen the most wonderful way there can be to give his life to the service of God. He would aim to bring God to us and to take us to God. How marvellous it must be to spend a lifetime in this way if it suits, and it certainly would suit Christopher. He'd been growing into it all this last year. He was so gifted in the right directions for a spiritual life, and so good with people, all kinds of people. How fortunate we were to have him working among us and to have him as a friend. We were going to have a lovely day of celebration.

We all arrived in good time at St Mary's. There were already many people standing outside the west doors. Christopher was there with his family, his parents, an older brother and two young sisters. They had travelled from West Kilmartin as had other relations and friends, and a few others from all over the country. Some faces were familiar to us from meeting their owners at last year's ordination ceremony, so straightaway we were able to give many friendly words of greeting and welcoming waves to those standing further from us. Besides Christopher, two other young men were being ordained that day: one, the Cathedral curate, also to be priested and the other, from a distant parish in the glens, was to be ordained deacon. Their relations and friends were there too and many of the congregations of the three

156

Strathlyon churches. For a while we stayed there, outside the Cathedral, in the sunshine or under the trees by the riverside and the many brightly coloured summer dresses added to the cheerful atmosphere of the occasion.

Soon it was time for us all to take our places inside the Cathedral. I thought we were very fortunate that St Mary's was no gloomy building but was rather well lit with white painted walls. The sunshine streamed in through the large stained glass windows and cast patches of rich colour over everything. Richness was the operative word that morning, nothing was skimped, every light was switched on, there were handsome flower arrangements wherever one looked and soon all ears were called to join the eyes when the organ began to fill the place with noble music.

I was one of Christopher's sponsors so I had to take my place at the front with his family. There I would have a good view of all that was taking place. Edward was the other sponsor, but he would come in procession with the other clergy and would be sitting in the choir. I had done my best to be sure I'd look neat but not gaudy. I knew I mustn't look like the bride, it's Christopher's day. Is he the bride, I wondered? And I decided not, but that he was the bridegroom, he's marrying the church and the church is the bride of Christ. That way of thinking I found very confusing. I realized I mustn't look like the bridegroom's mother either, though there wasn't much fear of that, for she was looking smart and lovely and elegant, and was, anyway, much younger than myself. I could be Edward's mother, I remembered; he's the same age as Philip and John, more or less. I couldn't be Christopher's grandmother either: I was, at least, too young for that.

So I was wearing a quiet sandy coloured summer suit with a pink frilly blouse and no hat. I supposed I looked rather like a biscuit, or an oatcake, though I'm hardly the right shape. Anyway I should, I hoped, melt into the background, and then I could enjoy myself.

I remember wanting desperately to pray. This feeling kept rushing into my heart with great urgency, but all around there was such a great sense of expectancy I found it difficult to detach my attention from my surroundings. I remember letting my gaze wander round the handsome interior of the Cathedral. I looked at the great height of nave and chancel, the tall coloured windows, the beautiful carving on

157

the choir and canons' stalls, all was designed to express our realization of the greatness and glory of God and help our prayers rise up to him with our worship, praise and thanksgiving.

The organ broke into the first hymn and the choir came out of the vestry followed by the servers and then the clergy robed in their copes. I saw Father Munro, Christopher's rector from West Kilmartin who had done so much to encourage him in his undertaking of the priesthood. I recognised him from last year. He was going to preach to us the next day in St Andrew's. And last of all came the little Bishop of Cairndhu looking the most magnificent of all with his mitre and crosier and gorgeous cope, followed by his chaplain, a deacon from St Columba's. The Bishop had bright dark eyes which had a way, it seemed, of piercing one, (especially myself), through and through as if he were measuring one's godliness. And my godliness seemed to shrink the longer he pierced. It wasn't at all a comfortable sensation.

The ordination service was threaded into the Eucharist, and I found myself swept along by the momentousness of the occasion. I clung on hard to the prayers which, though mostly in unfamiliar words, spoke of those things which I most needed to express.

The sermon was given by the rector of the parish near Aberdeveron in the Diocese of St Fergus where the Cathedral deacon had lived before coming to Strathlyon. He spoke of God's having become, through Christ's life on earth, touchable see-able, hear-able by us, and how bringing Christ to us is the true work of the priest, to make him real for us, not only in the Mass, but in the humdrum daily life of work. Christ is always with us in all we do, in all that happens to us.

Soon the moment came when Edward and I had to present Christopher to the Bishop. We recited together the words from the service sheet.

"'We present to you Christopher John. He is recommended by those in this church who know him, and by those who have taught and prepared him. We therefore ask you to ordain him.'"

Later I decided that these presentation sentences sounded very unCranmer-like. However often I'd repeated them over and over to myself during the last few days, I'd been unable to absorb them word-perfectly into my heart. Anything written by Cranmer is usually fairly easily anchored in the brain or mind. The whole long middle sentence seemed to me rather too clever, as if its author had been pleased with himself for writing it, rather than his being grateful for the inspiration. The rhythm was awkward and rather out-of-breathish. Fortunately, we were expected to read the whole thing from the service booklet, so I felt more comfortable about my incapacity to learn it totally by heart.

Soon the candidates went forward to prostrate themselves. I felt this was the most moving part of the ceremony. The choir sang the Litany of the Scottish Saints, which, of course, they sang very well and the beautiful words were clearly heard.

'Draw us to thyself ... sanctify our will .... lighten our darkness ... strengthen our weakness .... deepen our love... uphold the weak, raise up those who fall, and strengthen us all by thy power. O Lord, hear our prayer.'

And then came the ordination itself, the laying-on of hands by the Bishop and then by all the priests present. After that came the changing of vestments to suit the new status of each one, the giving of a Bible to all three and a chalice and paten to the two new priests.

I was definitely a bit surprised to find some rather feeble but very heartfelt tears coming into my eyes. I was also annoyed that the design of my new specs made it impossible to wipe away even those few surreptitiously enough for my comfort.

The Bishop then announced: "let us greet the newly ordained and one another with the sign of peace."

Edward, with a beaming and mischievous smile, surprised me with a kiss as his sign of peace, adding under his breath. 'Just for once', a reference to our not, in St Andrew's, having any such modern or disruptive happening during our Eucharist.

However, that day this disruption relieved the tension which had been growing in my heart, so my sign of peace to Christopher was a truly heartfelt hug. The Communion followed, and then the final hymn and the procession out of the Cathedral into the brilliant sunshine. After this there were many blessings and congratulations and taking of photographs on the steps.

We then all walked the short distance to the Cathedral hall for refreshments, wine and delicious snacks, accompanied by a few speeches. A little later still Christopher, with his family and a few close friends, including the Morlands and ourselves, drove to his flat near St Andrew's church for a substantial buffet lunch with more wine and more rejoicing. There were no more speeches, but lots of happy conversation.

We knew we were fortunate to have Christopher as our curate and he thought he was fortunate to have all of us. It must be a good omen for the future, I thought as Nicholas and I drove home, very thankful the day had gone so well and for the promise of a good future.

Later, after I'd changed out of my best clothes and relaxed a bit, I began to look back on the morning's events. I decided the unpeaceful peace hadn't felt as distracting as it usually does, and I wondered why. I mentioned this to Nicholas. Was it because the whole of the new ordination service was strange to me and the new Blue Book liturgy not much more familiar? If this were so, then I supposed, when the Bishop announced the sign of peace, the top of my mind, or whatever it is, was already active and didn't mind being called to attention. Normally in the Mass that part of my mind is totally inactive. I'm usually taking no notice of my surroundings except for knowing I'm one of those present and will soon be taken into Christ's Peace in the Agnus Dei and then to the altar rails for the Bread and Wine.

"I realise now, I said to Nicholas, "that this morning I'd forgotten all about its being Christ's Peace we were meant to be exchanging. Well, not totally forgotten. With Edward and myself our exchange of the Peace seemed just a lot of fun, though Christ, of course, was there in a way, in both out minds. We're great friends and love each other dearly but there was no need to say so in that way at just that moment, we've all week for that. Edward will have certainly remembered it was Christ's Peace he was giving me, but I certainly nearly forgot. I was concentrating on how much I loved everybody, especially himself and Christopher. All these loves of mine are for ever embedded in Christ, it's the only kind of love that's worthwhile. So, I suppose my almost forgetting was immaterial really. And Christ's Peace is part of the surrounding atmosphere in the Cathedral, as it is in every church, and is especially so and strongly in St Andrew's, don't you feel? It's always there."

"There's a very good letter on the Peace in the new Newspot by someone, a canon," Nicholas said. "He seems a sensible person. I meant to show it to you."

"Oh, let's have a look." Nicholas threw the paper across to me. I read:

"...'the liturgy is primarily a deep personal and penitential sacrament. We come to recall and to share in the Lord's Crucifixion and to receive the spiritual food of the most precious Body and Blood of our Saviour. As the old hymn says:

'Let all mortal flesh keep silence, and with fear and trembling stand:
Ponder nothing earthly-minded, for, with blessing in his hand,
Christ our God to earth descendeth, our true homage to demand.'

'Here lies the essential ethos of the sacrament. It is not a convivial social happening. In making it so, the modern Church has committed a grave doctrinal mischief ... Is it too late to signal a change of practice? To have the courage to lift this bodily greeting (i.e. the modern 'peace') from its present uncomfortable home and put it down in the real world where it belongs?'

"That's very good," I said and I thought so too. "Sometimes distraction does win. I find, on Sundays, it's hard to concentrate on what's happening at the altar, even in our own church. Our attention is taken around the building and the congregation, so many different people are moving about, taking part in this service. In a quiet midweek service we are able more easily to do so. But many people feel about this differently. They seem to enjoy some fairly noisy friendship at the start of the service and they love the 'Peace', which is no peace, in the middle, because they like to express their good and kind feelings to each other by some action. But I much prefer all to be as quiet as possible, always."

"So do I, but then I was brought up to believe that a quiet church was necessary for true prayer to flourish. There could be organised noise as in a hymn, but reverence, actually to show reverence, was necessary"

Soon after that I was really glad for the chance of an early night and so was Nicholas.

I thought about the two jolly parties: one in the Cathedral hall and the other at Christopher's. "It's extraordinary," I reflected, "how tiring conversation can be when one wants to do one's best for visitors, and however well disposed everybody is towards everybody else."

TRINITY:
CHRISTOPHER'S FIRST MASS

The next day, Sunday, we were all back in our own St Andrew's church again, Edward and Christopher, Jack and Jane, and the rest of our congregation, and of course, the many other visitors, friends of Christopher, for his first Mass. After the previous day's excitements I felt, in an unexpected way, as if I were drained of the possibility of prayer.

As we left Whinside in the car I'd felt as if, when I got to the church and knelt down, nothing would happen. All the excitement of yesterday must have been too much for my spirit or whatever part of me it was that had been affected. Even in the ordinary way some parts of my head or heart or whatever were never very securely strong. But I knew I ought not to feel like this, for really, I was full of gratitude to God, for his mercies and for his saving grace. I was full of thanksgiving. I'd expected to be borne up on a wave of hope for Christopher and his future and I needed to pray about this too. Instead, I was having to pray for strength for myself. He'd be full of joy for what he was doing and I felt our prayers would be of great importance that day, but now mine would be of the feeblest. I felt helpless and useless and empty.

Nicholas usually made a point of being early at church, for often he needed to see people about various monetary subjects. This usually gave me an opportunity to say Hello to friends as they arrived, but that day, however, I felt I'd better go quietly into the church without speaking to anyone.

I hoped people wouldn't think me rude, my not staying at the door to chat with them. I hope no one would be offended. They'd all be sure to talk to each other. Perhaps I wouldn't be missed. People have a great need to talk to each other when they meet after a whole week spent apart. It's only a very few of us who see each other when we come here between times for a quiet weekday Mass. So I went straight into the church and lit a candle below Blessed Mary's picture. Prayers don't need to have words and if later that day I could produce some words I knew it wouldn't matter if they were foolish. I'd ask Mary to pray for me, she'd do that better than I ever could.

I then knelt down in our usual pew and after a few minutes I managed to find a few simple words. In a little while the normality of things began to work in my spirit. I began to look around me. How lovely the church looked, I thought, with the sunshine sending beams of coloured brightness through the windows, lighting up the walls. Flowers in every corner added more colour and the polished brass and carved wood gleamed brightly from much loving care.

The pews filled up, and the organ began to play. Nicholas came to join me. The choir entered singing the Introit hymn. They were followed by the servers and then by Christopher, Canon Harper, Father Munro, and finally by Edward. Everything was on a smaller scale than yesterday at St Mary's, but I thought for this very reason the power of the Spirit seemed more concentrated, more pervasive of everything in the church. The music, the hymns, the settings of the Mass, the anthem, I knew I would love them all.

Father Munro preached. After yesterday's deep sermon, Christ showing us God, his Father, the Father who is in himself, he chose a lighter, simpler subject. He compared and contrasted Christopher with his saintly namesake.

"Offero," he said, "was a Canaanite and a giant. We can see our friend Christopher is no giant so far as height is concerned, though we may have a distinct impression the heart of a giant beats in him. It was Offero's ambition to serve the most powerful king on earth. When he discovered that the first king to whom he had attached himself was afraid of Satan, he changed masters and for some time served *him*. One day however, Offero saw Satan becoming filled with terror at the sight of a cross set beside the road, he saw that now Satan feared one Jesus Christ of Nazareth who had died on the cross. Offero at once left Satan and set out to search for Christ in order to serve *him*. He was unsuccessful at first, but after some time he met a hermit and asked him the way to Christ. The hermit replied that the way was through prayer and fasting, which didn't appeal to Offero all that much, his being more of a practical fellow. We suspect, though, that prayer and fasting may well appeal to our Christopher. The hermit told him that, instead of fasting, he could use his great strength to carry travellers over a nearby stream which at that time was swollen by floods into a torrent.

"Offero built himself a hut of boughs and cut himself a stave of a whole palm tree and unweariedly carried across the river all who called to him for help. One night he heard a child's voice crying out to be carried over. Offero went out into the dark and took the child on his shoulders. He was surprised to find so small a body should weigh more heavily on him that anyone he'd ever carried before. That night the winds and waves had risen fiercely and it seemed to Offero as if he would never reach the opposite bank with his burden. When he finally did so, the child told him that he was Christ, it was Christ whom he had carried, the Maker of the World, and the great weight he'd borne had been the whole world itself. Offero knelt down and worshipped the Christ Child who accepted him into his service, and his name was changed to Christopher. Before the Child vanished he bade Christopher plant his stave and immediately it bore leaves and fruit. You can see your Christopher has already planted himself among you and his work has already borne much fruit, more I expect than I shall ever know of.

"Christopher became a Christian and remained steadfast in the faith, for which he was scourged and then beheaded. Today we pray that your Christopher, too, will remain steadfast, but not come to such a death. On his way to the scaffold the first Christopher prayed that all who looked on him that day and put their trust in God should not suffer earthquakes, tempest or fire. That's why even nowadays images of St Christopher are frequently seen, often in cars to protect the driver on his journeys. Whoever shall behold St Christopher shall not on that day faint nor fail. It is probable your Christopher will not have such a miraculously sure effect on those who look on him, but I'm certain everyone of you will always be better for being with him."

Father Munro ended by asking his listeners to remember that *despair* is a word not used by saints or even by those who love God simply and strive to serve him.

"Some people say the Church is dying," he went on, 'others say God is already dead, but we know God is eternal life. It is not possible that he can die. On the cross Christ may for a short while have thought himself forsaken by God his Father and also by his disciples, who for a short while themselves lost their faith and ran away. But God cannot die and Christ rose on Easter Day. Remember that God cannot die. Christopher will help you take this truth out into the world, help you spread the Gospel, help you bring more and more people into God's love."

Then I let the old liturgy in all its blessed familiarity wash over me. By the time we'd reached the Consecration prayer I was feeling much more my usual self again, my heart and mind following all the words deeply. I was very conscious it was Christopher's voice I was hearing, as for the first time he offered to God the sacrifice of ourselves as members of Christ's body and brought Christ down into the Bread and Wine to feed us.

After the service Christopher placed a basket of red roses in honour of Blessed Mary before her picture, and a second he presented to his mother. Then he said the Thanksgiving and gave the Blessing and we all sang the final hymn with much fervour.

When we were outside again in the sunshine, grouped on the grass in front of the church, there were more congratulations and blessings, more kisses, more photographs, much rejoicing. Then Christopher went off with his family for a quiet meal, and Edward who'd had some friends come unexpectedly to Strathlyon, went off to have lunch with them. Jane and Jack had an old friend, Father Iain McAllister, a retired priest, staying with them. He was from the far north beyond Stara in the Diocese of Wyvis and the Griams. He had many years ago been their parish priest in Isla and then had later moved south to West Kilmartin where he had met Christopher. He thought very highly of him as a young man and had come to his priesting. So they'd invited Nicholas and myself to join the three of them for the rest of the day at Drummore.

TRINITY: AT JANE'S AGAIN

I was grateful that Sunday to Jane and Jack for their invitation to lunch. I could at that moment think of nothing I would enjoy more than to relax in their lovely house with friends who demanded nothing of me beyond my being myself. I knew there would be good food and drink which would put heart back into everybody including myself after the excitement of the weekend.

"I'm not ill," I thought, "it's just that I've temporarily run out of energy." I was realizing that in earlier times I used to be like this often, but lately not at all. Let's not worry, I decided, I'll soon be fine again."

I'd often envied Jane and Jack their lovely old house. Although it had been their home for only the last ten years or so, all their possessions fit in so well one could imagine their having lived there two or three times as long. There are comfortable chairs, old pieces of family furniture, cheerful thick carpets, good pictures on the walls; it made me think the design of our own house was very routine and uninspired in comparison. All the attraction of Whinside is in its beautiful setting.

I'm often a little nervous that, when people do come to our house, they will get a wrong impression of us. We've got a few nice belongings but neither of us has ever had the patience or the spare time and energy and money to put much effort into acquiring any more good things to keep them company.

Jane's lunch was excellent and enjoyed by all, and it had greatly strengthened me. The wine was good, but not so wonderful that every mouthful had to be savoured slowly. It could be enjoyed at the same time as we enjoyed our conversation. I still felt a little feeble and, after lunch, I was perfectly happy to sit on one of Jane's deep comfy chairs and listen to the conversation going on around me. Occasionally I joined in with an odd remark or two, when it was necessary to add a bit of common sense to what was being said. But I must have appeared remarkably silent for one who was usually bursting with instant comments.

Jack was talking about the clergy and their pay. He was saying the clergy's job was the most worthwhile and important of all jobs, so they ought to be very well paid. We need their help and advice more than anyone else's. His suggestion was that the words 'minimum stipend' should never be used because their very sound made people think of their being paid as little as possible.

"Perhaps," said Jane, "we could have stipends varying according to the responsibilities of each job, as happens in ordinary life."

Then everybody joined in. Priests were people to be looked up to, so of course they should be well paid. Jane thought it was wrong for people to imagine that having a vocation to the ministry equalled being content to be poor. Nicholas thought that appearances were a great help. If the rector looked cheerful and tidy and his house and garden also, this would encourage people to understand his worth.

I came in here, "I've often thought it would be a good idea to make sure the Rectory was as well looked after inside and out as our own homes are. I mean at least so far as the kitchen equipment is concerned, and the bathrooms. Also the decorations' being not too shabby. People should be able to go into a rectory and feel better even before any conversation begins. And really one does get better value from people if their surroundings are nice. It would show that we value our priests."

Iain McAllister was getting restless. He had been very much enjoying his weekend visit to Drummore, basking in Jane's tender care, but he didn't like what he'd just been hearing.

"I've been listening to all you've said and I've not agreed with any of it. I've got much too much money. Priests should be paid much less than they are at present and then we could have more of them, more people could have their own priest instead of sharing. I'm retired and with my two pensions, one from the government and the other from the church, I've much more than I need. Priests have become greedy. I had more than was necessary when I was working. Though of course I could give some away, which I did."

"Iain," said Jane, "is one of those pretty rare kind of priests who are totally wrapped up in their calling. They hardly spend money on anything except the basics of life. Except for your hobby, Iain, for your communicating with your friends on the radio. Your being a radio ham. Though I'm sure you make everything work for you in that way by ingenuity rather than by splashing out on posh equipment. But people like you are rare. Often priests are family men who want their children not to feel their father has money problems which their friends' fathers don't have."

Jack pointed out that some clergy had wives who worked so they could help with the total family budget.

"I'm not sure that's a good thing," Nicholas said. "Though we can't tell how many fewer wives would be working outside their home if their husbands were better paid. Obviously some women work because it's fun, or at any rate less boring than staying at home."

"I don't see how rectory life could be boring," said Jane, "though I can see some wives would prefer another kind of work. But it's not right to sniff at women who are 'only' clergymen's wives. It's a highly honourable job. Though that statement's against my preference for unmarried priests. If all priests were unmarried there'd be no clergy wives, and that would be a pity. We would miss them if there weren't any. They're often the best of women."

"On the whole there's enough money around," said Nicholas. "It's a question of altering people's perception of what's the right amount to put in the plate."

There was a pause, then Jack said, " I think we need to go for a walk after all that good food and drink."

"Yes, let's go down the lane past the Snoopy croft and back by the farm," Jane suggested.

"I'll stay here and relax," I said. "I'm surprised how exhausted I still am, limp and feeble."

"It's old age," said Nicholas.

"I expect so."

It was easiest to agree in words, though in reality I knew it was a lack of the Spirit in me, or perhaps the Spirit and I were adjusting to each other. But this was obviously not the moment to say so.

I was left alone. I sat quietly looking out at the sunlit garden and over to Cairn Dhu in the pale blue distance beyond the intervening wooded hills. I might be sitting quietly but my mind was not quiet, nor was my body relaxed, though in one of Jane's deep comfortable chairs it had every chance to be so. I suppose we have been busy lately, we

168

had to be in Strathlyon almost every day this last week, as well as, on Tuesday, there'd been an early start for Nicholas's meeting in Eaglesburgh. Probably Nicholas is right, it's old age, or partly so. Perhaps I can benefit from this idea, take advantage of it, do less and do what I do do more slowly. Or I could concentrate on those jobs which I enjoy rather than the chores, as much as that's possible.

I let myself listen to the few sounds I could hear. Two clocks were ticking in the room, a small one the mantelpiece with a quick tick and a skeleton clock under its glass dome on Jack's old bureau which ticked more slowly. There was also a grandfather in the hall with its slow, low sounding pendulum beat. Outside a distant dog barked. I fell into a light sleep for a minute or two, maybe more, then I woke up, feeling a lot better. I began to try to see if I could say some familiar prayers and in between let my mind wander down any avenue of thought that came to me. I was quite content and almost happy.

When the others returned from their walk, a refreshing cup of tea was greatly enjoyed, and after that it was soon time for all to leave for Evensong at St Andrew's.

I was thinking how much everybody loves Evensong. The choir shines in the canticles and anthem, and we join in the psalms and hymns. I love every minute. The prayers, too, are very peaceful in their nature.

'Lighten our darkness, we beseech thee, O Lord, and by thy great mercy defend us from all perils and dangers of this night.'

Everything in Evensong is comforting. But tonight? Will it work for me as it usually does? With this strange exhausted feeling I've got?

Then we arrived at St Andrew's. When the service began, I gave up thinking of the words which were flowing past me, I gave up wondering about whether I was concentrating or not. Sometimes I joined in a hymn or a prayer, sometimes I listened and sometimes I just let myself be there without worrying about anything. And always I enjoyed the music. The choir sang the anthem, "Jesu, joy of man's desiring,' which swept me away into a moment of reflection and remembering.

Canon Harper preached on a theme from that morning's Epistle: 'For God is greater than our hearts and he knows everything,' and this put a seal of comfort and encouragement on the whole day for me. The whole service worked for me in spite of my distraction. In the calm beauty of the church I felt soothed beyond my best hopes.

Later, after we'd got home and had some kind of a scratch supper, I went to bed, and as soon as I lay down under the duvet, I began to stay the Compline psalm which begins, 'In thee, O Lord, have I put my trust, let me never be put to confusion.' But when I got as far as,

'Into thy hands I commend my spirit, for thou has redeemed me, O Lord, thou God of truth,'

I fell asleep, I'd intended to go through most of the Compline service, especially through all the collects at the end which I knew well.

'Look down, O Lord, from thy heavenly throne ... Protect us through the silent hours of this night ... visit we beseech thee, O Lord, this habitation ... let thy holy angels dwell herein to preserve us in peace, and may thy blessing be upon us evermore.'

All those lovely words remained unsaid, though I expect, the remembrance of them comforted me through the night.

TRINITY: EDWARD TO LUNCH

Breakfast seemed fairly well ready, all the necessary oddments were on the table, the cooked food was keeping warm in the oven, and the coffee was making itself in its jug on the side. Breakfast is meant to be a simple meal but in fact there's more to be got out and put away than at any other time of day. All the same I usually enjoy breakfast. I'm always hungry for it.

At mealtimes I usually read my newspaper, the Warden Weekly. And I can't see what's wrong with that? Monks are read to during their meals, so, as there's no monk here to read to me, I have read to myself. And so does Nicholas. We always read during meals, we've all the rest of the day in which to talk to each other. But meals with friends are different, I think. They're celebrations, and at those times the food and drink should be as good as possible, (but not overwhelmingly so, not showy, not just chosen to show off the hostess's skill, not to interfere with the conversation). And then the food will combine with the words spoken between friends, (we hope there will be laughter too), making a lunch or evening meal memorable. The friends should want to look forward to our meeting again for another meal together another time.

Nicholas used often to remind me that monks wouldn't read anything so left-wing as the Warden, if they had a newspaper to read at all. And I'd always reply, "Probably not, but how do you know? Anyway I need to read a fairly pink newspaper to counteract you and the boys who are very bright blue and reactionary."

This was a permanently repeatable conversation, and occurred, I suppose, monthly.

That day Edward *was* coming to lunch so there was going to be a celebration. He often came to lunch and Christopher too. Though not both together. It was more fun to have them separately. Both Jane and I liked to give nourishing meals to two hard working young bachelors. To the aged grandparents even Edward seemed young and Christopher seemed very young indeed. I always enjoyed having them to the house. I thought the provision of food made as much contribution to the growth and strengthening of the church as to the strengthening of the two young men. It was always a simple family meal, perhaps I made a little special effort, but nothing difficult or fancy. There was always a lot to talk about, from church practicalities to church politics and personalities, projects and past events. All these PPPS's! Even Edward had not been a friend for so long that we were unable to surprise and amuse each other with unexpected views and ideas, each pretending to shock but producing only laughter all round. It was just like having one of our boys for a meal, a relaxed atmosphere and no ceremony.

After lunch, while we were drinking our coffee in the sitting room, I showed Edward what books I'd been able to buy in Eaglesburgh when we'd been there last week. Two were second hand.

"I was fortunate to find them," I said "First of all here's a *Synopsis of the Gospels* which includes also the parallels from John. You can see it's a beautiful book, with clear print on good paper. I was so pleased to have found it. And look here too, you never know what you'll find in a second hand book."

I showed him what I'd discovered tucked inside it when I'd got home. I produced a brownish page of a Sunday newspaper from nearly twenty years ago, and printed thereon was the heading, 'The New Sayings of Jesus, The gospel according to Thomas.'

"Let's see," said Edward. "How interesting. Oh yes, look there it is, the famous bit about Mary. 'Simon Peter said to them, 'Let Mary go out from us, because women are not worthy of the life!' Jesus said, 'See, I shall lead her so that I will make her male, that she too may become a living spirit, resembling you males. For every woman who makes herself male will enter the Kingdom of Heaven.'"

"How strange that sounds," I said. "It sounds like good propaganda for women priests."

"Yes, it is strange. But those words will probably turn out to be against women priests if we go into them deeply. Lots in the Thomas Gospel is familiar. For instance, 'Jesus said: Show me the stone which the builders rejected, it is the corner stone.' and again here: 'The harvest is indeed great, but the labourers are few: but beg the Lord to send labourers into the harvest'. What else did you get?"

"Oh, this too. I've not begun it yet, though. Jung's *Answer to Job*. I've been fascinated by Job for a long time and often I have a good idea of what Jung is saying, because he writes clearly and seems to understand what we're really like. And I also got this new book about Julian of Norwich. I need to know more about her."

Edward and Nicholas then discussed a few points which would come up at next week's Vestry meeting, a discussion which would make life a lot easier on the night and the meeting probably a lot shorter. Then it was time for Edward to leave as he had to make some visits before Evensong.

"Since Christopher came," he said, "I've more time to spend on each job, which is good. But all the same I never used to feel rushed. But I do need to go now. I need to cut the grass at home first before I do the visits. I keep leaving it for much too long a time, and then it grows too long. It's mostly my own fault, I suppose."

"Well, not necessarily so," I replied, trying to encourage him. "It's been raining a lot lately so the grass hasn't stopped growing and, also, in consequence of that rain, there have been days when you've not been able to get out and cut it."

"It's kind of you to find an excuse for me."

"It's been very difficult here too, as Nicholas knows. You've only to look out of the window to see how long our grass is."

TRINITY: JUNG AND A DREAM

One supper time shortly after this, I'd finished my newspaper and so was left with no reading matter to accompany my breakfast next morning. I needed a book to fill in the gap till the Warden or one of my birdy magazines should arrive through the letterbox. It was often difficult to find a book for mealtimes for it had to be one which would stay open by itself on the table. It was unlikely any new paperback would do this and even some old ones could be unco-operative. Neither should it usually be a borrowed book, or even a library book, because, however careful I was, there could be accidents. After some thought about all this I chose *Answer to Job* which I'd bought only the week before. Although it was a paperback it was old enough, being very second hand, to stay open with the butter dish placed on the far left top corner and my own plate on the diagonally opposite one nearest me. It was my own book so I'd no need to worry overmuch if the prunes when pierced with a fork should spray their juice over it as was their wont.

A bit ago, I'd read that reading is like a cleansing waterfall, it doesn't matter if you don't remember what you read for, so long as it's good reading, it's doing your soul good, but you must go on reading. You can tell if it's good for you, if when you have put your book down, you feel nourished rather than undernourished. That word 'undernourished' reminded me that it's often good too to think of reading as a food instead of as a waterfall. It doesn't matter if we forget what we read, so long as we go on reading words that will nourish our souls.

After breakfast I drove into Strathlyon to do some shopping and then I went on to Jane's for lunch. It was too windy for us to sit outside in the garden afterwards, but we were very comfortable in the sitting room with the garden door open. By now I'd got over my few days of tiredness, but, all the same, neither of us felt like a walk, so a little gentle conversation seemed in order.

I began to talk of a subject which had all day been uppermost in my mind. I'd had a dream in the night and I felt I must tell Jane about it.

174

"I must tell you," I said. "You don't mind, do you? It's not like an ordinary kind of boring dream. My telling you will help me decipher it perhaps, or remember it better, to have it well sunk in my mind, and then the meaning may come to me later."

As usual Jane was her kind self and she encouraged me to tell her everything.

"In the dream we were in the South of France, staying on the coast near Nice. We were driving into the mountains to look at a famous gorge, not one I'd visited before. About a mile or two before we came to the gorge itself, we and some other cars were held up by electricity workmen putting up new high tension cables between two pylons. (Towers I suppose they should be called). Very Electricité de France, one on either side of us, each some distance from the road. The French people from their cars were waiting with us too, standing around watching the proceedings. Beyond the overhead lines was a cliff-like line of mountains and the entrance to our gorge. Covering the mountain tops were clouds glowing a lovely strong pink in not very latish afternoon sunlight, (a dreamlike exaggeration, no doubt), bright against some more distant dark stormy clouds. Some cables were already up, strung tightly between the pylons and two others partly up, hanging in great curves, one still drooping down nearly to the ground, the other half way up.

"A man was standing, (he was so far away he looked like a pin man), on one of the tight cables. He was holding onto the cable above him with his hands stretched above his head. He was silhouetted against the sky and appeared to be wearing totally black tightly fitting clothes and a black skullcap. Then suddenly he was upside down, his feet still in some way fixed to the cable he'd been standing on, but his hands now on the cable below him. All of us held our breath. Then the man fell to the ground. This seemed inevitable to us, we were hardly surprised. It seemed also that we all knew who he was and yet no one actually knew him personally, as if he were someone known only through newspaper photographs or T.V. We accepted that he must be dead. I was asked to take a message, written hastily on a scrap of paper by one of the Frenchmen standing near us to the foreman who was away to my left, in a group with some of the linesmen. I could read only two or three words of this message which was presumably

175

written in French, and by the time I woke this morning I'd forgotten even those few. I can't begin to think what it might all mean, but when I woke I had the impression as one does sometimes that the dream was important and meaningful."

"It's very strange and very mysterious," said Jane. "But knowing you, I expect the solution will come into your head during the next few days. There must be a meaning, it's such an out of the ordinary dream and not connected with anything obvious you are doing at present. You've not been to France lately, nor are you thinking of going there soon, are you?"

And so we went on happily talking about many things until it was time for me to drive home for a meal and a peaceful evening with Nicholas who, as he hardly ever had a dream himself, (as you may remember), naturally wasn't interested in other people's, my own or anyone else's.

The next morning Jane rang up. She said, much more cheerfully than usual:

"David's just been on the phone from the office. We've got news at last! Prue has left Martin, it was yesterday everything happened, and at the moment she's staying with David in his flat. She can stay there for a short while. She didn't want to speak to us. She's too upset. That's why David didn't ring till he got to the office this morning. So he could talk to us without her hearing what he needed to say. Colin, her new friend, brought her round to David's last night. However she's got as far as asking David to tell us that she and Colin are hoping to come to see us sometime soon so we can meet him."

"How marvellous. It's this marvellous news we've all been waiting for. I do hope it will all turn out well and you will like Colin."

"We don't know any details, but that's not necessary, except to know she's safely with David. Jack of course is relieved and pleased too."

I went back to my household jobs with a light heart for Jane. One great long worry was lifted from her and I could rejoice with her. Whatever other worries she might in the future have about Prue they could wait for the day they came.

I was enjoying my Job book. I read it, not only at meals, but also after lunch and in the evenings, interspersed with other books which

176

were simpler or spoke of more familiar things. There was much in it I only half understood, though at other times I could understand very well what I read. I was used to plodding gently on through only partly understood chapters and I knew not to let myself be put off, unless, of course, most of the book was incomprehensible.

I thought it was very good about Yahweh forgetting to be omniscient and being surprised by the bad behaviour of the Children of Israel. It was good to read, too, that Job behaved in a morally better way than Yahweh, who allowed those awful things to happen to Job just to please Satan. And it's a helpful idea to think about God's oppositeness: if there is good in God, then, if God is all, there must be bad in God, too, though, all the same, that must be in a way we don't understand. It would be the opposite of what Jane and I'd decided the other day. An important part of Jesus's work was to overcome the Devil in people, to make him come out of them. Or perhaps it's like Edward saying: God is love, but if necessary, as it was in the Crucifixion, in order that his plans for our redemption could be carried out, he allowed evil to happen, he allows the Devil to act."

A few days later I'd reached the page in the Job book where Dr Jung writes about various aspects of Satan, his sowing of the tares, about his unsuccessfully tempting Christ to accept the role of a worldly ruler, about his successful temptation of Judas to betray Christ, (though that betrayal did not prevent Christ's dying a sacrificial and redemptive death). So, it seemed, we were back with the Devil versus Christ again.

Dr Jung give his version of New Testament history which I found fascinating and at one moment surprising. He writes that, before the beginning of the New Testament story, there had been careful precautions taken against Satan's interfering with Christ's divine birth. And on the occasion when Jesus sent his disciples forth as lambs among wolves, on a mission round the villages, the seventy returned with joy saying, 'Even the devils are subject unto us through thy name' And Jesus said unto them, "I beheld Satan as lightning fall from heaven.' And Dr Jung goes on:

'this marks the final separation of Yahweh from his dark son. Satan is banished from heaven and no longer has any opportunity to inveigle his father into dubious undertakings.'

Although Christ has freed us from our sins by his death, says Dr Jung. Satan is still here on earth. This must mean that, as Christ has banished Satan from heaven, we are safe here on earth only if we live in Christ and he in us. That means safe for salvation, I expect, not safe from suffering. Far from it.

Then came the surprise, for I suddenly *saw*. I understood this was my dream. The man in black whom we saw falling to earth from the electricity lines was Satan, God's dark son. If in my dream he didn't fall like lightning he certainly fell from electricity cables signifying lightning, for a squiggle, a zig zag of lightning is the symbol, the warning sign, fixed to every electricity pole.

It was strange that I'd had the dream before I'd come across what would normally be the cause of the dream, before my reading about Satan and his falling from heaven. And more than that - but how do *I* fit into it all? There was I in the dream with this scrappy bit of paper with its mostly illegible, or at any rate incomprehensible, message in my hand which I was taking to the foreman. Of all the people watching that afternoon, in my dream, I was the one who was given this message. And because it was my dream. I was sure the message must involve me in some way. Even if I'd not yet 'got the message'.

Oh! I *see*! I can *see* that the message on the bit of paper for the foreman and the message of the dream are identical. Satan has fallen from heaven. Of course, as I couldn't read the words, I didn't get the message. Now I understood the dream, and if I dreamed the dream again now, I would understand the scribbled message. Does that make sense?

I told myself to remember to tell Jane next time I saw her.

TRINITY: JUNG AGAIN

Jane came over the next afternoon (and Tess of course) and we walked up onto the hill. I told her about Job and about my, in the end, being able to decipher the dream.

"It was Satan falling from heaven I saw. Now, with Christ on earth to guard and guide us, we are safe from him. He's no longer able to make mischief in heaven, nor here either, so long as we love Christ and ask for his protection. Though I'm afraid Satan will make mischief still among those with already evil intentions."

"That's the meaning of your dream," Jane understood. "And that's what was scribbled by someone and taken by you to the foreman? That's a very neat and satisfactory solution."

"It's a marvellous feeling when the mind suddenly *sees*. Everything falls into place. No loose ends or hardly any."

"Though if Satan is still alive on this earth he should, in your dream, have got up and walked away, or even come towards you, for he'd not died."

"That *is* a problem. But perhaps it's that we all took it for granted he was dead, for such a fall would kill an ordinary man, which we supposed he was. We didn't know he was Satan. Well, I didn't know for a few days, not until I read about it in the book. Maybe he just picked himself up and disappeared into the maquis. He probably gathered a band of followers and they became dissident tribesmen and went about attacking people all over the world. Or probably worse than that, for dissident tribesmen need not be wicked, they may be dissident for good reasons. It's more likely they'd become dastardly dictators, or torturers, or kidnappers."

"Or housing profiteers, or drug pushers, or gutter press magnates."

"Anyway with Christ's death on the cross Satan is defeated not only in heaven but here on earth too, though often it doesn't seem like it. But he can't win any more, it's a rearguard action that's taking place. He can make things very uncomfortable for us, but not fatally so. With God helping us we shall for certain make it to heaven."

"That's what Edward says always on Good Friday. The cross is the victory over evil. I remember that."

179

"There are some very interesting ideas in the Job book which I don't completely understand," I went on. "They're not specifically to do with Job but all the same are important to us. Dr Jung is very good on myths and archetypes. I don't often think about archetypes and I misinterpret the word myth. I use the word as if it meant something not true, but that's wrong. He says for instance the birth of Christ follows a pattern already set out in previous history, people were already used to the idea of God coming to earth in a person. It was already a myth, it's already in our bones. That's what a myth really is: something which we expect to happen, which is needed to happen, and then it happens and is accepted as necessary for the world.

"Also it's not possible to demythologize Christ, Jung says, to see him as a man with no God-hood in him from conception as if the angel Gabriel had never visited Mary nine months before Christmas. Any Godliness he could have acquired would be only of the same order of Godliness as saints are able to have. If you try to do this, to strip him down, as it were, to a human being only, all that's left for us is a religious leader, and one about whom very little is known. And this man, born as a man only, couldn't be God incarnate. Jung says too that it's at the moment of the crucifixion when we see most clearly Christ as a human being, the divine myth is present in its greatest strength. That's like Edward's saying that Christ's own feebleness, his powerlessness on the Cross, is in fact Christianity's greatest and most enduring symbol. Our other great symbol, or image, is Christ as a helpless baby in his crib, powerless again. And we feel the strength of these symbols when we see them, their strength in pictures, something we're not used to these days when so much is in words for us to read. It's not possible to have religion without Jung's kind of myth. Religion is what we believe and it is essentially, it has to be, linked back to the eternal myth. What we need has to be true. What we need cannot be untrue. Myth is not fiction, it consists of facts which are repeated, which happen, over and over again. If the life of Christ is 'largely myth', that's just what expresses its universal human truth. And a myth does not work only inside a person, in his mind and soul, but also outside him, in what happens to him and what he does."

"That's very good," said Jane, "I agree with you about the difficulty with the word myth. 'It's a myth,' one says, meaning it's something often said but not true. Whereas in fact a myth is a universal truth."

It wasn't very interesting on the hill. The sky was colourless, and the countryside seemed rather dreary, there were no birds singing, spring time was truly over, nor were there even any birds to see, nothing to enliven the scene.

"Let's go down to the Willow Loch. The moorhens and dabchicks should still be there. They can't leave the loch till the young can fly and it takes them longer to learn to do that than it takes small garden birds who can immediately flutter from twig to twig. I've not seen any coots here at all this year."

We dropped down into the little valley and came to the loch under cover of the willows and birches. Tess was fortunately very quiet when told to be on these occasions. After a short time we saw two well-grown young moorhens and heard a dabchick. If the parents had any young they were invisible.

As we climbed up the hill again away from the loch, I said, "There's a very good bit in Dr Jung on Job about Mary and the Assumption. I'll try to make sense of it. I think that he, Dr Jung, is saying it's been necessary for us for a thousand years to have a Queen of Heaven, and now here she is, Mary the Virgin. And there's Christ, the Divine Son of no human father whom we also need. It's again what Jung says about the necessary things becoming true. Because of her Immaculate Conception, of her being free from all sin, Mary belongs to the state before the Fall. All these ideas are necessary to us as archetype and myth, it's necessary for us to have Mary as Queen of Heaven. We have needed and we have a deep longing for, a Mother to be an Intercessor for us, we need her to take her place alongside the Trinity.

"Yahweh, in the beginning, (I should have said this before), was married to, or perhaps one should say, balanced by, Sophia who is Wisdom. But later she, Wisdom, Sophia, was more or less forgotten by Yahweh, who instead became wrapped up in the Children of Israel and their doings or rather misdoings. This we can see happening in the Old Testament. Dr Jung says this lack of Sophia needed putting right and Mary is the equivalent of Sophia, is her successor, replacement. Mary is Wisdom. I've not explained this very well, but we have a need for this myth to happen. It sounds convincing when Dr Jung writes it, which he obviously does better than I've explained it. Mary is sinless, she is Wisdom, she is our perfect Mother."

Jane said, "Well, I've often thought if people kept Mary more in the forefront of their minds and in their hearts, we'd hear less abut this need for God our Mother. I can agree wholeheartedly we need Mary to fill this gap, and she does this better than any untried modern idea. It seems right and natural for us to say, 'Pray for us, O Holy Mother of God.' It's all very satisfactory, especially as now from your Jung book we see how necessary myths are and what they can do for us."

We walked down the hill and across the field, rather than scrambling straight down the slope, towards Whinside. I went on talking to Jane.

"There's another interesting section in Jung's book about the difference between male and female, masculine and feminine, men and women. Perfection is what a man, a male human being, is looking for; he aims for perfection. Women on the other hand are by nature needing to be complete. These ideas are not totally clear to me, but I think I understand them a little, so I'll try to explain. Jung says, if women strive for perfection they forget about their complementary role of completeness and are no longer truly and completely feminine. I can see this if I think of sportswomen, or, these days especially, professional business women, all striving to do well, striving for perfection each in her own way. We can see the more they succeed, the more perfect they become, the less complete, the less like women they become, I mean the idea, our idea of a woman.

"The more perfect a man becomes the more male, masculine he is. When women are exceptionally good at any specialized and (originally male) career, they have to work so hard their life becomes unbalanced and their other side, the womanly side of themselves, their completeness, is neglected. Women aren't created for perfection, but for completeness, not for perfection itself but it's complementary part. Completeness is always imperfect, Jung says. If I can't define this satisfactorily, I can see it when I think of all the sides of a woman that go to make up her whole person and none of these sides or aspects is perfect. It's those varied facets growing together which make her complete in her woman-ness, womanliness."

"That idea would work with headmistresses, don't you think?" said Jane. "I say headmistresses because I've come across them in my life more than business women. There are some who do that difficult job so well they're hardly like women any longer. I can feel a bond with most women on the whole, but between myself and some headmistresses, I can feel only a barrier. This doesn't happen with headmasters, or businessmen. They can aim for perfection in their job and this suits their maleness. I can admire them as men and be friends with them quite easily. And the same applies to priests. I can admire their gifts and their holiness and be friends with them. But women are more suited to something other, even if I can't describe what it is."

"Nor can I describe it. Jung says women go on growing in depth, and also of course they *can* give birth (though they don't all wish to), and this realizes, brings to reality, the idea of growth. Men in their perfection are sterile in Jung's meaning. Well, yes, in a way they *are* sterile. No human man played an active part in the incarnation. Joseph's part was of very great importance, the loving human and legal father of Jesus, who made a home for Mary and her Son, and took decisions for their welfare as a father does. So - ."

And then I told Jane about the Gospel of Thomas, in the paper cutting I'd found, and about Mary, and Jesus's saying he would make her male so she would become a living spirit and enter the Kingdom of Heaven.

"I think it might be, it's a possibility, that the word 'male' here in this context, can be replaced by the word 'perfect' in the sense Jung is using it in this part of his book, what we've been discussing. Mary is already complete, the completely sinless Mother, but truly a Mother, and Jesus wants to make her 'male' in inverted commas, and perhaps we can use that word in Jung's sense of 'perfect' as we have been. So you see, there's no reason why Mary, Queen of Heaven, should not be both complete *and* perfect. She is a unique person. What applies to her need not apply to any other woman. In which case the argument about Jesus in the Gospel of Thomas saying Mary should be made male is no argument for women priests. Yes, Mary can be both perfect and complete because of her part in the Incarnation. If any other woman strives for perfection she forgets her completeness, her womanliness, whereas Mary does not.

183

"And now I've read about this I can explain better how I feel about women priests. I understand the priestess question now more or less as this: for a woman to become a priest she must strive to become perfect as a man is perfect (in Jung's way of talking), but this can happen only at the expense of her completeness, her womanliness, which after all must be wrong, unnatural and very difficult."

"It's quite a new idea, or new to me, a new way of looking at the whole problem," said Jane. "I've never really thought about it before. It's very fascinating."

"There are lots of other things in the Job book which are helpful. For instance, Jung says, 'Don't say that, if a thing is psychological, it has been explained AWAY,' which people are saying all the time. 'It's only psychological!' 'For the psyche,' he says, 'is REAL.'

"I was thinking too," I went on. "Dr Mascall says women don't need to be ordained priests, (or rather, he's quoting someone else. I forget whom). Because of Mary's part in the Incarnation, women begin life already a step nearer to God than men are. Women can be mothers in their own right as Mary was, but no man was Christ's father, as we were saying. He says men are fathers only by proxy, or as you might say in a kind of detached way, sometimes not knowing even, or even not wanting to know."

"In fact really women are super people."

"Except the bossy ones. I don't like to think *they* are very good. Nor silly women. They give me the pip. It's those who live with Mary's words continually in their hearts who are wholly women: 'Behold the handmaid of the Lord. Be it unto me according to thy word.'"

"And that means 'according to God's word' not the traditional 'be a second class person' idea often found in men's thinking."

Jane added. "And all people, including all men, are meant to give their lives to God. To listen to his words."

"I don't know whether I've made all this clear, whether you can understand it at all."

"I think you've made it very clear. All along I felt I was following your points very well. I'm not sure I could tell them to you back again, though. I'd have to read the whole book myself first and get all the ideas running through my head in a better order than they are doing now."

TRINITY: THE WRATH OF GOD

One afternoon I'd been picking runner beans. It was a job I loved very much. Our runner bean row, (or actually, it was more a circle of strings reaching to the ground with the bean plants climbing up them towards a point), is about the only place in the garden which creates an impression of the tropics. All that pale green liana effect, the floppy leaves, the sprays of red flowers, and later the beans, hanging in clusters, it all makes a lovely forest to hide my head in. I can peer inside amongst the foliage, looking for beans, and give myself the illusion of a great area of lush growth going on for ever. Courgettes almost make a jungle too, although so low down near the ground my face can't get lost amongst them as it does in the beans. Their stalks and leaves are so splendidly exotic in a way which makes it hard to find the courgettes themselves hidden underneath. But the leaves are horribly spiky and I often get some nasty unexpected pricks.

I'd been looking forward to tea time, for then, as soon as I sat down, I'd be able to get out the book on Julian of Norwich, the one I'd bought in Eaglesburgh at the same time as the Job book. When the moment came I sat in my armchair with my mug of tea and opened it.

After a very few pages I discovered the style was woolly. On persevering a bit more I found myself disagreeing with the basic premise, that there is no such thing as the Wrath of God.

"I'm so disappointed," I said to Nicholas, when he came in from the late afternoon's watering of his greenhouse tomatoes. "My book's hopeless, after all my looking forward to it so much. The author says there's no such thing as the Wrath of God. He says God is never angry with us, he only seems to be so because we put our own crossness onto him. He says God is always loving and that Julian says this too. Well, yes, up to a point, we do say God is love, but he is also just, and righteous and almighty, so there must be in him an ability to be wrathful against evil. We wouldn't be able to feel about him as we do, if we didn't believe him to be full of wrath against, for instance, concentration camps, or cruelty to children, even if he wasn't against all the people involved. He must be wrathful against sin even if not against the sinner, though I suppose the two are joined together until

185

the sinner comes to see his sin as such and confesses to God and is forgiven.

"I think the author is mixing up two kinds of anger," I went on. "He talks only of the anger which results from people being thwarted or crossed, which could never be God's anger. Only incomplete people expect never to be thwarted or crossed. I certainly don't. I'm often both. God couldn't be bad tempered either. Only incomplete people are bad-tempered. I think, and I expect you do too, that God's wrath is like that of a loving father who's slow to anger and is saddened when it becomes necessary to show it. He's always full of love for his erring children. There is no hate in his anger. Hating is also a sign of incompleteness, I think."

"You're quite right," Nicholas said. "We're taught a lot about God's wrath. His enemies' plans and actions are its most usual cause, those whose acts are evil. But it's aimed also against any wrong his beloved children do when they're not concentrating on his will. But that last wrath never makes his love for us any the less."

"That's what I was thinking. The author suggests this idea of a wrathful God puts people off Christianity. The word Christianity should suggest to them love not wrath. He and Julian (so he says) think of God as always showing his loving side, even to the wicked. Well, God's ready to forgive all those who, when they realize their sins, confess them and try to do better in future. We believe God is sad when we sin and his wrath continues until we confess and ask for his forgiveness. Then all is wiped away, there is perfect remission. This is what we believe, and that's what you were saying. After all, Christ's coming to earth and dying was for us, for our redemption."

"I can see you'll be throwing your book into the WPB in another five minutes." And then Nicholas sat down with his mug of tea and the newspaper and concentrated on that.

I went on thinking about this problem to myself. Edward often told us about the Wrath of God and of the severity of Christ. I thought of what Dr Hunter said in a book I'd read not long before on interpreting St Paul. He says the Wrath of God is God's holy love reacting against evil, and, though Jesus laid a new emphasis on the love of God, the divine reaction to evil is still an awful reality. It's God's holy displeasure at sin. His Wrath is not incompatible with his Love. The opposite of love is hate, not wrath. Jesus was severe with the

Pharisees because although they were very holy in their own way, they were proud and unforgiving with it. Holier than thou, as one might say.

I was disappointed that a book I'd so much looked forward to reading had let me down, so to speak. It would have to go into the next church sale. I was sure I didn't want it. I'd certainly not even finish it. Really I ought to put it straight in the bin so that no one else could buy it and read it, so as not to pollute anyone else's mind. It wouldn't make much more than tenpence at the summer sale so the church wouldn't be losing much.

I remembered another disappointing book I'd once bought, that time about St Paul. The authoress wrote more about Paul's life than about his teaching for she didn't believe in the saving grace of Christ. Also she kept making rash statements such as 'Everybody knows'. I remember one sentence: 'It is a well known fact St John wrote his Gospel in his old age at Ephesus and therefore it wasn't to be relied on.' Well, maybe, I thought. But some people aren't so sure. How could I have gone on reading that kind of thing? The day our bin lorry had been due to come round I'd put it out to be collected and suitably shredded with the other rubbish. And that's what I'll do with this book about Julian likewise.

I did read as far as to discover that the author of this book on Julian said that the ASB has banished the Wrath of God from our church services and this makes it all the more to be recommended as *the* prayer book for today. That's awful. No wonder this country and its church and its people are in a mess. The Bible and Prayer Book have plenty of wrath in them, especially the Psalms; well, everywhere really. In John's Gospel one can read, (I had to look this up for the exact words but I knew they were there),

'He that believeth on the Son hath everlasting life: and he that believeth not the Son shall not see life, but the wrath of God abideth on him.'

In a way, calling God's wrath down on ourselves and falling from grace are not entirely the same thing, and yet when we sin we do fall from grace and deserve his wrath. So in my mind the two are closely connected. We are continually falling and then calling to God to forgive us and lift us up again. Having followed Edward round the Stations of the Cross in Lent, I know very well indeed we are falling all the time. We can fall physically as well as spiritually, and Christ, in his humanity, fell too on Good Friday, though not through sin as we do, but from pain and exhaustion. All our life we're continually falling and picking ourselves up over and over again, but we know there's God's loving hand to help pick us up and comfort us and give us courage to press on through life with renewed strength. Our own suffering doesn't last forever nor does God's wrath. Christ died in order that forgiveness should become a reality. His forgiveness is there for the asking, when we have truly repented. When Jesus died on the cross, the disciples and Mary wondered what had happened to God's love, until Easter Sunday. It can be the same with us. The resurrection works for us as it worked for them. It puts everything right. That's in a psalm too.

'The Lord upholdeth all that fall, and raiseth up all those that be bowed down.'

He will lift us up but we have certainly fallen first. But I've written about this before.

I've heard Edward say that when Jesus fell on the way to Calvary he wasn't suffering for his own sins as we should have in his place, that would be impossible, but for the sins of Pilate and of the Jewish leaders and for all the world's sins and for our own sins too, and, because it was God who suffered, he felt this pain all the more, more that we would feel it.

It's very difficult, though, to make people understand that turning to God and following Christ won't make life suddenly free from the risk of falling or free from God's wrath. Temptations will still besiege us all and we'll give in to them, often almost without thinking. I must choose a better book for this evening. But at that moment it was time to think of supper.

Later I said to Nicholas, "I suppose it was because Julian went round saying all would be well that people have connected her with this softening down of the Bible and God's wrath. She must surely have meant all would be well *in the end,* in the last days, after all the awful apocalyptic happenings, when women had better be barren, and other terrible things. After all *that,* all will be well. But I do need to read a good book about her.

Some months later I did buy a better book about Julian and was pleased to read these words of hers,

'If there be anywhere on earth a lover of God who is always kept from falling, I know nothing of it - for it was not shown me. But this was shown: that in falling and rising again we are always held close in one love.'

TRINITY: PRAYER AND BELIEF

It was a bright sunny July day. There was a wind blowing from the north-west, always a good direction to keep the air clear and cool and yet allow the sun to warm the sheltered hollows. Jane and I decided to walk down through the wood to the loch, and for a change to turn left and walk along towards the caravan site. There we would be able to start our climb back up the hill.

"This way, Tess," called Jane.

After we'd walked down the drive of the big house and had turned along the lochside road, the fields on our left sloped gently up away from us to the Long Wood which ran along the whole length of the hillside until it met the wood of the broken rocks, the Coille na Creige Briste. Beyond and above these trees, but hidden from us at the moment, was Whinside and its neighbouring houses. On our right were scrubby patches of birch, alder and brambles growing in the few feet of grass and pebbles between the road and the water's edge. Every so often there was a little bay and in one of these we sat for a short while, each of us on a suitable boulder. We watched the dinghies from the sailing club opposite reaching and tacking in various directions, their helmsmen taking advantage of the good breeze. Tess paddled a bit, then cast around for interesting smells and finally came and lay down beside us.

"I was going to say," I said to Jane. "Christopher lent me a book on prayer. It's by a monk who studied in India. I thought it was going to be marvellously helpful. I read about how to relax by noticing what parts of the body are pressing on something and what parts are being pressed on. And listening to what sounds could be heard and to accept them as only background noises. I found both those ideas were very good. But when I began actually to read right through the book itself, I discovered that every exercise seemed to be taking a long way round to God. One section was about concentrating our attention on our nostrils and the air going in and out of them, this for hours on end. I did try it myself, but not for so long of course. People like ourselves don't have that kind of time. I suppose it must work for some, well obviously it does, or people wouldn't do it or write about it, but it didn't begin to work for me. And after all a few words of St John of the Cross bring me nearer to God in two minutes than thinking about the end of my nose does in ten or more.

"Also it seemed to me that the God I would find by following the Indian book's ideas might be anyone's God, whereas I'm looking for, and need to find, our own Christian God, the God of the Trinity: Father, Son and Holy Spirit."

"Yes," said Jane. "that reminds me I've often wondered about Thomas Merton. When he died he was on a journey to meet people of eastern beliefs, to compare their different ways of contemplation, their different ways to God, with our western ways. He was attracted to the idea of finding a common ground which east and west could share. Would he have wandered away from the Trinity? I'm not sure whether to be glad he died then, or whether he would have returned home more secure in our own traditions that he was before."

"Thinking of different people's ideas about God and so in a way about different gods, reminds me of what Father Munro, Christopher's old rector, said, when he was up here for Christopher's priesting. One of the young deacons, who was also here, liked to make out he was very advanced in his views and we were very old fashioned. That part's true I expect, though it doesn't make him right and ourselves wrong. He was saying what lots of people like to say these days: that Mary could have given birth to a daughter and then we would have worshipped God the Daughter. It sounds very improbable but how can we argue about it successfully in simple language? Father Munro, though, replied at once, his words coming out so swiftly, without hesitation. You could imagine he'd said the same thing many times before to other young and only partly educated deacons.

"'That wouldn't be Christianity,' he said. 'We believe in Jesus Christ, in God's only *Son*, our Lord.'

'That's the best answer to many of these strange modern views, such as God's perhaps being our Mother, just to make a change. It isn't Christianity, Christians believe in God the Father, in Jesus his Son, and Mary was his Mother. Really I can't conceive why all the bishops and high-up clergy don't say this firmly at once to squash these pointless ideas. Jesus came to earth as Lord and Shepherd so he could come only as a man. (I know there are many women shepherds nowadays, but men are more usually in our minds for that job). We do believe God is a spirit and we worship him in spirit and in truth, but when we think of him as a Person he becomes a Father to us. It's Jung's archetypes all over again. How could we possibly, just casually, or even thoughtfully, swap one archetype for another, Mother for Father, Father for Mother, without noticing what a completely different religion we'd created, different fundamentally.

"Anyway," said Jane, "the angel said, 'Thou shalt conceive in thy womb, and bring forth a Son, and shalt call his name JESUS."

"It's not necessary to invent a God the Mother. For apart from our always having the comforting remembrance of blessed Mary's presence in heaven as well as her life story in our hearts, we know there are no qualities a mother has that a father can't have too, deep down in him, however differently they're manifested. And vice versa. Their roles are usually different in life on this earth, for physical reasons such as bearing babies and suckling them, and for reasons of temperament, but mostly because of tradition. Both fathers and mothers are or can be loving, caring, anxious for us, understanding, forgiving but firm, generous. There's no need for us to imagine God as female, not as male, or as neither, if that were possible."

"Father Munro was very interesting to talk to, wasn't he?" Jane put in. "I mean, to listen to. I agreed with most of what he said so of course I thought he was a very good person with some very sound views. Apart from his discussing the sex-of-God question he was saying there was no need, if one were a beginner, to study Paul's Epistles at first. It was sufficient to concentrate on St John's Gospel, perhaps for the first five years. I love John's Gospel and have relied on it more than on any other of the four."

"So have I. And Paul, according to Father Munro, wrote nothing that isn't in the Gospels. I'm fond of Paul though, I'm intrigued by him. I like to think of each of his letters as a kind of paté, a concentrated and very nourishing food. You can find many of John's ideas in Paul's letters. The ideas about love, and the cross, and finding God the Father in Jesus Christ, and our being in Christ and he in us."

We could hear the baby buzzards calling from their nest in the wood as we got up and walked further along the lochside.

192

"Let's turn up here," I suggested, when we came to a gate, "and miss the caravan site. It'll be very busy just now. From here we can go straight up to the wood and then scramble up through it to the field above which is the one below our house. We can hear the baby buzzards calling now. When we get there they'll be carefully silent."

When we were in the wood there was complete silence as I had promised. And in a minute or two later we came out into the turnip field below our house. Because of the turnips and their ridges and deep furrows we walked round this field too and then finally climbed over our lower garden fence assisted by strategically placed slabs of sandstone. Then I sat on my old brooding stone with Jane beside me as we had often done before. In front of us was the lovely view over the loch to the far mountains.

"What we were saying," said Jane, "about God's being a Father or a Mother reminds me about how very surprised I was to read in Newspot not long ago a suggestion that we should perhaps say the creed less often because it's become irrelevant. I thought that was an awful idea. How can the creed be irrelevant when it's basic? God is our Father in the creed, that's quite clear. Perhaps the author of the letter want to change to God the Mother and so the sooner she learned to manage without the creed the better she would feel about things."

"I saw that letter too. I often think of the creed as a kind of very old and very well worn path or alleyway of granite setts, uneven through much use, leading between old houses in an old city, taking us directly to where we need to go, rather that having to use a wider, easier, though longer, main road or by-pass. Or else I think of it as the paving stones of an old Roman road leading us safely in a straight (of course) line over a high moorland wilderness where we couldn't because of this well-marked track ever be lost, even in a mountain mist. I feel I should say the creed more often than I do, not less."

"What is good too about the creed," said Jane, "is that the longer you live the more you grow into what you believe and with more confidence. The creeds aren't something you could ever grow out of, not at any rate once you'd grown into them. Or I wouldn't have thought so."

"Finding the right way to pray though isn't easy," I said feelingly. "And yet one is compelled to pray by something outside one. I feel that prayer is only the way of learning where I'm to go, wherever that may be."

Jane said, "We all need to grow as well as to go somewhere, but you need to especially, I think. And you need to feel yourself growing as well as going. Do you feel God is pulling something out of you? He's putting something into you where it's taking a new shape and later it will come out as a new something. I don't know what."

"That's it, I think. Though I don't know what either. I feel compelled to go somewhere. Maybe to search for the source of the love that surrounds us, though we know it's really within us. All the same it's deeply hidden and needs much searching for."

And then, of course, it was time for Jane to go home.

TRINITY: TWO SPANISH SAINTS

As I've said (or I think I have) Christopher has a very good selection of not too erudite religious books, so when I expressed my interest in St John of the Cross and St Teresa of Avila he lent me a slim and simply written volume containing a little about each of them, illustrating some of their thoughts and teachings by extracts from the writings.

For instance, St John wrote about possession:

'To possess the heights of Mount Carmel you must let go of all other things. Now that I wish for nothing I have all without wishing. Now that I seek for nothing I have all without seeking. Love the beauty of the world but don't try to possess it for yourself, then it will be yours.'

I thought this was a marvellous idea which could save anyone of us an infinity of fretting for what we can't have, of saying 'If only I'd something or other ... (Edward, I remembered, had long ago told us never to say 'If only ... and I realized I should think about this advice every day and not just from time to time; life would then be very much simplified). It's so easy to want to possess what we love. Children want to possess lots of good things just because they can see them, anything that attracts them. I often have to remind myself that even what I own isn't really my own but lent by God. It seems important to be certain about this, to see the truth of our not being owners of anything. 'All that we have is thine and of thine own do we give unto thee.' We say this prayer every Sunday in the Mass.

Therefore, if we believe, seriously, that all we have belongs to God, we shouldn't be devastatingly hurt by any loss. I needed to realize that even the place where I lived, Ardness, which I loved so much, and all the countryside around, and the house, Whinside, and all that was in it, none of these things or places belonged to *me*, not even the parts I 'owned'. None of Whinside was Nicholas's or mine but lent only to be our home for the time being, a welcoming home for us to live in but not for boasting about, or showing off to visitors. When I'd learnt to give up the idea of possessing all those things, then I should find I was able to love anywhere as my home, and I should all the more enjoy my present one for I'd be no longer fearful of losing it. I saw that if God did take my home away I ought not to mind. It wasn't mine to keep, even though I'd wanted to stay in that lovely place for ever. With God's help I should be free in my mind to go and live anywhere he might send me without suffering any great sense of great loss. Everywhere, anywhere could be my home, though we must look after, as well as we can, wherever it is we're sent to. And, after all, everywhere and anywhere I found myself, there were sure to be people who needed friendship and all kinds of help.

I'm sure it's important to learn to let go of people we love as well as letting go of things. We know we must let go of our own children when they grow up, like swans shooing last year's cygnets off the pond which has been their home ever since they were hatched. Everyone is God's child. Everyone has his own free will and his own life to live. We should never try to rule the ways of others. Let's give our love for our children and friends to God and then he will use that love for them in the best way possible. We should relax and accept his care for them, that he will love them and protect them, he will take them to himself.

I saw that Nicholas wasn't MINE, he's God's child though I was needed to look after him as he was to look after me. This is true for the boys too, they were not MINE, and anyway I'd had to learn to share them with Joyce and Christine, to learn to hand them over to their wives who were more their own age and more suited to the job now than myself. Francis Bacon wrote,

'He that hath wife and children hath given hostages to fortune.'

When a person we love, or anyone really, becomes older, nearer his life's end, we shouldn't try to hold him back, try to keep him here in this world with us. We believe heaven is waiting to welcome people, so we should let them go with thankfulness. And we need never be far from those who've died. We believe in the Communion of Saints, that they are safely with God, with all his children. We can pray for them and ask them to pray for us. We can feel near to them and although we are bound, at first, to find communication with them difficult, in time we shall learn to overcome this. What a lot there is for us to learn.

As well as writing about not possessing anything in order to possess all, St John writes about the night. I don't enjoy the darkness of the real night, the one that comes every twenty-four hours. I try not

196

to think often about that one. But the darkness that's somewhere in the soul is a night I wonder about a great deal. For as far back as I can remember, I've felt this night must in some way be not entirely threatening, that its darkness is not frightening but encouraging and comforting. St John writes that we should remember God works in us in the dark moments of life more than he does in the sunny ones. In the darkness of the soul we meet God as completely as we ever can do in this life, much more than during the bright exciting days.

Where St John is a saint of the night St Teresa is a saint of the day. She's very practical. She says we need to build up an image of Christ outside ourselves before we seek him within us, otherwise the inward gaze may reveal only ourselves which we may mistake for Christ. There need be nothing complicated she says, about this outward image we have of Christ.

'You will find it very helpful if you can get an image or picture of this Lord - one that you like - not to wear round your neck and never look at, but to use regularly whenever you talk to Him, and he will tell you what to do and say.'

St Teresa is very realistic about good works and loving our neighbour. How can we best help our neighbour? She says we should start where we are, with people near at hand, not with ambitious schemes. It is the amount of love we give which counts, not the size or importance of our task.

'The Lord does not look so much at the magnitude of anything we do as at the love with which we do it. If we accomplish what we can, His Majesty will see to it that we become able to do more each day.'

She says too, that in giving all to God, in drawing nearer to him, we learn to be more outgoing. Our love in God as it grows flows out all the more easily to other people. It's from the life of Jesus in us and ourselves in him that we learn more about loving our neighbour.

There was lots more, of course, but these are a few of the useful ideas I've remembered. I'd read about these two famous saints before, I would have like to read still more about them but I felt, at that time, I needed a little bit of lots of different people's helpful writings. Here I'd just dipped into someone's selection and had taken out a few good ideas.

TRINITY: AT THE RECTORY

Having parked the car in its usual place behind St Andrew's church, I walked the short distance along to where Edward lived. I was coming to photocopy some notices I'd written the day before. The rectory was one of several more or less similar but not identical houses set in a quiet wide street. For one about a hundred years old it was an unusually light and pleasant house, built in the local pinkish sandstone, not rambling or gabled or gloomy, nor with tall narrow depressing windows, quite the contrary. And above the entrance porch was the date 1887 in curly numerals carved into the stone in deep relief. Over the outer door was an oblong of stained glass with 'St Andrew's House' in red letters surrounded by green leaves on a blue ground. There was a balcony over each of the bay windows of the two main front rooms, either side of the front door, and a smaller central one over the porch. In the stonework above each of the two main bedroom windows was a carved decorative shell and above each of these was a little gable topped by a wrought iron fancy spike.

Every time I went there I was happy to see the furniture and decorations inside were quiet and unobtrusive but as agreeable and comfortable as the exterior was elegant and interesting. Also, every time I went there, I felt really welcome and relaxed. I was almost surprised this was so, though it's not kind of me to be surprised that Edward's house should be so well arranged and yet not in any way overpoweringly posh with matching furniture or swish fitted carpets. Edward would be hurt if he thought I was surprised his house should be a home that welcomed visitors, that I should expect things to be sparse or bleak or uncomfortable just because he wasn't married. It's not only women who know how to be comfortable. Good heavens, I know of a few women who've no idea.

Hugh Watson, the Provost of the Cathedral, was with Edward discussing some of the many things which often need to be discussed by two neighbouring rectors. (Hugh's work is much the same as Edward's but on a rather more exalted scale). Nicholas and I were friendly with Hugh and his wife Fiona. She and I always found lots to

198

say to each other when we met but, sadly, we'd never visited each other's homes.

"That's a pity really," I thought, "it's probably due to Nicholas and my living not in Strathlyon but out at Ardness. And Fiona is busy with her three children and also with all she does to help Hugh at the Cathedral. But most of all I'm sure it's due to the fact that these days everybody's lives are so full that putting on a meal for anyone except one's very nearest and dearest is an effort. I'm including Edward and Christopher, of course, as certainly our nearest and almost dearest for they more or less count as part of our family.

"Come in, Betty," Edward called, "have some coffee, Hugh's here. Come in and say Hello."

Hugh was beginning to tell Edward about the Cathedral shop and how, earlier in the summer, he'd invited someone to come and advise about improvements. He'd thought she might have good ideas about the best things to sell, or how best to display them. There was very little room in the Cathedral shop and it seemed important to make the most of all the space they had.

"However, being used, I suppose," Hugh was saying, "to looking at much bigger and grander churches and cathedrals, the lady seemed to think we ought to have a Visitor Centre on the grass or under the trees by the riverside. I had to get her to come down to earth and into the actual, rather than her imaginary shop. She was determined though to explore the whole building, looking for some larger space, as if we hadn't already done so ourselves. We don't want a large shop. We want to sell only a few church orientated things, so visitors can find something small to spend a little on and easily carry away with them.

"The expert lady kept forgetting, or seemed to be forgetting, about the true purpose of a church. To her it seemed the commercial or secular or display side was more important than worship. She didn't seem to realize the vulnerability of the holy atmosphere of the building. I thought this was sad. Our cathedral isn't a great and famous place with hundreds of visitors daily. People come here in twos and threes and they expect to find a church which is used for prayer. She talked about weddings too as if we often had grand social ones, lovely brides and bridesmaids with elaborate dresses, to be looked at and admired. These would attract people, she thought, into the church, they were spectacles rather than occasions for prayer among friends with rejoicing and hope.

"Do you think," I asked, "it's to do with the less reverence people in general seem to feel nowadays? Even some grown ups often don't appear at all awe-struck by the special presence of God in our church. And when our Sunday School children come in towards the end of the service, they don't creep in but hurry up the aisle and then wriggle into their pews and go on communicating with one another, as if they didn't know they had come for another kind of communication, Communion. I don't think that's good."

"I think you're right there," said Hugh. "The accent *is* much less on reverence now, it's more as you might say on having a party with God."

"I'm one of those who definitely need a holy atmosphere," I went on. "I notice whether there is one or not. Some people say any old place will do for the Mass, as well it has to sometimes, but not if it's not necessary. In St Andrew's, and in St Mary's too, there's a great feeling of all those people who've been before us and left shadows of their prayers on the walls and this thought (a mental vision as it were) draws out our prayers from us. Our prayers come more easily and sweetly than in some other churches. Don't you think, Edward?"

"That's true. It was one of the good things that struck me at St Andrew's from the beginning, from the day I first came to see the church. And it's grown on me."

"But there's some very odd and puzzling in the way reverence has been disappearing," I said. "I discovered not long ago, in the Mass, in the old intercessions, when we pray for all people and this congregation here present, which is the first time ordinary people like myself are mentioned, a phrase has been left out. The prayer used to read, as you will remember,

'And to all thy people give thy heavenly grace, and especially to this congregation here present, that *with meek heart and due reverence,* they may hear and receive thy holy word, truly serving thee in holiness and righteousness all the days of their life.'

"It's those words 'with meek heart due reverence' which have vanished, and I can't see for what reason they have been taken away. It couldn't be to save time. I feel they are conditional in their meaning and therefore important. You know what I mean. Only if we have meek hearts and are attending with due reverence will we hear and receive God's holy word."

Hugh and Edward both agreed. Hugh said, "It's sad when good phrases, or even whole sentences are taken away. It's happened too often lately. Anyway the aim of the shop is to provide visitors with something to spend their money on, to remember us by, and to add something towards making it possible for God to continue to be worshipped at St Mary's. We all know balancing the books isn't the main purpose of a church, but no church can exist unless the books do balance. And the shop helps just a little towards our being able to carry on God's good work."

"*Anyway*," I said. "I came to do some photocopying, so I'd better get it done or Nicholas will be agitating. He's talking to Duncan about the swing doors that won't swing and how much will it cost to put right?"

TRINITY: HOLY WOMEN

One evening in the middle of August I was walking round the garden looking at the progress of summer. There'd been a dry spell, the grass hadn't needed cutting for a week or two and had become the colour I described as bright brown, not pale or dark but quite a strong, even a foxy colour. The whole effect was untidy though, for there were patches of different lengths of grass, long tufts in odd places and even green areas where the ground was damper or more shaded. However the apple crop promised to be good.

I was contemplating and recalling the super service we'd had at St Andrew's for the Assumption of Mary. I was beginning to understand about the idea, what is involved and why, about Mary's part in the coming of Christ, in the birth not only of Jesus but of Christianity itself.

People, that's to say, the human race on earth, or on part of the earth anyway, were ready for the next stage of being brought closer to God. We were ready to have salvation brought to us, ready for a redeemer to take away our sins. Mary, a young woman living in Palestine received the Angel's message about carrying God's Son in her womb. She said 'Yes' to God, 'Be it unto me according to thy word,' and 'Behold the handmaid of the Lord'. So Jesus is wholly a man, Son of this Mary, and he is also wholly God, son of God the Father by the Spirit. When he grew up, her Son showed us the Father in himself. Mary gave him her care and support all through his life on earth, apart from the times of wondering, rather naturally, what on earth he could be up to. She was there with him when he died on the cross, and at his coming on the first Easter Sunday.

For all this it was necessary for Mary to be a perfect woman, a perfect mother, the most perfect that could be imagined, whom no one else could ever equal in any way. It was impossible she could be sinful even in the way that saints can be sinful, and it follows from this that her journey from this world to heaven at the end of her earthly life should take a different course from our own.

She had no need for any last judgment, nor to suffer in purgatory. St Peter didn't need to use his keys to unlock any doors for her, they were already held wide open. Her body could not, like ours, be left in an earthly, earthy grave. It had to be that she would leave this world in a way as different as possible from our way, in fact, to be taken up directly into heaven. Because of the part Mary played in our redemption, she deserved the best we can imagine, though our imagination hesitates for we know well enough not one of us deserves anything, all that comes to us is a pure gift from God. The Assumption of Mary is a gift from God too, a gift to Mary, and also a gift to us. We need Mary to be at the side of her Son in Heaven, and at the same time to be for us ever approachable, always ready to listen to us in our moments of despair and in our moments of joy and thanksgiving. She is our new mother. Our need for the Assumption of Mary is made clear in Jung's book, the book he'd written on Job.

The more I think of everything, not only of Mary, but of Jesus and his being the Son of God as well as of Mary, of the Spirit who comes from both the Father and the Son: of this Father and Son relationship which has been from all eternity, each eternally loving the other; when I think of the whole Christian idea, of its way of life, its light and its truth, of our spiritual nourishment by the Bread and the Wine, of Christ's Body and Blood given for us, binding us to this religion; how we are taken up into him, into his mystical body; the more I think of all this and contemplate its completeness and the way it all holds together, each part interlocking and complementing and perfecting each other part; the more I'm convinced there is nothing else we can need for our journey through our earthly life. Because of our belief, heaven is brought down to us on earth as we make our life's journey. Or, to put it another way, as we step out along the road of life, we can feel the lightness in our heart telling us that half of ourself is already in heaven.

The next day Jane was coming over anyway, and, as the weather, although not sunny, was warm and windless, I thought we could go for a walk through the wood on the far side of the trig point hill. This was partly because it was a lovely walk and partly for me to show Jane where the woodpeckers had nested in a hole in the rotting trunk of a dead birch. And now partly it was because I had these new ideas to talk about. Jane would be sure to have more helpful ones. Or at least she'd put everything in a clearer perspective for me.

"What I really wanted to say," I said to Jane after we'd inspected the woodpeckers' nest site and we'd turned to go out of the wood to walk over the heathery part of the hill and made sure Tess was following. "was to ask you what you thought about the Assumption of Mary and her part in the beginning of Christianity. About all the completeness of what we believe about Christ and about Christianity's total perfection. God is here with us whether life is going badly or well. However great our despair and our need for help, God is here to listen. There's the Trinity with its dynamic love, the Holy Spirit going from God the Father to Christ his Son, showing us this love, what true love is, and Christ's coming to show us the Father. You know it all as well as I do and better. I don't think it would be possible to conceive of a more wonderful system of belief, if those are proper words to describe this indescribable thing."

"Yes, I've thought about this often. The best psychiatrists can't cure people's minds or souls in as sure a way as true Christianity can. Even the best psychiatry must work better when topped up by the Holy Spirit. In fact whether we need psychiatrists or not we all need topping up with the Spirit most of the time. I agree with your thoughts about this perfection and completeness. None of it needs altering though our reactions to Christianity will change as we grow in the Spirit. The Spirit helps us grow. Mary's part in all this is important, or rather essential, as the Mother of Our Lord. Happiness can now become joy, which is infinitely more enduring than plain happiness and will survive many trials."

"I feel that," I replied. "Happiness is usually just for now, for today, when people and things are being nice to us, but joy transforms the past and lightens our way into the future."

"That's what I mean. Joy comes from inside one. And joy is what Christ brings. Happiness can be from circumstances, though it's very pleasant when it happens and certainly not to be despised."

When we got up to the trig point we sat down on the dry closely cropped summer turf and looked down on the loch. At first the spiky dead bits of grass stuck into our legs, but we bent our knees and tucked our feet up under them and made ourselves comfortable leaning against the white concrete post.

"On a large scale map of around Ardness I got the other day I saw this hill is really called the Hill of the Meeting Place of the People," I explained, "rather than Trig Point hill which is only our own name for it. You can see it could be a sort of Thing, a meeting place only it's name's in Gaelic, the Cnoc na h Eiracht, (cnoc beint a little hill as in 'knock' with a k) and not in Norwegian like Tynwald or Dingwall. We've just come through the Coille or Wood of the Hill of the Meeting Place of the People. It's easy to imagine those who lived hereabouts, in past pre-Christian ages, sitting around on this patch of clear grass where even the gorse doesn't grow and cover it over, discussing things of great moment; it's a good shape of hilltop, broad and smooth and grassy over quite a wide area, and with super views all round. All the taller hills and mountains are a long way away."

"And that does make it the right place for both a trig point and a Thing," said Jane. And then she added, "It's jolly to see the gentians in flower up here, even if these aren't blue at all, but only a wishy-washy purple. They're a lovely interesting shape, very unusual. At this time of year too, the harebells are beautiful. I love to see them growing in the walls along the sides of the road all mixed up with ladies' bedstraw. Their soft blue goes very well with the bedstraw's yellow and both go well with their background of grey stones and the dead pale beige grass of this time of year. Bright green grass would spoil the effect."

"That's like Turner, do you remember? He hated green vegetation - not an artistic colour for landscape, he thought, - preferring to paint during the summer in Italy where there'd be very little bright green anything.

"Thinking of the Assumption," I went on after a pause, and Tess had come to lie down beside us, "made me think about all the other women besides blessed Mary who've helped me. Mary has such an important part, as we've been saying, no one else can touch her, but there are others: Mary Magdalene first of all, even if, perhaps, she is three separate Marys. I like to think she's the sister of Martha, the Mary who sat and listened to Jesus' teaching, and also the Mary who poured the expensive ointment over his feet, as well as the Mary who was forgiven much, if she was called Mary. But it was certainly she who was first to see Christ on Easter morning.

205

"I love Martha too," said Jane. "She who was the first to meet Jesus when Lazarus died. She heard him say, 'I am the Resurrection and the Life, he who believes in me shall never die.' And she understood."

"And what about St Catherine of Siena who said that *of course* God could have created each one of us completely perfect both physically and mentally if he had wished, but in fact, he chose rather that we should need each other's help and love. That's a very encouraging idea, don't you think? For it does much to explain part of life's seeming unfairness."

"That's true. None of us is intended to be self-sufficient, totally independent of others, like little disconnected islands in a great Pacific Ocean. Love flourishes best where help is needed and given. Of course we should take care not to be annoyingly and unnecessarily dependent on other people, never selfishly and thoughtlessly taking advantage of people's willingness to help. If we stop for a moment to think we can all see there are others in greater need than ourselves."

"And there's St Teresa of Avila who had saintliness more or less thrust upon her, in spite of herself."

"And thinking of one Teresa must bring us to another, or to two others: there's Thérèse of Lisieux who suffered so much we find it hard, or I do, to understand the direction of her suffering and saintliness, but really it's worth while giving time and trouble to try to understand."

"And Mother Teresa of Calcutta. It's wonderful how much she has accomplished with God's help in this age which is so often said to be anti-God and faithless, and how she has found so many people to help in her work."

"I love to think of all the women who will remain unknown and yet are saints, whose lives and achievements and their overcoming of difficulties are known to only a few people, or only to God."

TRINITY: A FUN SERMON

Although there was no sun to speak of, there was not much wind either, so Jane and I went on sitting up on the Trig Point hill and talking about things in general and what interested us in particular. There was no rush for us to be down again at Whinside yet awhile. Jack was away in Eaglesburgh so Jane was free of any ties. Tess was sitting down quietly beside us.

"I was thinking too," I went on, "about St Anne and in what ways she's important to us, and the marvellous sermon Edward preached on the Sunday evening which was also her Evensong, if you see what I mean. It was a very interesting sermon, and very funny really, very typical of him. He'd not prepared it, of course, it came straight out of his head as often happens. He used the idea of St Anne herself and those of the first and second lessons: Eli falling off the seat backwards by the gate and St Peter with his sheet's being let down from heaven full of beasties. The idea must have come to Edward as an inspiration while he listened to the readings, those outwardly very disconnected stories. You'll remember, how he set himself a kind of acrostic of ideas, three ideas to be joined together to make, in fifteen minutes, a complete sermon full of God's love and how it works. He put his watch beside him on the edge of the pulpit and we sat, or I did, fascinated, enthralled, full of attention, wondering how he would make it all work out."

"I do remember it very well. I couldn't see how all the separate bits were going to be organized to make one sensible whole, an illuminating story that would hold together. Just think how often we've sat through some other people's much longer and carefully prepared sermons with only a fraction of the interest of this one, not leading us, either, to any better an understanding of the Gospel."

"Let's see if we can remember the details and the reasoning," I suggested. "The main points Edward made were, one, that a naive view of the world often gives a sharper and therefore more memorable picture of God's truth than any highly spiritual or scholarly exposition can do. Two, that we are all God's children whoever we are, however old we are, or wherever we come from. And three, God is everywhere but more concentrated in some places than in others.

"He began with St Anne and the church in London, in Hoxton, which is dedicated to her. Each year on her Day they have, well, we hope they still have, a grand procession, carrying her statue round the streets, singing about St Anne, Granny of God. St Anne was, still is, the mother of the Virgin Mary, the Mother of Jesus, and therefore St Anne is the Granny of Jesus, that is Granny of God. This is the naive idea and from this follows the idea that, as we are all related to each other anyway through Adam and Eve and the evolution of the human race, so we are all related to St Anne and the Virgin Mary, and so we are all kinsmen to Christ. We are all cousins of God. You can see these two points clearly here, the simple idea of St Anne's being Granny of God and the idea of our inter-relationships, no one is not a child of God.

"The first lesson was in 1 Samuel. There's a battle going on, not unusually, between the Philistines and the Israelites. Eli, the old priest, is sitting on a seat, watching, by the wayside, outside the city of Shiloh. He's anxiously awaiting news of his sons, Hophni and Phineas, who are in danger. As he waits, there comes running up to him a man with his clothes rent and earth upon his head. He tells Eli his sons are dead. Eli takes this news stoically, as he also takes the news that thousands of Israelites have been killed in the fighting. However, when he is told that the Ark of the Covenant has been captured by the Philistines, he becomes very upset indeed and falls from his seat backward by the side of the gate, and 'his neck brake, for he was an old man and heavy.'

"Why was he more upset by the loss of the Ark of the Covenant than by the death of his sons and of so many Israelites? To the Israelites the Ark was the dwelling place of God. God was in those days still the God of the Israelites only, and even they could find him only in the Ark. Therefore the Ark was their most treasured and holy possession, the home of their God. This notion of God's being only in one definite place, the Ark, seems to be a naive idea to put it mildly. Nowadays we think of God as being all around us and even in us, immanent, as well as out there beyond everything; transcendent: not in one place only but in all the universe and beyond.

"All the same we do understand about God's being more concentrated in some places than in others. As God was present in the Ark for Eli, for us he is concentratedly present in the Bread and Wine, Christ's coming to us in the Mass. Consequent on this we also think of his presence in the tabernacle where the reserved Sacrament is locked away safely at the side of the altar. But he's found most concentratedly of all in our hearts and, because of this, we can take him around with us and share him with others.

"And this is the second idea: Eli's view of God helps us to understand, by his misunderstanding, one of the basic truths of God, that his holiness is all around us though more concentrated in special places. Eli thought of God's being in one place only, while we know he's everywhere though not always in the same strength as it were. Now it's your turn!"

"I remember!" said Jane. "In the second lesson, in Acts, Peter learns, in a trance, something contrary to what he used to believe, that nothing God makes is common or unclean. 'What God has cleansed, that call not thou common.' He's told he may kill and eat anything that's set before him on a sheet which has just been let down from heaven. All those 'manner of fourfooted beasts of the earth, and wild beasts, and creeping things, and fowls of the air' which are in the sheet are clean and may be eaten. None of them is unclean for God made them, created them, he hasn't just cleansed them, they've been clean from their creation.

"He learns also, at the same time, though rather against his wishes, that this loving all God's creation applies to people as well as to all beasties. Now, at the same time a centurion, Cornelius, is warned by God, by a holy angel, to send for Peter, who is in Joppa, as we know, having his trance. He's to come to Ceasarea where he, Cornelius, is living, so that he can hear Peter's word, hear his explanations about Christ. Cornelius is a devout man, a gentile. He prays to God always with all his household. So, while Peter is contemplating the significance of his lesson with the sheet and its animals and just beginning to understand the implications, two servants and a soldier arrive to ask him to return with them to Cornelius in Caesarea, The Spirit tells Peter to go with them and doubt nothing. His decision to go isn't an easy one for him to make, for in those days it was considered inappropriate for a Jew to call on a Gentile in his home, but happily he's learning his lesson rapidly.

"When Peter gets to Caesarea he tells Cornelius and his household he's pleased to visit them as 'God has shewed me that I should not call any man common or unclean.' And he continues, 'Of a truth I see that God is no respecter of persons'. (that's to say, God isn't impressed by worldly rank or station), 'and in every nation all who fear him and work righteousness are accepted'. This is the third point. Whoever we are we should relate with other people considerately and with politeness. There's no rule of uncleanliness to separate us from each other. Peter then expounds the Christian faith to Cornelius and the Holy Ghost falls on him and all his household. But none of Cornelius's family or servants has yet been baptised with water, so this has to be done now, in the reverse order from usual, so that everything shall be made complete. I'm not sure now, you go on again."

"Well, there's not much left to say. We hardly need to draw all the ends together as we've been doing that as we've gone along. I'll try though. First of all at Hoxton, we saw how we are all kinsmen together and to Christ, and this was expressed in a naive way, thinking of St Anne as Granny to Jesus. Then we saw Eli's naive view of God's being the national God of Israel only, and concentrated in one place, in the Ark. And we too believe that God, although spread throughout the universe, his creation, is concentrated in the Bread and Wine and also and especially in our hearts. Our hearts are the temple of the Holy Spirit and as we go around in this word we take this concentration of God with us. Thirdly, in Peter's story we saw how as God made all men clean, we can accept our interrelationship to each other and to God, and back we are in Hoxton again watching the procession."

"It was a super sermon. I remember it so well because it was so very clearly told to us. Also because we were involved in its progress. We felt it was our sermon being unfolded before us. Of course all Edward's sermons are about the Gospel message. He makes us understand how we can love God more and work for him all the better. But it's often his more informal sermons we enjoy the most, isn't it? especially on Sunday evenings."

After a pause I said, "If we go down the hill a little to the left of here, we can then walk straight across the field and climb over the fence by the straining post. The field's clear now the silage is gone, so we can walk across it without harming anything, it's the best and easiest way back to the house."

"Yes, let's." We uncurled our legs and got up and walked down the sheeptrack and then across the field and into the lane and so on to Whinside and some welcome tea.

TRINITY: FRIENDS AND VOICES

"You remember what you were saying the other day," said Jane, after we'd refreshed ourselves with some welcome tea. "about not always seeing people's best sides. It made me think of how one is friends or not so much friends with people. It's not always one's own fault, for often one's pushed into dislike or helped into friendship. And some people are naturally friendlier than others, it's easier to be friends with them. Though we need to try to be nice to all. I suppose, and not show our dislike. Though Christ showed his dislike of the Pharisees."

"That's true," I replied. "It's an interesting subject. You can see it well in Edward and Christopher. Edward is especially self - sufficient. I never worry for a moment that he mightn't be quite content having that whole house to himself. He doesn't ever look or sound lonely in it, and of course during the day there are often people around, coming in and out. Christopher is different. I find myself wondering if after all he wouldn't be happier with a wife."

"That's very true. He's a much more outwardly friendly person. As you say he seems to need company. But he's good with people and so he can have lots of friends, and he does already have lots of friends."

"But it's not so simple really," I went on. "Edward has lots of friends, though probably fewer here in Strathlyon than elsewhere, they're likely to be scattered around the world, and he has friends in a different way. It's much easier for me to be friends with Edward than with Christopher, though I'm friends with both. Maybe I find Edward easier just because Christopher does already have lots of friends here. If some one has already lots of friends, I know they'll not need me, that they're sociable people. Anti-social people are much more interesting, at least often they are to me. Though Edward's not really anti-social, far from it. But he's got a kind of detachment. He's fun to be with but I know he'll be all right when I've gone home. It's true enough, though, with him, that our minds often work in the same ways. We often both take the same view of something and then we laugh and that makes a bond."

"The thing about Edward is," said Jane, "he's so transparent, transparently good. But at the same time he's so human, he's full of humanity. And he sees the funny side of life. He brings holy things and everyday life together."

"Yes. If I ever feel awful about anything and tell him about it, he understands at once why I'm feeling awful. He says to remember always that 'whatever happens, God loves you,' When he says that, it sounds real, true. Those words spoken by him carry conviction because he himself believes they're true. And I feel better straightaway. It's so heart-warming. Their truth sinks into my whole self. Until of course I need to hear them again. 'Whatever happens, remember God loves you'."

"Some people," Jane went on, "complain that Edward visits only the county families, they think he should spend more time with ordinary people."

"And yet other people complain he's too fond of going to the Glen Gowrie to meet his friends, though it looks a very respectable pub to me."

"It certainly is. David often goes there when he's staying with us, when he wants a change of company other than his old parents."

"And", I added, 'they say Edward goes to the wrong end of town too much, but that's a silly idea. There can't be a wrong end of town in God's view of Strathlyon, which would be Edward's own view, a clergyman's view."

"I agree. That can't be right, though I see what people mean. Jesus too was accused of being a friend of publicans and sinners. Some people think that's a bad thing to be, they were brought up to be careful about strange people. Jesus showed us just the contrary. God created and loves all of us."

"For after all," I said, "Jesus knew, and he said, whole people don't need a physician, it's the sick who do. 'For I am come to call not the righteous but sinners to repentance.' I'm sure he wasn't at all solemn and disapproving when he was amongst his less presentable friends, when he went to eat with them. I'm sure he would have been cheerful and entertaining as he tried to make them understand about God's loving them whatever they'd done before. And I was thinking, in this country, in these days, it's not so much believers who are wicked in spite of their believing and need to repent, though of course they do, but it's more those who've never heard of the Kingdom of God at all. They certainly need to hear about God and be encouraged to realise that God is love, that he'll love them in spite of their not believing up to now."

"And there's another kind of misunderstanding," I said, Some people complain there's not enough mission outside the church, that the Gospel should be taken to those with no religion, especially people in this country. But then parish people grumble and criticise priests who do so, like Edward does, go out to visit non-church people. They say their rector should concentrate on his flock. People do expect impossible things and whatever happens it's wrong for somebody and they always tell you so."

"I remember Edward saying once," said Jane, "that church respectability is a disgrace. He was meaning that church people who worry about respectability are like the Pharisees, thinking about what shows, whited sepulchres and all that, what other people will notice. They're afraid of being thought not quite - *respectable*. They're afraid to do a right though lowly action because others will despise them for it. They'd criticise Edward, or any clergyman really, if he should go to help 'unrespectable' people."

"I've thought about this too," I said. "For instance, I often feel a bit ashamed when I come to church in my best suit or coat and best shoes. I feel I'm looking much too *respectable*. And yet in honour to God I can hardly come in my worst clothes. Anyway that would embarrass Nicholas. And Edward, too. I have to remind myself it's only my outside that's looking respectable like the Pharisee and the poor old publican is still very much alive inside me. Also, if one's reading an epistle or lesson at the service, it's discourteous to wear 'unrespectable', unsuitable garments, scruffy or bizarre, for *they,* the clergy, will have taken trouble to be in their correct and decorative garments, and so we ought to take the same care."

"But really, I suppose, the Pharisees thought of respectability equalling goodness," Jane said. "They needed respectability to give themselves confidence, that's what they'd been taught, I expect, and lots of people even nowadays are much the same. Jesus didn't need a similar boost, as it were, because he had no false feelings of

214

unworthiness to overcome. he was able perfectly to communicate with God, he was a perfectly well balanced person."

"As we were saying," I said. "some people get a bad name for themselves because they are doing good in an unpopular or 'unrespectable' way. But Jesus said:"

'Blessed are ye, when men shall revile you and persecute you and shall say all manner of evil against you falsely, for my sake. Rejoice and be exceeding glad: for great is your reward in heaven.'

"Nicholas as well as Edward, needs to be connected to that idea. He often has to say things which make him unpopular and people are nasty in return. I have to remind him about his reward in heaven, to cheer him up, to make sure he remembers he's blessed. But I don't think he's convinced, anyway certainly not for long."

"I often think, or wonder rather," Jane said, changing the subject again, "as we were saying, about what makes people friends with each other. It's not just thinking the same things, though that helps, but there's also got to be a difference to make a friendship interesting."

"I've thought a lot about that, too." I replied. "Friendship between two people needs something unconscious to be happening, outside what can be explained. It's therefore not easy to analyze. So far as I can see, it's caused by, or comes about by, odd connections at the beginning. It can be something in the way people stand, or how they move their head, or an eyebrow, that attracts. Or with myself, I find it's how they talk, what kind of sentences they use, and the voice, and the funny inflexions in the voice, and after a bit you can feel there's a bond somewhere. It's not only the subjects that get talked about, though they are important. The attraction may be mutual, or it may not be. It certainly may not be."

"In a way that would explain what Edward says in his sermons about our understanding God not with our reasoning mind but with our heart. And, if you remember, it was the way he said *that*, which had such an effect on you. It changed you altogether. You became really and truly a Christian. It was in his voice."

"Yes, and it was unexpected. It was due to his voice and not to our being friends, because we weren't, or hardly, at that time. I noticed not long ago, another thing about voices too. Gentle, clear voices can make holiness seem just at hand, or even really surrounding one. For instance, it can happen in the quiet weekday Mass, especially when Edward's taking it, the whole service appears seamless. It flows straight on. He makes all the little bits, those which are different for each day, smoothly fit in so you would never know. And it's his voice that does it. On the day I'm remembering, there were only the two of us, himself and me, in the Lady Chapel, and everything flowed so perfectly all the way through from beginning to end, I felt there might have been neither of us there but only the Holy Spirit. The familiar words were spoken as if there were only one voice in the church, they seemed to hold the Spirit captive. He and I, as people, individuals, seemed unimportant in comparison with the reality of what was happening. The Mass was happening and we were the Spirit's instruments or voices, and there was Christ himself in the sacrament, present with us in the world. And I thought, then, at that time, this must be how it ought to be, how it always ought to be, though with a crowd, or even with only a few people, it would probably be impossible.

"That day I'd slotted myself in at the start and came out at the end feeling quite a different person, washed and dried and smelling much nicer and more prepared for life and marvellously nourished too. Normally I hardly ever open my eyes during the Mass, but that day, when I did so, I saw only the back of a beautifully embroidered chasuble, with its sprays of silken flowers and not really anyone, any person, there at all, certainly not Edward. Everything was melted into the holy background of the altar and reredos. Well, perhaps I don't mean melted so much as blended, everything had blended into the Holy Spirit."

"We have some beautiful chasubles at St Andrew's, haven't we?" said Jane. "Besides that cherry blossom one there's the very soft red one with the very dull warm gold trimming and a panel of roses and grapes down the back. Not overdone, quietly suggested, everything very subtle. It used to belong to Father Pearce. And the lovely brighter red one with lots of little red and gold flowers surrounded by little green leaves, that was Father Colin Stephenson's. They have histories which in some way add to their beauty as well as to the significance of the service. It's odd to think in these days, in many churches, many people have given up being interested in their priest's backs, and shortly all those lovely chasubles will be stored away in vestry cupboards waiting for whichever generation it will be that returns to the old ideas and comes to rescue them. There's sure to be a kind of revolution or homecoming one day. I do hope so. In the meantime, if we ever had to have a change a St Andrew's, and we had to have a priest who faced us I'd have to learn to keep my head down all the time like you do, instead of only some of the time."

"What we are being asked to admire and appreciate these days is so unsettling, all those services which are *different,* and the difference is said to be the admirable thing. I heard someone say not long ago about a special Mass that was being held. 'We wanted it to be *different.*' The show, the spectacle, the entertainment, it's more like audience participation, rather than the Spirit drawing our worship into the sacrament. I read about this a few months ago. It's in my Remembering Book. It's St Augustine, but used by somebody else. I forget by whom. Let's see."

My Remembering Book was handy, just by my chair. I got hold of it and opened it and quickly found the words I'd written:

" 'It's not for us to change the liturgy, the liturgy is given. If the liturgy doesn't fit us now, it's for us to grow into it. It's not that we should be making something of the liturgy, but rather that it should be making something of us, moulding us.' "

And then I'd quoted directly from what I'd been reading:

"'The liturgy faithfully celebrated should be a long-term course in heart expansion. It is the Holy Spirit who prays in us, who prays in the liturgy, who is the soul of the liturgy, the life in it.'

"That's what I've just said about Edward's gift of disappearing and letting the Holy Spirit take over. It goes on,

"'It's a very shallow idea to think too much of the joys of fellowship, or even of our own spiritual refreshment. This isn't the purpose of the Mass. We are there to hear God being offered to God on the altar of God and that is the most infintely satisfying thing that could ever be.'"

"That's really very good, and quite a change from what's said mostly these days."

It was more than time for Jane to go home, even though Jack was away on his travels, so we got up and went out to her car.

TRINITY:
OLVA COMES TO ARDNESS

August went rushing past, September had already come. I found, nowadays, every day went rushing past, and the weeks and the months too, even the years. After all, I thought, it's natural it should be so at my age. If I were two days old, a day would be half my whole life; if I were a year old a day would be 1/365th of my life; if I were ten years old now it would be 1/3650th of my life. Now I'm just seventy and a bit, but we'll say seventy, a day is - (where's my calculator? Let's see, 365 x70 = 25,550) - 1/25,550th of my life. No wonder each day whizzes past so fast.

At Westlake I used to think of August as a non-month, a time when people took their boats down to the Straits for the regatta or went away to other more distant places. Our sandy soil always dried out till the ground seemed like a desert, the garden drooped and faded, the veges didn't live up to their promise after all our work, and there was always a water shortage so we couldn't use the hosepipe. It was lovely on the sandhills though, I remember the hot dry dusty atmosphere which suited the time of year. The melilot was over, but the evening primroses were in flower and dwarf mallows straggled across the sandy paths. There were very few birds about yet, though happily swallows and house martins and swifts, those lovely summertime birds, were still dashing around the sky, making the most of the last of the summertime insects. The few remaining garden birds were silent, the others had left us for a gypsy life in the fields. Even the shore was deserted except for noisy parties of blackheaded gulls returned from their breeding places. Wherever I happen to be, these days, their screaming calls remind me always of August at Westlake. In September things began to come to life again, people returned from their holidays and the waders came back and fed again on the wet sand left by the ebbing tide.

It's different here, around Strathlyon. August never seems dead in the Highlands. There's always the heather flowering on the hills. That's much more beautiful, excitingly so, than I'd ever expected. It's not at all a vulgar gaudy purple, but a soft colour which blends with the surrounding greens and blues.

What had been happening here at Ardness? It had for once been a fine summer in Strathlyon, lots of warm and sunny days. And contrary to expectations, Nicholas and I hadn't been too busy, we'd several times been away with the caravan.

John and family had been to stay, and that was all a great success. They'd enjoyed their sailing. They found it a good idea to hire a boat from the boat centre across the loch, and they'd had quite a few days with enough but not too much wind. Philip and his family had gone camping in France, but they'd be coming north for the half-term week in October.

I was wondering, too, how Edward was enjoying his holiday in Mexico. By this time I could imagine him on his way home via the States and he might be even now with his friends in Dallas of all places, where, surprisingly, there really are some normal people living. I can imagine, or perhaps, really, I can't imagine, all the animated conversations that would be taking place. He'd soon be home, he wouldn't be sorry and nor would we. He's like Nicholas and myself in that way, he loves to get back home again to his own things and to his friends. Going away is fun, but coming home is even better, especially to here. Ardness is such a super place to live.

Christopher was going away during the next month, September, to see his family. And there's a girl he's going to see too. Is it *a* girl friend or *his* girl friend? I don't know what to wish, except that I wish the best for him with lots of happiness.

A week or so after this, one evening when Nicholas was out at a Scout leaders' meeting, I was enjoying myself, reading about Hooker and Andrewes and Charles Wesley and others in a book by Canon Alchin, a book on some forgotten strands of the Anglican Tradition. Then just as my mind was far away the telephone rang.

"Oh bother," I said, "or perhaps it's Oh good! We'll see." It was Angela, my sister from Olva. She and Peter were proposing to pay us a visit, for two nights, in the middle of the following week. They'd decided, at last, to make the effort to uproot themselves and come over to Ardness. It was not possible with the Landrover for them to make the double journey in one day, but with three days away we, two sisters, would have one whole day together.

"How lovely, how marvellous it will be to have you. How good of you to come so far. Nicholas will be thrilled too. All news can wait till we meet." I was already feeling excited at the prospect of the great visitation.

Later Nicholas returned and I called to him while he was still in the hall. "Guess who rang. No, you never will, not who nor why. It was Angela. She and Peter are coming to stay. Two nights. Next week. Can you believe it? After all this time. Leaving their fastness. And all to come to see us. I hope it will be fine for three whole days. Everything must go well. I must plan some good food for them, but simple, easy. I suppose the dogs can sleep in the kitchen, or in the Landrover. Where did they sleep last time? But that was so long ago, perhaps it was even different dogs in those days."

On the day of the visitors' arrival I was ready for them in good time and anxiously awaiting the moment the Landrover should appear. The weather was beautiful. All day an early September golden calm hovered over the loch and over the distant mountains away to the west. I wasn't *really* anxious. I remembered Angela was always an easy person to have in the house. She would be sure to say she loved the view, her bed was comfy, she'd slept well, she didn't mind when she had a bath, probably wouldn't bother with one, she enjoyed her food, was always hungry for meals. She would talk effortlessly and amusingly about life on Olva, her past life, our joint past family, her present family. Peter, on the other hand, often made me a little nervous, he might, I often felt, have preferred a different kind of meal, his bed might not have seemed so comfy as he said it was, when he had a bath in the evening, I wondered whether he might rather have had one in the morning.

I don't really need to worry about Peter. His conversations are so amusing and good tempered. It would be fun if we could meet more often. But Nicholas wouldn't really enjoy staying on Olva for any length of time and certainly not to live there, or even anywhere on the West Coast. I'm adaptable, like Angela too. We can easily learn to love what our husbands love. Learning good points about places is only a knack, a way of looking at things. Most women are particularly good at adapting themselves, making anywhere into a comfy home. It must be something to do with survival. A comfy home breeds happy families, and they are the ones who survive best. Or do they? Yes, of course. If children can see love in their home working for general happiness, for them and their parents, they're more likely to stick to God and do well in their lives.

The evening passed very successfully. Thank goodness. The meal was much appreciated and everyone was in good form. The conversation was relatively sparkling. Peter's streak of humour made Angela and myself feel our words were shining rather more brightly than usual. We all spent a good night, including the dogs in the Landrover, and next morning Angela and I went off early into Strathlyon to do a quick bit of shopping. We left Nicholas and Peter to take the dogs a walk over the hill and then do some jobs in the garden.

After I'd guided Angela into the most hopeful shops, and several sensible but attractive purchases had been made for an island winter, I asked her if she'd like to have just a quick look into St Andrew's to see the changes and improvements made since her last visit. We'd left the car behind the church, so going there wasn't out of our way. We went inside, and I lit a candle and said a prayer much more hurriedly than usual as, of course, my mind was on my sister. I'd hoped she would be appreciative rather than non-committal; it was unlikely she would be scathing, but in fact, she was enthusiastic about everything. It was so many years since her last visit, that all she saw seemed new and fresh, even the light through the windows struck her, and the carvings and gilding on the reredos and the altar rails, the eagle lectern, the simple stone font with its carved lid, the diversity of kneelers in many colours. She admired the changes and especially the new figure of St Andrew in fibreglass, she liked his sightly modern style.

"He was meant to be timeless," I agreed. "Certainly we'd not wanted anything modern, but I agree with you, he is attractive. He commands attention. It was sad when the old one got broken."

We also inspected the new lighting and carpet in the Lady Chapel and its newly painted white walls. Then we returned laden to Ardness.

After a quick snackish lunch we all got into the Landrover with the dogs. Nicholas directed Peter and he drove us to Glen Clare, a little valley not far away. There, in a convenient spot, we left the car and walked up a track through the birch woods towards the loch. The leaves and bracken were hardly yet beginning to turn, but what gold there was shone in the sunshine. The heather was fading now on the hills, but the fly agarics under the trees were becoming red, waiting for their little gnomes to come and sit on them. Robins were singing again with much sweetness.

Angela and I walked behind the two men, who as men can do, strode on ahead regardless with the dogs leaping around as little energetically as spaniels might. We began reminiscing, talking and looking about us, happy to be together, enjoying ourselves quietly. After a bit we were discussing the differences of opinion between the church and wonderful new medical discoveries.

"It does seem as though," I was saying, "the church often discourages the use of these helpful ideas. We pray in our intercessions for doctors and nurses and their work with the sick, and this must include those who do research. But when wonderfully helpful things are discovered the church is often against their use."

"I sometimes think," Angela said, "about women and the womb. As you say there are so many helpful things that can be done for us, but there seems to be a general feeling around that, if we no longer have our wombs, we are hardly any more to be described as women. It's odd."

"I agree. I'm delighted not to have *my* womb any longer. I don't feel any different now as a person from how I felt before, except that I'm always well and there's no more trouble. If I do feel I'm any less a woman, it would be because I'm growing aged, which would happen anyway. But clergymen seem doubtful. Look at all those letters we've been having lately in Newspot about the moral view. Of course, I forgot, you're spared Newspot, lucky you."

"It's men. They don't have to cope so they don't look for hopeful changes. They imagine women to be helpless and dependent creatures but at the same time expect them to be able and willing to do lots of boring chores in the house."

"I don't think it should matter in the long run if some women were unable to have babies. That used to be more the case than it is nowadays. Though it must be sad for those who really long for one of their own. There are too many babies anyway in this country, in the world, too many people altogether and there is such a marvellous choice of jobs for women to do these days."

"It still happens too that mothers may have more children than they feel able to look after properly and yet feel abortion isn't for them."

"Having your baby adopted too must be a very difficult decision to make. A very young baby will still seem really part of yourself. It's all so sad. And not really sorted out yet. I feel sorry for some people."

"It *is* so sad for some. We've both been lucky - fortunate - with our own families. More or less just what we wanted and hoped for.

Nicholas and Peter were well away in front by now, so we sat down on a lichen-covered rock to await their return. We could see Loch Clare at the end of the glen shining in the afternoon sunlight.

After not so long they and the dogs returned and we all made our way back to the Landrover. Peter thought they'd seen a young osprey fishing in the loch. Nicholas was less sure. It had been away on the far side and, sadly, against the light.

"I do hope it was," I said. 'I wish I'd been there."

"You could have been," said Nicholas. "You didn't need to talk so much, nor sit on your rock."

"It was very enjoyable, what we did. We don't really mind missing a question mark osprey, or even a truly one."

On the way home, Peter took us out for an evening meal at a country hotel, which was very pleasant and much appreciated. Their visit was acclaimed a great success and there was talk of a repeat in two or three years time.

Next morning, the Landrover and its occupants received a cheerful send-off and I could return to my much loved daily routine, very grateful that all had gone so well.

TRINITY: ALL ANGELS

A day or two after the feast of St Michael and All Angels, that's to say, round about the end of September, I was contemplating the fact that I wasn't at all well in with the idea of angels. I realized they'd never played a great part in my life. I'd always known about them and, of course, I recognised them when I saw them decoratively depicted in great old master paintings, with beautiful wings, bandeaux of flowers around their heads and lovely flowing robes in various rich colours. But I'd never thought of them as being actively helpful spirits who could be with me through all the difficulties of every day, that they could influence and help my life of prayer or meditation, my trying to live with God and in his ways with the world.

I was quite a bit ashamed of this neglect, for I was sure that angels could help us all, they could use their spirit presence all around us. I remembered Edward's being good with angels. He often mentioned their being present to help and encourage us, to save us from hurting ourselves more than if they had not been near. I remembered too, when I'd ever accidentally made a great error with consequent repercussions, and had told Edward, he would say, 'But you should have thought of all the angels who were all around you, helping and supporting you.'

I felt there was a gap in my mind and I ought to fill it. Here was some great help I wasn't taking advantage of. That afternoon the weather was mouldy, too wet and stormy to go out into the garden. I could spend some time trying to find out, to teach myself a bit about angels. I would enjoy that, even if I didn't get very far.

So with my Bible, Concordance, loose-leaf pad and writing implement, I settled down in my comfy chair.

I began with Abraham and read about the three men who come to visit him with a message for Sarah that she will have a son. Abraham at once recognises these men as angels and so he runs to meet them from the tent door and bows himself toward the ground. He tells Sarah to make some cakes and he himself kills a calf for them to eat with butter and milk. Then I read about the angel who, just as Abraham is about to sacrifice Isaac, his only son, calls to him out of heaven, 'Lay not thy hand upon the lad'. Abraham turns to the angel and immediately sees a ram stuck in a nearby thicket which he brings out and sacrifices instead.

Next, I read about Moses finding a bush on fire. He has gone by the backside of the desert with his father-in-law's flock of sheep, and then, on Mount Horeb, he discovers this phenomenon; the burning bush, although on fire, is not burning away. There's an angel of the Lord in the flame who calls to him out of the midst of the bush that he, Abraham, will deliver his people from the Egyptians and lead them to a land flowing with milk and honey.

There's the story of Jacob and his ladder with angels ascending and descending, and, in the story of Lot, it's angels who come and warn him to leave his home in Sodom to avoid the brimstone and fire which will soon fall on the town. 'Escape for thy life', the angels say. 'Look not behind thee.' But, as we all know, Lot's wife did look back and she at once became a pillar of salt.

Then I came to my favourite angel story, Balaam and his donkey. Against God's wishes Balaam rides out on his donkey with Balak, a prince of Moab. An angel of the Lord appears to the donkey but not to Balaam, who cannot understand why the donkey is behaving so oddly. First, it turns aside into a field, then it crushes Balaam's foot against a wall, then it falls down under Balaam, who, mystified at the beast's behaviour, smites it with its staff.

The Lord then opens the donkey's mouth. 'Am I not thine ass? Was I ever wont to do this kind of thing to thee?' And Balaam answers 'Nay' . And at last the Lord opens the eyes of Balaam and he sees the angel with his drawn sword in his hand, and, of course, he bows down his head and falls flat on his face.

Then I found the story of three heroes, Shadrach, Mesach and Abednego in the burning fiery furnace and with them is a fourth person who is in the guise of an angel and who delivers them from harm, the three who have trusted in Israel's God rather than in the golden image.

Further on I read about Daniel who was cast into the den of lions. King Darius goes next morning to look in the den anxious to see what has happened. But he finds God has sent his angel to shut the lions' mouths and Daniel is unhurt.

After a bit, I came to the New Testament. The archangel Gabriel comes to Zacharias, a priest of the Temple, to tell him that his aged wife will bear a son who's to be called John. Zacharias expresses his doubt and Gabriel who isn't used to his words being questioned is annoyed and causes Zacharais to become dumb until the day of his son's circumcision. On that day there is a query among the family about a name for the child, for John is not a family name. Zachariah has to ask for a writing table so he can write, 'His name is John.' And they marvel. And his mouth is opened immediately and his tongue loosed, and he speaks, and praises God. This baby will grow up to be known to us as John the Baptist.

Again, as we know, the archangel Gabriel comes, this time to Mary, when the time is ready for Jesus to be conceived in her womb.

'Hail, thou that art highly favoured, the Lord is with thee; blessed art thou among women. . .Fear not, Mary for thou hast found favour with God. And, behold thou shalt conceive in thy womb, and bring forth a son, and shalt call his name Jesus'.

Nine months later, in the deep wintertime, some shepherds are abiding in a field near Bethlehem, keeping watch over their flocks by night, and the angel of the Lord comes upon them, and the glory of the Lord shines around them; and they are sore afraid. The angel tells them not to fear, for this day a saviour is born and they shall go into the city and find a babe wrapped in swaddling clothes lying in a manger.

Another time Paul is on board ship, as a prisoner being taken to Rome, and a great storm rages, the ship is about to be wrecked on the island of Malta, but an angel of God comes to tell him no one will lose his life. Although the ship is lost, broken up on a reef, all swim or are washed ashore safely. When they have scrambled onto the land Paul lights a fire probably, I expect, to help dry their wet clothes, and he is bitten by a viper coming out of the heat of the fire. He suffers no pain, is not ill, and the natives, the Maltese, who expect him immediately to drop down dead, seem disappointed that he survives unharmed.

I also noticed that, when God needs to say something important about future times, there are often many angels, or the multitude of God's heavenly host, all together in the sky.

'and immediately after the tribulation of those days shall the sun be darkened, and the moon shall not give her light, and the stars shall fall from heaven and the powers of the heavens shall be shaken: and all the tribes of the earth shall see the Son of Man coming in the clouds of heaven with power and great glory. And he shall send his angels with a great sound of a trumpet and they shall gather together his elect from the four the winds, from one end of heaven to the other.'

There are more angels in the book of Revelation including the archangel Michael, he whose Day it was that started me on this search.

'And there was war in heaven; Michael and his angels fought against the dragon; and the dragon fought and his angels. And prevailed not; neither was their place found any more in heaven. And the great dragon was cast out, that old serpent, called the Devil, and Satan which deceiveth the whole world: he was cast out into the earth, and his angels were cast out with him.'

St Michael has used his sword to good purpose against the dragon. I realized this was what Jung had written about, what I'd dreamed about, what I was reading about in the summer.

Christ, after his resurrection, cast out the Devil from heaven, but he, the Devil, and his angels are still around on earth, infiltrating into everything, even into Christ's church, as we can see when we look around us.

Then I saw it was not quite like that. I remembered Edward's words, last Easter, on Good Friday, on the subject of the sixth Word from the Cross. *It is finished.* With Christ's death on the cross the battle against evil was won. The Devil is defeated, he said. He is no longer in heaven, the war against him was won when Christ died on the cross.

Why doesn't this seem so, I wondered. Why are we still struggling against evil? Why do we still need God working in us, helping us in our fight against evil as we strive to spread his kingdom? Edward has told us it's because we are still clearing up after the battle that was won when Christ died. When that is done Satan and his army of fallen angels will have been totally destroyed. At last God's kingdom will have come on earth as it is in heaven.

I was happy, I'd enjoyed my afternoon's occupation. It had been very good fun, and, at the same time, very good for me. Of course, I sighed, I expect I'll forget about angels many times again, but not so often as before, I hope. There's lots more marvellous words and descriptions in many other stories than I've told you here. Make a point of reading it all for yourselves, it's worth it.

227

TRINITY: BETTY HAS A COLD

One evening in early October I'd gone to bed feeling perfectly well. Quite myself. When I awoke in the morning there was a scratchy feeling in one side of my throat. Oh, dash, oh, bother, I said to myself, I don't want to have a cold just now when there's so much happening. I'll put some aspirins in my early tea, that often sends this kind of scratchiness away.

But they didn't. Neither did some more in my breakfast coffee. And all during the morning the pain in my throat increased. Sherry at lunch-time helped a little, lessening the pain and cheering me up, but I didn't want to take to drink, even sherry. That would *not* be a good idea.

Actively doing things and concentrating hard on thinking, these two activities helped a little, but there was always a battle going on between the pain and the attention needed for the job I was trying to do, whatever it was. Each took away from the other, the pain from the attention and the attention from the pain, so while I worked, as much as the pain was less noticeable, the job was less well done.

Then I remembered suddenly those sucky things. Where were they? I thought I'd better try one. And so I did. The first one did seem to soothe my throat somewhat, but the taste left in my mouth when the sucky sweet was finished was awful. I sucked another one and the taste got worse.

By next morning I felt I'd a golf ball situated somewhere between the back of my nose and the back of my neck and it was trying to swell up into a tennis ball. But I got up, there was no point my staying in bed, there'd be nothing of sufficient interest there to distract me from the pain. Anyway, I knew the time would go past more quickly if I kept as busy as possible.

By tea time that day there was not much change so far as my head was concerned, but in myself I began to feel terribly droopy, as if I ought to be lying down flat. I knew I shouldn't take any notice. I didn't feel *ill*. I wasn't ill. I wasn't threatened in myself, my life still felt strong in me, though I was worried by the awful pain in my head and now by this feebleness. Why was I so bad at coping with pain? And this wanting to lie down? As if my strength were going to run out.

It was only my bodily strength failing me, my brain was quite clear. It was strange, I wasn't really like myself. Although my brain was clear, I couldn't pray. I felt cut off from God. I didn't seem able to ask him to help. My mind seemed rigid, or perhaps brittle. I could have added up figures or even explained about the Trinity, or about Baptism, but I couldn't have said: 'O Lamb of God, that takest away the sins of the world, have mercy upon me,' and have meant it in my heart.

And then I remembered. But of course. I'd been like this before. It was quite a long time before, and I'd forgotten, it had gone out of my head. I used to feel like this, especially, when I was still at the very beginning of learning about God, about his love for me, before joy came. It was my kind of desert. It wasn't like the grand desert as described by the holy contemplatives, it was just a small variety, but not very pleasant all the same. I'd been so cheerful and busy lately with daily work, I'd been enjoying each day and at the same time making plans for the next few months, deserts had quite gone out of my mind. I'd been too busy for dry spaces to form amongst the green growth of my jobs. But I was glad I'd remembered about deserts. If this was my desert returned, I knew what to do to make myself feel less awful.

I'd not yet learned to prefer the desert to ordinary life as Thomas Merton suggests we shall when we've grown near enough to God. But it wasn't Merton who helped me at this point so much as St John of the Cross. In the book I've described before I'd read another helpful idea of his. He showed me how I might be able to transform my desert, and from his words I was able to write this prayer:

'Dear Lord, help me.
My heart and soul are dried up.
Help me to see this dryness as really a great happiness.
Thou art freeing me from myself.
Taking the work from my hands.
Take my hand and guide me in the darkness as if I were blind.
To an end which I know not,
And by a way which I could never hope to travel
With the aid of my own eyes and feet
Howsoever good I might be as a walker.
Help me to remember thou art in my sadness,

Thou art leading me along a way I could never find for myself,
Leading me to the Spirit.'

After I'd said this prayer slowly and rather hesitantly and more than once, I felt comforted, reassured in my mind and heart. The evening passed more happily than I had expected. Nicholas and I had a bit of fun watching a comedy series on the box which had been recommended by Philip. It was quite funny, we decided, not too silly or annoying, which was a change. All the same, I wished there hadn't been a laughing audience. I know when I want to laugh, I don't need to hear others laughing to jog my reaction. I don't want to be told when to laugh.

I went to bed early. But before that I inhaled, putting some dried rosemary, thyme and sage into a bowl, adding boiling water and then sitting with my head and the bowl under a towel. This is always good for the tubes in one's head and chest, it seems to relax some of the painful tightness, and as a bonus the face has a good cleansing in the steam which opens the pores. After that, I put some aspirins in a hot-watery mixture of honey and lemon juice. Whisky's meant to be good, I know, but its taste is so horrible. I don't really enjoy honey or lemon either but fortunately on this occasion my affliction had dulled my taste. Even whisky might have been tolerable that night. Perhaps, I thought, I should try it the next evening. Then I took my drink to bed with me.

I didn't like having to fuss over myself like this, but I supposed it was worth it. It's all right for husbands, they get their inhaling basin and whisky drink brought to them in bed and they can moan and groan about themselves and it doesn't seem to do them any harm. I mean, if I moaned like Nicholas does when he's got a cold, I'd make myself feel much worse. And it's simpler to get my own bowl of inhaling stuff and the hot drink rather than have to explain to Nicholas what I need. Though if I were actually really *ill*, he would do all kinds of wonderful things for me. He asked me, this time, if he could do anything, but it wasn't necessary. I was very touched at his asking, but I could still look after myself. I wasn't really ill. I'd not got a high temperature, or flu. Flu's terrible, it affects the whole mind, almost the soul. When I'd ever had real flu I felt I might shortly die, and, what's more, didn't really care, one way or the other. Now, I hadn't got flu and I felt quite reasonable. I was still able to think. And I felt not at all like dying. At that moment I was just limp in body and I was in pain. It's possible to be in awful pain and yet not be ill, ill in the sense of not being oneself. That's the trouble often. One is so much oneself the pain stays painful. If the nervous system were depressed the pain would be somewhat dimmed also.

When I'd finished my drink, I lay down and put my head under the duvet. The warm air from inside the bed helped to keep my tubes clear, and I was able to breath more easily. Nicholas came to bed soon, he turned out the light and was soon asleep.

Then I began to say my prayers. I tried to pray the pain might be taken away from me, but I could find no words to help, nor were my feelings any good; nor could I make a prayer without words as I sometimes can. There seemed to be obstacles placed in the way of every kind of prayer I tried. I lay there in very real suffering. At least that's how I remember it.

Though the suffering wasn't a grand kind like some people have. It would be sure not to last beyond a few days. Next week I'd be fine again. It wasn't a dramatic kind of suffering either, everybody gets beastly colds, or nearly everyone. This kind of affliction is certainly not glamorous. My nose and all round it was red, my eyes looked peculiar, my voice sounded very strange. And it's not good for me to be miserable, it doesn't suit me. It's not a very moral thing to be miserable either; being so can affect others and make them feel awful and miserable too, or cross, which is worse.

I lay quietly for a minute or two, then in that wonderful way these things happen, an idea was born in my mind. Another way of looking at things might be this, I thought: if God is not going to take my pain away, instead of my praying, "Please dear God, take my pain away.' perhaps I should say, 'Dear God, I offer you my pain. I don't want it. Please will you accept it?"

So I prayed: "Dear God, accept my pain, please."

It was marvellous. At once I felt changed. I was no longer forcing myself to pray, the words were coming into my mind as of their own accord.

"Accept my pain in the same way as you accept my love." I went on praying. "Accept my love and with it my pain."

Then I saw. I knew, and I understood: love and pain are very closely connected. When I put my pain at the side of my love and offered them both to God in the same way as I had on other nights offered my love only, my pain was changed. It hadn't gone away, there wasn't really any less pain, but it was transformed. All the threatening and unbearable part of it was taken away, and I was left with a different, less menacing pain. The pain had become something that seemed to join me to God as love did, rather that separating me from him as it had up till that moment.

Then I remembered the presence of angels around me and the collect from Compline.

'Visit, we beseech thee, O Lord, this habitation; and drive far from it all the snares of the enemy. Let thy holy angels dwell herein to preserve us in peace, and may thy blessing be upon us evermore.'

Just before I fell asleep I had a glimpse of something else, or another truth, a truth which I'd read about only, not one I'd ever experienced, something I thought might happen to others but probably never to myself. This night God came so much into my pain, I thought I might be able to begin to believe it would be possible to welcome pain because it brought God closer. Would this ever be possible for me? I wondered. I was almost asleep, but the idea was strong enough in my mind for it to leave its memory clearly with me through the night and into the next morning.

When I awoke, after some peaceful hours of sleep, I really was in much less pain. There was a thought of recovery on the horizon of my mind. I was still very dreamy and much wrapped up with the ideas of the night before, but the approaching morning definitely looked brighter in my expectancy than had those of the last two days.

I'd read about other people discovering this, about pain and love, but I'd never thought I would ever discover it for myself. What a marvellous difference it makes to life to know our prayers are truly so much part of the great Prayer which goes on all the time, to know these illuminations can come from God to speak to us, and change us, and make us all the more part of himself.

Now I thought, I understand why my prayer for my pain to be taken away wasn't answered in the first place. and why the aspirins and the sucky sweets did me no good. It was that a new lesson was being prepared for me. It was necessary for the pain in my head to be bad and persistent enough for me to stop resisting it and to hear this new message about pain and love.

I got up but didn't get dressed before breakfast.

"I think," I said to Nicholas, 'what I need most is a lovely bath, without hurrying. I'll have one after breakfast. Then this peculiar lethargy of mine can enjoy itself while I'm relaxing and at the same time the warm steamy air will be helping my nose."

My bath was indeed a great success. Afterwards I felt so much better, so much more my usual self, really relaxed in my body. The hot damp air had penetrated the stuffy parts of my head just as much as any inhaling had but with much less trouble and more naturally, though I did go on inhaling, the effect of the herbs was so good in spite of the bother.

I told Nicholas how beneficial my bath had been.

"I'll have one every morning now instead of a shower, until I'm recovered."

"That's good," he said. "I'm very pleased that for once you're going to relax a bit. It's about time you didn't go pressing on through the day so fast, it's time you stopped trying to achieve so much. You need to think of enjoying life a little more; even if you get behind in some things, you should learn to think about having a little pointless moderate enjoyment."

Recovery came slowly but surely over the next week or month or so. The leisurely morning bath was very enjoyable and it became a permanent part of my daily time-table, so far as possible.

"It's good," I remember saying to myself, "for I can meditate and brood about things and plan for the day while I lie in the lovely warm water with no rush. I must have been iller than I thought as I seem to be taking so long to recover "

And then to Nicholas I said, "It might, you know, be a good idea if I began to be my age. It might be very pleasantly advantageous to begin not to do so many things, those I don't really care much about. I've said this before but it can't have worked. You'd agree, Nicholas, wouldn't you, so long as you still get semi looked after, as at present?"

"I like that semi-looked after. It's about right."

"But you would hate me to be hovering over you all the time, and my not having lots of interests and occupations of my own, wouldn't you?"

233

"Yes, of course, dear." he said, rather unconvincingly.

"What I mean is, I'd like to go on doing all the enjoyable things and do less of those that are exhausting or tedious or both. Then I might have more time for reading and perhaps for writing. That would be fun. Perhaps for instance we could let part of the garden get a bit wilder."

"I can see signs of that happening already."

"Though a lot of that's because we've been living in this house long enough for the bushes and things to have joined up and we can't get in between them any more. I think that's good. There are mysterious places in the garden where no one goes. That's beautiful, that's just as it should be, a green wilderness full of the never visited unknown."

One day, as soon as I felt more myself, more or less normal, Edward brought me my Communion, for I'd missed a midweek Mass as well as the last two Sundays. He stayed to lunch. There didn't have to be any fuss made over his coming as he was counted as one of the family, as I've said.

"Edward's as good as a tonic for you," said Nicholas as he got out of the store cupboard a bottle of something else stimulating - and fizzy.

"That's true. I should soon recover completely if he came every day."

"You wouldn't be having this fizzy stuff every day though, you know that," Nicholas replied.

I certainly did cheer up as the meal progressed and I began to think of some of the funny things that had happened to me in the last few months or so. Something to make the others laugh.

"You know how we tease each other about which of us is the most practical, or the most logical, or the one whose head is best screwed on, and I have a job not to be bottom of the class every time. Well, it must have been last winter, for I was wearing gloves and they are part of the story. I was wandering through Sparks to pick up some odd items of food, and in my usual cheery way thinking about something totally different from the matter in hand; probably about what the company of heaven really looks like when they're there together with all the angels and archangels, with whom we laud and magnify God's glorious name, evermore praising him and saying ... when I suddenly found I'd only one glove. Oh, dear! Where was I last? And back I went, retracing my steps. There amongst the avocado pears, the rough crinkly brown ones, was my glove, totally camouflaged, patiently waiting for me to come and rescue it. One of my ancient, semi-efficient, thermal gloves, bought years ago, but still useful, and I expect by now irreplaceable. I'd said to myself accusingly, 'Neither Nicholas nor Edward would *ever* leave *his* glove in the avocado pears."

The men both laughed as they were expected to and looked at each other, affecting resignation. 'Poor thing,' they seemed to be saying. 'She will never grow up. We gave up hope long ago.'

"But all the same, Betty," said Edward kindly, "for whatever reason you allow your head to be in the clouds, you must learn to keep at least one foot on the ground. And concentrate on what you're doing.'

I felt much better after lunch because of the cheerful company around me and about a week or so later, but not till then, was back again to my usual cheery self.

And in my quieter moments I often though about all I had learned while I had been unwell.

TRINITY: MORE BOOKS

Autumn was very good and colourful that year. The sun shone most of the time and any rain there was fell mostly at night or when we were, anyway, tired from all we'd done during the sunshine hours. When Philip and Joyce and the two boys came up to stay for their half-term, our good luck continued. On two days we hired a mini-bus so we could all travel together to enjoy the scenery further afield, amongst the mountains or over on the West Coast. At night, Philip and Mike slept in our caravan with Lucy, who was very well behaved, while Joyce and Bob occupied the spare room. Everything ran smoothly, especially in the kitchen, for Joyce and, as I've described before, Philip were as practical and unfussy as Nicholas and I were ourselves. Philip did some good work helping in the garden, too, and the bleak unhomely strip light over the kitchen table where we had our meals was replaced with a three spot arrangement. A great improvement, I was very grateful to Philip for organising that.

When they'd left for the south again I mourned their departure, but I was also greatly relieved, for, it's always true, an increase in the number of inhabitants in the house by two hundred percent is a strain on the nervous system. Then, a few days later, when I was almost settled back again into normal life, I drove into Strathlyon to catch up on my shopping.

On my way into town I had to wait a minute or two, as usual, at the Drummond Street lights and my thoughts turned, also as usual, to the problem of love and its different manifestations. A long traffic-light wait is a good place for a short, but ongoing contemplation.

I decided one thing was clear to me, it was that our love for people works for us as an example of how we can love God. If we didn't love our own nearest and dearest we would have no idea at all about loving God, nor how to react to his love for us. This means too that it doesn't matter how much we love our friends and relations or people in general. It doesn't matter how much we've ever fallen in love with someone, even if we'd found ourselves absorbed in that person every hour of the day, for, when we do find we've grown into a totally absorbing love for God, we'll recognise it as having much in common with our earlier experience of loving a human being. And so, we'll understand our new feelings. And we'll see the differences too. For with God it will be a lasting love, and it will be much less fraught. Less fraught because God's love is sure and reliable. Even the best kind of love between humans can and probably will change. I don't mean that people are in general unreliable, but their love for each other is not sure and certain from the very beginning and on into the future in the same way as God's love for us is sure.

And in discovering how enjoyable it is to do things for our friends whom we love, we find an example of how we feel when we do things for God. And doing things for God must include loving those who aren't our friends, those for whom really we wouldn't normally have any feelings at all. It's marvellous how it's all worked out so we are helped to understand God's love.

At last the lights changed and I drove to the little parking place behind St Andrew's where I left the car. My first objective was the second-hand bookshop along the riverside. I'd not been there for ages as it's quite a step along from the shopping centre proper. There, in the shop, on the very crowded shelves where there's every kind of book, I found Austin Farrer's *Saving Belief.* It was on a handy shelf and clearly named, as if it were waiting for my arrival, to fall into my hands and be carried away. I then made a few visits to two or three necessary but lately avoided shops and after that I went into the Cathedral shop to look at their usually very good selection of books, the small paperback variety, before they closed for the winter. I walked back to St Andrew's where I went in to say a quick prayer, and then drove home.

Now I felt myself well equipped with reading matter for the next few weeks when the evenings would be getting darker and longer. And I could borrow other books from Edward or Christopher.

So that evening, at teatime, I began reading first of all this book of Austin Farrer's. I'd read one or two of his before and I knew I'd find him a pleasure to read, as good really as Dr Mascall though in a different way. In one chapter he's discussing the Trinity. He says the doctrine of the Trinity doesn't pretend to make God intelligible. It lays down certain requirements, such as: if God is to be God, the Godhead must be more perfectly One than any one of us humans is one individual. And also this Godhead must allow for more outgoing mutual love than can ever exist between any two of us. We don't know how these two opposing requirements are reconciled, we know only that they must be. When we consider the distinction of persons in the Godhead it's obviously a better doctrine of God that any other. This distinction of persons makes the highest sense.

Dr Farrer also comments on and explains a question about the Holy Spirit which had puzzled me for a long time. It was a question of words: The Holy Spirit is the Third Person of the Blessed Trinity. Why *Person*? The word means the same now as it did in the time when doctrinal definitions were being made. The word person, Dr. Farrer says, does not have to refer to a human being. It's misleading to think of the three Persons of the Godhead as a parable, as a story, about three characters. The revealed parable of the Godhead is a story about two characters, Father and Son, though the first of these is not a human father, but the First Person of all, and the Second Persons is not son to a man, but Son to his God. And the Father does not merely beget the Son, he also indwells in him by his Holy Spirit.

Why was the Holy Spirit called a Person? Dr Farrer says it was because the Romans could not hit on a better word. What they were trying to say is this:

'The Spirit is the divine life, is God, God the self-bestowing or indwelling. The first other whom he indwelt was the eternal Son, himself also God. The Holy Ghost is God, yet the Trinity is not (in human terms) a society of three, but of two, inspiring and inspired.'

Now I could understand all this much more clearly than I ever had before, and I felt I needn't any longer be afraid I might be misinterpreting the theology involved. The divine inspiration, the Spirit, enters into our souls.

'If a man has no sense of what it is to be inspired, even in his prayer, we shall talk to him in vain about the Holy Ghost. Association with Christ and inspiration belong together, the impact of Christ opening us to the Spirit of God, and the Spirit of God inspiring our response to Christ.'

I was enjoying my new book very much. Several points I'd not understood before were now clearer in my mind. It was all very cheering.

Another of the books I'd bought, in the Cathedral shop this time, was *The Name of Jesus* by Bishop Kallistos Ware and after I'd finished Dr Farrer's book I began on that. It was about the Jesus prayer, the Name of Jesus. In it, I noted, we need to learn how to be silent in prayer, we need to learn how to let prayer speak to us. We should listen to the voice of prayer in our own heart and then we'll understand it's not our own voice we're hearing but the voice of Another. We need also learn to stand before God with the mind in the heart, (as Edward has told us) and to go on standing before him unceasingly day and night until the end of our life.

The author explains about the Jesus Prayer: *Lord Jesus Christ, Son of God have mercy on me, a sinner.* This, or one of its variations, can be said at any time, slowly or fast, concentrating hard or letting it be as a background to life. There are several variations for us to choose from: 'Lord Jesus Christ have mercy on me' or any other even shorter version down to 'Jesus' on its own.

'The Name of the Son of God' writes Bishop Kallistos. 'is great and boundless and upholds the entire universe.' There is power in any name, but the name of Jesus is incomparably powerful. 'We make a name come alive by mentioning it. Speaking a name immediately calls forth the soul whose name it is, and so, when we repeat the name of Jesus, the power and the glory of God are present and active in us. The Invocation of the Name has a sacramental character, it is a sign of Christ's invisible presence and action.'

Then I recalled that once, when I'd mentioned to Edward that my prayers had no power in them, and I regretted this, he'd promptly put my mind at rest. 'It's not ourselves who can have any power, it's God. We need only ask God in our own simple language and he will hear us. It's God who created all things and all people and who goes on creating us continually all our lives. We can't make ourselves to have serious hearts with which to pray deeply, we must leave this for the power of God.'

The third book I'd bought, the second from the Cathedral shop, was about George Herbert, priest as well as poet. It includes 'The Collar', 'Love', 'Aaron' and 'The Flower'.

I've been keen on George Herbert ever since I first got to know his hymns, or rather, since I first realized which of the hymns we sang

in church were his. I loved them for their simple and clear words,
which bring out their meaning easily. I loved,

> 'And the cream of all my heart
> I will bring thee.'

> 'Seven whole days, not one in seven
> I will praise thee.'

> 'And what I do in anything, to do it as for thee.'

The first poem in the book is 'The Collar'. Here Herbert describes his
need to rebel against the discipline of God. This discipline is the yoke
or collar against which Herbert revolts. He addresses God in strong
direct language, longing to escape:

> 'I struck the board, and cry'd. No more.
> I will abroad.'

This yoke has up to then brought much dissatisfaction into his life.
But at the end of the poem he is glad indeed to hear God's voice.

> 'But as I rav'd and grew more fierce and wilde
> At every word
> Me thoughts I heard one calling, *Child!*
> And I reply'd, *My Lord.*

The second poem in the book is 'Love'. Everyone who knows the
works of Herbert at all will know this one. At first Herbert resists
God's love:

> 'Love bade me welcome; yet my soul drew back,
> Guiltie of dust and sinne'...

> 'I the unkinde, ungrateful? Ah my deare,
> I cannot look on thee
> Love took my hand, and smiling did reply,
> Who made the eyes but I?'

> '...And know you not, sayes Love, who bore the blame?'

Christ has taken the blame for our sins, so how can we refuse to sit at his table? We have to overcome our hesitation quickly and we read, with gratitude:

'You must sit down, sayes Love, And taste my meat:
So I did sit and eat.'

Of course you must read through the whole poem yourself. It's quite short.

Canon Mason ends his discussion on this poem with the words:

'Love bids us welcome. God, who has made us without our aid and intends to reward us beyond all our deserving, bids us welcome. And when our sad humility protests that he cannot go so far and we will not be honoured in this fashion, then he deals firmly with us. Quick-eyed Love, observing, anticipating, taking us by the hand, smiling tenderly and ironically, tells us not to be silly.'

The third poem is entitled 'Aaron', a priest of the time of Moses. My reaction, when I'd read it through the first time, was that I never would really understand it. Canon Mason calls it

'a version, a highly coloured version perhaps, of the Anglican Ordinal. The ministry is appointed for the salvation of mankind, to communicate the knowledge of God in Christ, that vital truth, that fellowship in holy things which will secure their eternal salvation.'

As bishops say (or used to say) to our future priests in the ordination service, regarding the flock whom the new priest will shepherd:

'Have always therefore printed upon your remembrance how great a treasure is committed to your charge. For they are the sheep of Christ.'

I knew these words were in the old Prayer Book, in the Ordinal. I wondered, though, if they were still in the new Ordinal? No, they were not. How sad, another tragedy.

Every verse of this poem 'Aaron' has the same rhyme at the end of the corresponding line in the other verses which gives the whole poem a marvellous effect of wholeness and completeness. I was glad I'd persevered. It was marvellous how the meaning, at first hidden from me, gradually revealed itself.

241

'Christ is my only head,
My alone only heart and breast,
My onely musick, striking me ev'n dead.
That to the old man I may rest
And be in him new drest.'

I was very pleased that the fourth poem, 'The Flower', was included in this book. It's about Herbert's shrivel'd heart and so, as I was familiar with such things, I understood much of it at the first reading. I'd been thinking of my own heart as a shrivelled old potato, and here was George Herbert with his shrivel'd root as a simile for his heart. I wasn't alone.

'Who would have thought my shrivel'd heart
Could have recover'd greennesse?'

And yet in springtime, it did recover.

Herbert's heart recovered and so did mine. I could see, though, his shrivel'd root was not a potato, but rather more the root of a herbaceous border plant, one which retreated underground in autumn and shot up again in the spring.

(Potatoes were perhaps not yet, in Herbert's time, grown in Britain).

'It was gone
Quite underground; as flowers depart
To see their mother-root when they are blown;
Where they together
All the hard weather,
Dead to the world, keep house unknown.'

And

'O that I once past changing were.
Fast in thy Paradise where no flower can wither!
Many a spring I shoot up fair,
Offring at heav'n, growing and groning thither:
Nor doth my flower
Want a spring-showre,
My sinnes and I joining together.'

242

I would have loved to be past changing myself, but Herbert made me realise this change of feelings from gloom to cheerfulness is ourselves crucified in Christ and rising again in him. In life we are growing and changing continuously. Changeless*ness* can come only after our death and resurrection, with our coming into God's Paradise, his garden.

'These are they wonders, Lord of love,
To make us see we are but flowers that glide:
Which when we once can finde and prove,
Thou has a garden for us where to bide.'

For me, this was the best poem of the four. It opened my eyes to completely new truths which set my mind on a better course than it had ever been on before.

A week or two after I'd finished this last book, Edward lent me *The Glass of Vision,* another of Austin Farrer's books. So one day, soon afterwards, I was sitting in my chair after lunch reading it, quietly taking in all that came to me from the printed page, when suddenly, I came across this wonderful paragraph:

'Science cannot help us to consider the voluntary passion of Christ, its intensity and elevation of being in its divinity. We need to keep unblocked the road by which a serious and realistic wonder advances through the contemplation of Christ's manhood into the adoration of his deity, that it may lay hold upon the Eternal Son, who, hanging on the Cross, is enthroned in Heaven; who, lying in the sepulchre, lies in the bosom of the Father and standing in the upper room, breathes forth from the heart of all being the Paraclete, the Holy Ghost.'

As you can imagine, I needed to read those words over and over again, before I could understand their deep meaning and then, after I'd begun to see more, I found I needed to read like a thirsty person needing to drink glass after glass of pure delicious water. They were not easy words expressing a simple idea, nor were they joined to each other in a straightforward way. I had to to take them slowly, inwardly digest them, before I could benefit from them.

Although the complex phrasing of the paragraph had seemed at first, to hide its meaning from me, it was just this complexity which drew me back and back again, to persevere in its re-reading, and arrive in the end at, hopefully, its full sense. The depth of this meaning reminded me of the well of water ever springing up in us to everlasting life. It wasn't truly that water, which, our having once drunk of it, we'd have no need to drink any more, for I had to return many times to these words. But there were reflections of that same water in Dr Farrers's words; They quenched something in me and satisfied me more than any ordinary everyday words had ever done before.

I could hardly imagine what life would be like without books. How dull it would be if printing had never been invented. Nowadays words arc so clearly reproduced on paper that reading can be a pleasure, the eye takes everything in easily and quickly, even if sometimes the mind needs a second or third perusal and some effort is required. In books there's an ever-renewable feast, it's certainly ever-renewable because there are more enjoyable books in existence than any one person could ever absorb in all his lifetime.

TRINITY:
THE SLOE LANE AGAIN

Towards the end of October, Prue brought her young man to see her parents. Jane and Jack were both pleased with Colin. They all drove over to Whinside for a short elevenses visit one day, which was fun. Colin was a few years older than Prue, he seemed a sensible person but not so sensible as to be dull. In fact, Jane told me, he was very well-informed, but never boring about it, always seeing the funny side of things. This suited Prue, who herself had a very quick mind and sense of humour. He was training to be an accountant and would soon be fully qualified. Prue had just got a job in a local bank which she hoped, with her good A-levels, would lead to something more interesting than just being a teller behind a glass screen. Colin was living in a very small flat in west London and Prue would live there too. His flatmate had kindly moved out to share with another friend. They were planning to get married at Easter. The wedding would take place in London and afterwards they would visit some of their nearest relations on both sides. They didn't want a church wedding, nor any family to be there at the registry office, except David.

Jane went back with them both to London, where she stayed for a few days with a friend not impossibly far away from Colin's flat. She was glad to see Prue comfortably settled with someone who was easy to get on with, and who seemed to have his heart and mind in the right place. She was sorry the wedding wasn't to take place till the spring, but it would be silly of her to fret about this beyond reason after all she'd been through.

Then she came back to Easter Kilcoy and, two days later, drove over to Whinside to tell me more of all the latest. After a lunch with much converse, we decided to walk down past the big house to the loch.

There was much to talk about, there were implications to be imparted to me and my reactions to these discussed. Of course, I was anxious to hear about everything, having met Colin for just that one very short time. I was hoping after a longer acquaintance to like him very much, not that I'd probably ever have the chance of this, with their living in London. But all Jane told me that afternoon promised well. I hoped he would have the patience needed to live with Prue, whom I personally had often found rather exhausting.

"I'm so glad that beastly business with Prue's awful young man is over," said Jane. "It used to weigh on my mind. It's hard to do nothing, even when there's nothing to be done. All one's learnt about prayer and acceptance seems rather insubstantial when suddenly something serious affects one's own family."

"It's easy to think," I said, "that one's defences are quite good, until they are attacked. That time when Philip went into hospital with a fierce appendix, there was nothing we could do for the first day or two except wait, and I felt so ill with anxiety, much worse than I could have imagined."

"Ordinarily, our minds know that God's in control, but when something awful happens, it's difficult or even impossible to feel this to be so. It's hard to remember too that God can turn all things to good, even tragic ones. Sometimes it must take years before any new good begin to show enough for those involved to see it. When Prue went off with Martin I felt horrible, almost sick, especially at the beginning. In the end, though, I more or less stopped worrying. I just had to learn to be patient, not to press Prue to do anything, to wait for events to show *her* what to do. It seemed to us so obvious that she and Martin weren't suited to each other, that sooner or later there would be a break. When Colin appeared and impressed himself on her, (though we didn't really know what was happening *when* it was happening, it was only through David we heard anything.), I began to feel more myself and able to enjoy my food and sleep again."

When we came to the lochside road we turned right and after a little while turned right again into the sloe lane and then upwards towards the trees and right again towards home.

The lane was very overgrown that autumn, no tractor had been through to clear a way. We had to push through thick spiny growths of brambles and hawthorns to reach the upper end where the blackthorns grew with even fiercer spikes and spines, though not reaching out as far as the brambles did. It had been a good year for sloes and Mary-next-door had been very pleased to gather some to make her good sloe gin.

"Jack says Duncan isn't too well," said Jane. 'Margaret is worried about him. I can't make out what his doctor says. They don't seem to want to discuss the question with anyone."

"I'm sorry, oh, dear. I'm not awfully fond of him. He's so *tedious*. But he's good and he works hard for St Andrew's. he saves us a lot of money, Nicholas says. He knows the best people to get for each job that wants doing."

"Christopher will be back at the end of this week," Jane remarked again suddenly. "I wonder how he's got on."

"I wonder if he'll get married. Perhaps we shall hear more about the girl friend when he returns, though I'm not saying. Now I'm as old as I am, I think I've become wise enough to let things happen and not be surprised, or not often. And certainly not think of foretelling anything."

After Jane had gone home, I had a little spare time before preparing the supper. I began my usual job of writing out next week's list of services and saints' days, the Kalendar, in my best italic hand, not really at all professional as I very well knew. But it impressed the uninitiated and was legible as well as reasonably decorative, a better alternative to vague, untidy, scribbled lists, which was all most of the congregation aspired to, or illegible grey typewriting.

"It's odd, this writing business, calligraphy. This italic lower case stuff doesn't really suit me. I much prefer to write notices using capital letters. Then each letter has a life of its own, stands up on its own, and it does so even more strongly when it's placed in a word with other letters, though that sounds contradictory. And given a bit of luck with the spacing, the whole notice will then take off and become itself, full of vigour, attracting eyes to look at, to read its message and inform the brain. I think that's where the magic comes in. Each capital letter seems to form itself for me rather than my having to draw it, and the final result appears on paper in spite of myself. The notice has a life of its own. It's mystifying, for, when it's all done and I step back to look at it with detachment, it doesn't seem to be mine at all but someone else's, or nobody's. I can stare and stare at it as if I were drinking it all in, as if it weren't mine at all, as if I'd never seen it before, as if it has been conjured up from nowhere. It's all very odd.

Christopher returned from his short break with the news that he was engaged. Of course I was surprised, in spite of my having discussed it with Jane, and then surprised at myself for being so. He had met Felicity when he'd been at college in Eaglesburgh. Her father was rector of a parish in the Marches diocese. She had been studying to be a deaconess and was now working in Melthorne at the cathedral there. She wasn't sure if she wanted to be a deacon. Probably not. It wouldn't be very easy if she were married to Christopher anyway. She wasn't yet used to doing two jobs at once.

TRINITY: MORE SERMONS

Duncan Forbes, our St Andrew's secretary, had missed one Sunday at church and when the next one came round he was still away. We were told that Mrs Forbes, Margaret, his wife, had said he was very tired, he had no energy, he seemed to want to spend quite a large part of the day in bed. He was in no pain. His doctor, who was very kind and helpful, had been coming regularly. There was no need for him to be in hospital. The nurse came every other day. Margaret was a very capable and organised woman and her daughter, who lived in the next road, came round to be with her father for part of each day. Edward was worried about him, for, when he'd been to visit him during the week, it seemed that part of himself had already drifted away into the next life.

I was sorry, that second Sunday, to see Duncan was still missing. It was difficult to know what to do. If he were in hospital, in Balmore, it would be simple to pop in for a moment or two with a card, or some flowers or fruit, but to call at their home seemed such a disturbance. I didn't worry too much, though, for Nicholas would know what we should do for the best.

In spite of thinking about Duncan, I enjoyed that morning's service. We all sang well, and the choir especially well. Canon Harper preached on not letting the sun go down on our wrath, from the Epistle, which I enjoyed greatly.

At Evensong, it was Edward's turn for the sermon. He preached from the second lesson which I'd read in Duncan's absence. 'Love worketh no ill to his neighbour: therefore love is the fulfilling of the law ... it is high time to awake out of sleep: for now is our salvation nearer than when we first believed.

Well, with Duncan's being away, we didn't have to listen to his mini-sermon at the beginning of the lesson. And the real sermon was good. Edward always is good on love. He spoke of how the love we feel for each other, for our families and friends, can show us how we should love God. That's what I was meditating about when I was last stuck at the Drummond Street lights, but the remainder was different. There was, Edward said, more we could learn from such a love. When we love another person very much we want to share everything with him, even to give him all we have. It's the same with God. If we love God with all our heart, we will want to give him all of ourself, all of our time and all our possessions. As it's a joy for us to help all the people we love, similarly it's a joy for us to give our best service to God. And, because he loves us, (he's loved us from all eternity), so likewise he gives us all we need and in abundance, more than we can desire or deserve. We must believe that. We mustn't forget God is giving of his love all the time. It's high time to wake out of our sleep and understand this. With the love God gives us, we must love and turn it into action, into doing good to others. This is the fulfilling of the law and the Gospel.

I could feel I was beginning to understand this. And God's love, as I'd said, works the other way too. We can learn from the way we react to God how we should react to people. When we've learnt to give everything of ourselves to God, then we'll truly love others in the way we ought to. That's to say, we'll help others, not in a grumpy or half-hearted way, having to make an obvious effort to do the right thing, doing it as a duty, but we'll want more than anything to help others, we'll find ourselves full of love for others, an overflowing love which will be looking outward for those who need help.

The Good Samaritan didn't hesitate before he turned aside to help the robbed and injured man. Nor did he wonder how little he'd need do to help him, what was the least possible he need do. He did all that was necessary without hesitation. I'm still not like that. I can feel myself glooming about the bother and effort and the often boringness of helping people I don't know well, or whom I don't like very much. I love helping people I do love, that's quite a different thing. Everyone likes to do that. But if I loved God as I ought, I would love to help everyone, including my enemies and the unknowns, even the most awkward and difficult people.

As we went out of the church after the service, it was already dark. It was really winter now. I much prefer the long light evenings of summer. I love coming out from Evensong into the daylight. I never really feel sure of myself when I'm out in the dark, though one can hardly say it's really dark outside St Andrew's with the street lights all around. In the summer evenings too, when we come out of church, the swifts are still screaming round the rooftops. It's an exciting happening, ears and vision co-operating, the birds dashing as well as screaming. It's lovely, too, when it's dusk enough for the unfamiliar bats to come out from the tower to fly in circles overhead, when it's dark enough for them to emerge and yet still light enough for us to see them.

Later that evening, after I'd helped Nicholas count the collection and we'd put all the week's cash into bags for the bank, I was thinking about St Paul and his favourite subjects, love, the cross, being in Christ. I then remembered, one Sunday, only a month or so ago, Christopher had preached on the effect of the cross on our lives and on the world.

'God forbid that I should glory save in the cross of our Lord Jesus Christ, by whom the world is crucified unto me and I unto the world.'

He'd explained about the cross being the foundation of our faith. And then had gone on to elaborate on this these and St Paul's ideas. All time is divided between what happened before the cross and what happened after, and this is well shown in the New Testament. The friends of Jesus became amazingly changed people after the crucifixion, they believed about God differently, they thought of the world and its relationship to God in an altogether new way. St Paul says everything must be considered in the light of the cross. There is no way for us to come to God's love except through the cross.

I remembered there was a time when I hated crucifixes, I was afraid of them, of their portrayal of suffering. But that was before I believed in Christ as our saving Lord, before I understood who he was and what he did for us. The suffering is still there in all crucifixes, but there's also a calling to us to acknowledge our salvation, to understand that the weight of our sins has been taken from us. With Christ's suffering and our redemption, we can look on the cross with thankfulness and adoration.

It had been a super sermon, very deep and helpful. So everyone had thought, judging by what they said to Christopher as they went out afterwards. Or nearly everyone. It was only Trefor Pari-Jones who had to stop to complain.

"What's all this nonsense about crosses? We don't want to hear about this kind of thing."

"I don't know why Trefor comes to St Andrew's," I'd said to Nicholas later that evening. "It must be something from his childhood."

"Well, he obviously believes in a different kind of Christianity from ours," Nicholas had replied. "But he believes in Christ in his own way, I expect. It wouldn't be tactful for us to ask him. And it wasn't right of him to speak like that to Christopher in everyone's hearing."

"In a way I wish he would leave St Andrew's and go somewhere else. He obviously doesn't enjoy coming all that much. I would feel more comfortable if he didn't come. It's not pleasant to have an anti-St Andrew's person in our midst. As I've said before, he might be teasing, but it didn't very much sound like teasing tonight."

TRINITY: ALL SAINTS

The following day Nicholas and I decided to take a card and some flowers to Duncan at his house. He and Margaret had a little modern white house in a pleasant road of fairly similar houses. Each one was surrounded by a beautifully tidy garden. There were not many flowers now, at the end of October, but I knew, in spring and summer, there were great displays of every shade of colour, of every kind of flower, short and tall, and in between. It must be very good soil here, I thought, slightly enviously, everything grows so very well. The gardens, though, weren't very big, so it wasn't surprising their owners could keep them so extraordinarily tidy.

Margaret came to the door when we rang and she showed us into the sitting room. As well as the garden the house was very tidy too. Margaret must be very organized, I thought. I was sure she was - not like myself.

Her daughter was with her that morning. She was both capable and jolly. We didn't see Duncan, but sent fond messages to him with the card and flowers. Margaret said he had, for quite a few months now, been finding things beyond his strength. Not everything had been beyond him, but he'd seemed able to do less and less as the days had gone on. The last thing he wanted to give up was St Andrew's, and especially he'd wanted to be at the Sunday services. He was very sad to have missed these last two Sundays. He was worried about some letters he'd not been strong enough to answer. Nicholas took them, telling Margaret not to worry, and, above all to see Duncan didn't either. As treasurer, Nicholas knew all about what was going on in the church, and he would have everything in order for the next Vestry meeting in a fortnight's time.

"Do tell him not to worry. His work's always been so well done, there's never been any confusion. Seeing to these will be quite straightforward. Do your best, Margaret, won't you, to persuade him we'll manage all right, though of course we're missing him."

"What do you think?" I asked Nicholas as we drove home.

"I've no idea," he replied.

"Is it his heart?"

"Perhaps. I'm not well up in medical things."

"Margaret's funny, she doesn't want to talk about symptoms. Well, it's not funny, it's natural. Symptoms can sound frightening when you talk about them. It might make the ill person worse if one talked about symptoms unnecessarily. It must be he's not in hospital because there's nothing that can be done for him there. He's got two capable women at home where he's much happier to be. He's seemed much older lately, hasn't he?"

Two nights later Duncan fell asleep at his usual time, but he didn't wake the next morning.

It was marvellous, I thought, he should die quietly at home and not to have been in Balmore for weeks, not to have to be away from Margaret. It was good for Margaret, too, not having to trail up to the hospital on the bus. Perhaps he just got tired of living. Perhaps he felt himself called away for something God had in mind for him. Margaret would be good about that and not try to hold him back.

This year All Saints Day fell on a Sunday. I enjoyed this. Only for the last three years or so had I been interested in saints' days and other similarly important occasions, or not even for as long as that. I was rather unhappy about this, or, perhaps, regretful was a better word. I had, indeed, wasted most of my life out in the wilderness. But this year, as things were turning out, there'd be, on the Sunday, special prayers and sermons and hymns about saints. I'd be able to fill up some of the gaps in my knowledge of such things, gaps which can sometimes embarrass me. It doesn't actually matter all that much if there are gaps in what I know, I'd probably be the only one to notice anyway, but I'm conscious of my ignorance and can't help feeling a little guilty about it. I certainly ought to know more about saints than I do, who they were, what they did, what we think about them, how they affect our lives today. Their personalities and their lives are fascinating to read about, even, or especially, those from long ago. If I'm lucky enough to find a good book about them.

The morning service lived up to my expectations. That's to say, I was able to concentrate on the prayers quite well, to follow the lessons and to enjoy the sermon. And then, too, the actual Communion seemed very meaningful this time so didn't rush past me with only half myself concentrating on it, and I'd suddenly find it was all over. This quite often happened, and I'd be very upset, I'd feel quite bereft, as if I'd lost someone or something. Though I knew in my head my concentrating didn't matter, the service was happening and I was present there and not intending to be absent-minded. And finally I'd enjoyed singing 'For all the Saints' with my best breath.

Of course. Who wouldn't? It's such a satisfactory hymn, so long as we're allowed to sing all the verses, including the starred ones, otherwise it's all over too soon and I feel cheated of something good, something I need. We begin each verse on the second beat of the bar. I don't understand why this should be helpful, though it does seem to give us just the kind of push to get things going. I must confess, though, to beginning sometimes on the first beat. '*Thou* wast their rock ...'and as I would probably be the only person doing so I wouldn't be heard anyway and so there would be no harm. We had the good Proper Preface for the day, too:

'the multitude of thy Saints compassing us about with so great a cloud of witnesses to the end that we, rejoicing in their fellowship, may run with patience the race that is set before us, and together with them receive the crown of glory that fadeth not away.'

I knew it was really from the Epistle to the Hebrews: that as we are compassed about with this great cloud of many saints, we can lay aside every weight, and also the sin which doth so easily beset us, and we can run this race with patience. But the crown of glory that fadeth not away is in St Peter's first letter. It's marvellous how much the Bible is used in our prayers, in the Prayer Book. What are the bereft next generation going to miss? They won't know, though, but all the same I'm sorry for them in their loss.

These words of the Epistle put everything in a nutshell: how we think about the saints and what they do for us. I like the cloud of witnesses. I always think of the poster we have on our bathroom wall, it's of a cloud of butterflies, the blues, the coppers and the hairstreaks, hovering over their plants. To me, they seem to be witnessing constantly to the glory of God their Creator. They don't have to rest, being in a picture, they can go on hovering, flying around, perpetually. I like, too, the idea of running the race with patience. It seems to indicate it must be a long race where patience is more needed (and probably stamina, of which I have extraordinarily little) than speed.

All the words of the prayer are good, too; strong, direct and strung together with a marvellous rhythm.

Edward preached about the Communion of Saints. Whether we mean the real Saints, those who are canonised for their holiness, or ourselves who, as church members, are working for saintliness, praying for holiness, this is their Day. We are all individuals who will be gathered up into heaven when we die, we'll become members of that great company of holiness.

At Evensong Jack read the second lesson. I decided, yet again, that he did read extraordinarily well. He read from Revelation about the Book which only the Lamb that was slain can open. The beasts and elders fall down before the Lamb. Each one of the elders has a harp and a golden vial full of odours which are the prayers of saints. The voices of many angels are saying:

"Worthy is the Lamb that was slain to receive power, and riches and wisdom, and strength, and honour and glory and blessing... all this be unto him that sitteth upon the throne, and unto the Lamb for ever and ever.'

These words ring with Handel's marvellous music even when they're only spoken, especially when Jack's reading. He'd know about the Messiah and have the sound in his head when he came to these words.

Christopher preached on the day's Gospel, the Sermon on the Mount. And I noticed, especially, 'Blessed are the peacemakers, for they shall be called the children of God.' He mentioned Duncan Forbes's being outstanding at peacemaking, always appreciating another person's problems, always listening carefully, (his getting it wrong about the tower window being due to the coming of his last illness - my one thought here), never jumping to hasty conclusions or judgments, often trying to bring two people to understand each other.

"We have lost a peacemaker," he said, "but the results of his peacemaking will live on here at St Andrew's. We will remember his saintliness in action here."

TRINITY: ALL SOULS

The following day was All Souls Day. This was the day chosen for Duncan's funeral. I thought it was a wonderful idea to have a funeral on All Souls Day. And it was indeed. The service was held at St Andrew's in the early afternoon, followed by the interment in the old Strathlyon burial ground. This was set in a picturesque site below a wooded hill, a little distance back from the river. I'd not often been there, but each time I had I'd decided I wouldn't mind being buried there myself. The surroundings were all so leafy and sheltered and calm and quiet, and not gloomy.

Edward sang the Requiem Mass. Almost all the St Andrew's congregation was there with others from the Cathedral and St Columba's. There were many also from other churches and from the town in general. In fact, our church was rather overfull. Duncan had lived all his life in Strathlyon and was well known to many who had enjoyed his open friendliness and very practical help.

Everything about the service was very moving, the music and the words and there being so many people who wanted to come, out of affection for Duncan. I was moved above and beyond tears. There was real sorrow, there in the church, but it was tempered with thanksgiving for so good a life quietly relinquished. There was rejoicing that Duncan's faith would bridge the gap between his life and what would come after. All this inspired people to forget themselves. The Holy Spirit was all around them. I thought everyone must feel his presence and find their hearts lifted up.

Edward spoke of losing our life in order to save it. This we try to do here in our wordly life, offering all to God. Then, at the end, we die in order to rise again in glory, as a seed has to die when it's sown in the ground before a new life bursts out in beauty. Duncan had spent his life learning to live for God. In dying he would go on to the glorious life with his Redeemer.

At the end of the service Edward took a sprig of bright yellow-leafed berries, which he'd broken off one of the bushes in the church garden. He dipped it in holy water and sprinkled the coffin, saying at the same time,

'Go forth upon thy journey from this world, O Christian Soul,
In the name of God the Father who created thee,
In the name of God the Son who died upon the cross for thee,
In the name of God the Holy Ghost who breathes the life
    of God into thee,
In the name of Blessed Mary and all the Saints and Angels
    who wait for thy coming.
May thy dwelling be this day in the new Jerusalem,
Where, with Lazaruss once poor, thou mayest inherit the
    riches of the Kingdom of Heaven.'

When the coffin was brought out from the church to the top of the steps at the west door, the single bell tolled, in acknowledgement of another Christian soul's passing from this life to the next. Then Edward spoke the words of the Nunc Dimmittis:

" 'Lord, now lettest thou thy servant depart in peace according to thy word. For mine eyes have seen thy salvation which thou hast prepared before the face of all people, to be a light to lighten the Gentiles, and to be the glory of thy people Israel.'"

Then Nicholas and I drove with some of the others, including Jack and Jane, to the burial ground. Nicholas had been requested to be there as an office-bearer of St Andrew's. There was a fair number of us following the coffin along the narrow twisting path to the newly dug grave. With the late autumn sunshine gleaming on the few remaining leaves on the trees and on the rich black and silver velvety fabric of Edward's cope, he led the procession of mourners, declaiming,
    " 'I am the Resurrection and the life, he that believeth in me ...'"
but the words were lost on the gentle breeze before they reached me, who was following quite a long way behind. But they were not really lost, for I knew them well. The Gospel over again. This was the Requiem service for that day, All Souls Day. This would have been our service today in the church if there had been no funeral. I was thinking too of the Epistle:
    'Death is swallowed up in victory. O death, where is thy sting? O death where is thy victory? Thanks be to God which giveth us the victory through our Lord Jesus Christ.'
    These words have a stronger and more encouraging meaning for us when they're said about someone we've all known well.

258

On the way home, as we turned off the main road for Ardness, I asked Nicholas suddenly who he thought would be St Andrew's secretary now.

"It's for the Vestry to decide of course, but almost certainly Jack, I hope. He's been asked and has agreed. It would be good. As you know he's got the ability, mental and practical. And the time."

"And he's used to writing intelligent letters which is more to the point.

"Poor old Duncan," I went on. "I wished I'd been fonder of him. I found him so difficult to communicate with. He often didn't seem to approve of my attitude to life in general. And yet many people loved and respected him. Well, I respected him because he was good, even if I found him not easy to know well. He was very solemn, wasn't he? Even when he was being funny. That used to make me want to laugh, for the wrong reasons. And usually at the wrong moments. And, of course, he always knew best. There were really only two sentences I could safely say to him. One was 'Yes, of course' and the other 'That's right'."

"He certainly did think he knew best," said Nicholas. "I was always having, myself, to say, 'Yes, of course', and then I would go away and do what I thought was right, in the way I chose."

"He was a bit like you are, only in the opposite way. I mean I mustn't say to you 'Are you sure?' or you get mad and say you wouldn't have said anything unless you were sure. It's not like myself. I often say things just to see what happens, like flying a kite. It's more fun. One can find out quite a lot that way. About people as well as about things."

Then we were silent for the short length of road before Whinside and I thought about all the times in my pilgrimage when Edward hadn't tried to put me right in my working out of the faith. Nor had he often directed me more surely along the path to the Holy Spirit. He'd always let me make my own progress in my own time, even if I made many side-trackings and sometimes even reversings. 'Hesitant skating' were words which seemed well to describe my method of getting though life. Though he'd always help me when I asked him, I found in the end it was really the Holy Spirit who did the guiding, and who better? But Edward was always there patiently to hear about my progress, and he would have stepped in to rescue me if he had really thought it necessary.

TRINITY: AN AUTUMN PICNIC

I can understand, I was thinking, why real contemplatives want to love the desert, to live through whole days when God seems absent. They're always aware of what I was forgetting when I had my cold. They know, when they feel abandoned by God, that he's still more than ever with them, hidden deep in their soul. There, at those times, he can do more for them than he can in those moments of bliss and spiritual consolation which we, beginners in the faith, so much long for. It's hard for us to imagine how anyone could have a preference for the desert, and yet, if we could remind ourselves of God's nearness, or God's working in us, we would rejoice at finding ourselves apparently forsaken. But we can't choose how God will come to us, or when. We have to wait with hope and lots of prayer, and remember, as St Teresa said, God loves us all and he values simple prayers and good deeds as much as he does advanced devotions. The prayers of those in the first outer mansions of the Interior Castle are as valuable to him as the prayers of those in the innermost.

I was relaxing in my morning bath, feeling, in spite of all the strains and excitements of the last weeks, really not at all like the old woman I was intending to become. Now it was time to get out of the hot and comforting water, get dressed, collect some food for a picnic lunch, and leave Nicholas something organized or semi-organized for *his* meal at home. I was going out for the day with Jane to see the autumn colours. Nicholas would take me into town, for he was going to see the St Andrew's auditor, but after that he'd be in the garden tidying up, a very ongoing - as the saying is - autumn job.

We drove into town and met Jane with her car as arranged, then we, she and I, made our way gently westwards into the hills and to Glen Lodda. This was one of the loveliest glens for an autumn outing and every year we came, if we could, to see the trees in their brightest and most beautiful golden colours. Early November was not too late in the year for a visit. In the Highlands the seasons, especially spring and autumn, are much delayed. Even by this date there were oaks still in their dark green foliage.

At first we drove up a wide and level valley where the river flowed from one side to the other in slow curves between green or rushy fields. From time to time we could see an oxbow lake, just as one learns about at school, or an embryonic one, half formed. Fascinating. Low hills covered with golden birches rose up on either side of us, once we saw a buzzard soaring in the sunshine, and another time there was a heron by the waterside looking hopelessly mournful. We came to our journey's end, to the car park at the end of the public road, its flat space covered with a golden rain of needles dropped by the surrounding larches. Here we left the car, and as Jane switched off the engine we suddenly could hear on our left a small stream come rushing and tumbling out of a deep and narrow ravine. Nearer to us we could see it dashing past where we were standing on its way to join the main river in the wider valley.

We decided to carry our solid food with us, but leave the coffee for our return to the car. After Jane had called Tess and helped her through the stile we climbed a steep path to find ourselves in about ten minutes out of the ravine and into the sun at the top of a cliff where a small stream fell into the river below. From here we could watch the sunlit water falling down into the deep shade of the gorge below us. We ate our lunch here sitting on tussocks of bilberry.

There were varied kinds of trees here, those around us in full sun and the lower ones in deep shade. There were birches with cascading slender twigs, each with its ration of bright leaves shining like miniature golden lanterns; there were aspens, especially elegant, their branches spreading themselves out just so far, and then their supple ends suddenly drooping decoratively down towards the ground. A few groups of dark blue pines contrasted with the rust and gold of the majority of trees, but this depth of colour made all the other falling and fallen leaves glow all the more brightly. Down in the ravine itself only a shadowy light penetrated. There all was gloom, though not a sad gloom, the colours were muted but golden all the same, a shadow gold, as if in another key, a minor key, as opposed to the major key of the sunlight where we sat. And the noise of the river, in spite of its drifting up from the darkness below, had a happy sound, no sad shadow could muffle its cheerful rushing and tumbling down between the stones.

261

"If I could paint all this," said Jane, 'all this wonderful mixture of colour and shape, the dark ravine and the trees up here in the sunlight, it would be super. But I never could. My normal blotchy method would be useless, it wouldn't explain anything of the beauty. It would be super, though, for anyone like John Sell Cotman, for he would simplify all he saw, he would make sense of the world without spoiling the magic. Perhaps I'll take some twigs home and hope to paint them before their leaves fall off or they lose their colour. The bog myrtle and dwarf willows are lovely at present. They'd go well with Michaelmas daisies or berries or hips, or even autumn crocuses; they're all in our garden at the moment."

"That would be a good idea. It should be lovely." I encouraged her. "It would be lovely to have even a sketchy record of the glorious whole surrounding us today."

We didn't hurry over our lunch but continued to admire everything we could see.

"Do you ever feel," I said suddenly, after we'd more or less finished our food, 'that praying can be rather a bind? That it would be much better to get on with some active work for God? I suppose it's because I've not been used to prayer all my life. I would miss praying much less than you would. I know we need to praise God and thank him for our blessings and to confess our sins to him and to intercede for others, but as a beginner, I often want to *do* something special rather than pray."

"I do sympathize with you. It's good to remember though, St Teresa says doing things for others is often as good as prayer, or better."

"That's true. I remember reading that. I ought to take lots more opportunities of helping people, even if it's only in cheering them along on their way through life."

"Also," said Jane, "we need to find time for the things we really do enjoy, such as coming here today, and not feel guilty about it. It's good for us sometimes to do something which is thoroughly enjoyable and quite useless, except we'll feel all the better for it afterwards, and we'll remember the whole day for a long time to come. It's just as wrong to push ourselves into good works too hard and too often as it is to have too many days off. It's good for us to see how lovely God's world is, especially when we're so fortunate as to live in such a beautiful part of his world. We shouldn't forget, either, that good deeds on their own aren't helpful. It's the Spirit working in us, bringing God's love to us and taking ours to God which makes us do really worthwhile god-directed good works, works done for love of God, not for ourselves, not for acquiring merit, not to score well with God."

"That's what St Paul says, isn't it?" I said. "That well known bit about love or charity, whichever you like, in Corinthians. Without love the tongues of men and of angels are nothing worth. And if I could have all faith and could move mountains there'd be no point if I'd no love in me. And I could give all my goods to the poor and my body to be burnt (that's not likely fortunately), if I have not charity, I am nothing."

We then scrambled down the path again to the car, had our very welcome coffee and began to drive leisurely towards home. We were in no hurry, so shortly we took a side road and crossed the river into a narrow lane running along the other side of the valley.

"One time when Nicholas and I came along here," I said, remembering, "there was a wonderful scene with masses of cattle being collected from the hills further up the valley. There weren't any obvious cowboys but many landrovers and much lowing and mooing of beasties. I took a lot of photos but none came out. I'd not wound the film properly into my camera. It was rather an awkward camera that way, it happened more than once. I was very disappointed at first, but then I began to think that perhaps God was trying to discourage me from taking photos."

"You mean that perhaps he was wanting you to learn not to be too puffed up with how good you are with your camera."

"Well, I know I'm not good really, not seriously good. Not like really gifted, well-known photographers. I just have some good luck occasionally. But I thought the idea of not trying to be an expert would help me enjoy what I do but not in competition with other people. I shouldn't get too serious about photography generally. There are other more important things God wants me to do.

"What you're describing is a very good example of what Edward means when he says 'it doesn't matter.' You mustn't get upset about such and such a thing because it doesn't *matter*."

"Yes, it *was* a good example. After all this time I can see it doesn't matter at all that I've got no photos of that day. And if I'd had some good photos I might have boasted about them to my friends which would have been silly or they'd have stayed disregarded, mouldering in an album with no one looking at them."

"Do you think any redwings or fieldfares will soon be arriving?" said Jane, after a mile or two more. "I would have expected to see some here today."

"There are lots of berries for them anyway. It would be lovely to see some bramblings this year. I don't feel it's really been a proper winter unless I do."

We arrived back in the outskirts of Strathlyon well pleased with our lovely day out. Jane took me home and then drove herself back to Drummore.

ADVENT: ST ANDREW

One day, later in the month, Edward came over for the usual lunch and general discussion on parish affairs which he often had with Nicholas. While we were relaxing with our coffee afterwards I asked him. "Edward, dear, please, I know I've asked you before, but it just didn't sink into my brain. It's something to do with the sky. Why is St Andrew the patron saint of Scotland? There's no offence meant against your country in my not knowing this, for I've even less idea of the connection between St George and England. I could look it up in my aged encyclopaedia, but it's easier to ask you, and your direct answer will be much more reliable, I expect."

"It's not difficult, I'll tell you. There was going to be a battle. The King of the Scots, who was called Achaius, who doesn't sound very Scottish, and the King of the Picts who was called Hungus, who does sound possibly Pictish, were going the next day to fight against Athelstane, who sounds English all right, grandson of Alfred the Great. They, the Scottish and Pictish Kings saw, the evening before the battle, clouds in the sky shaped like a St Andrew's cross. (And this was in the days before, of course, aeroplane trails made this kind of thing something quite normal). This interesting sight turned out to be a good omen, for they were victorious against Athelstane. As soon as possible after the battle was over, they went barefoot to the kirk of St Andrew, which happened to be nearby, and there they made a vow to adopt his cross as their national emblem."

"Thank you. Now. I shall remember. But, with those funny names of the kings, I'm not surprised I forgot."

"This year, does Advent Sunday or St Andrew's Day come first?" asked Nicholas. "Last year they were both on the same day, a Sunday."

"You're not thinking, Nicholas," I chipped in quickly. "The first Sunday in Advent must be on a Sunday, the one that will allow there to be four altogether before Christmas Day, and St Andrew's Day must be on the thirtieth of November, whatever day of the week that falls on. If St Andrew's Day was on Sunday last year, it must be on Monday this year. If you think in your mind of the thirtieth, that is St Andrews's

Day, moving to the left along the days of the week, like you think of your birthday moving in the same way, and the First Sunday in Advent moving to the right against the dates, which are getting smaller all the time, you'll be all right. It's easy. Just remember, though, Advent can never begin before a certain date in November, which I've temporarily forgotten, and when, as the years pass, we get to there, it jumps forward, or backwards, whichever way you look at it, again, into December and you begin working backwards, or forwards again. And of course you must allow for a hiccup for Leap Year whenever that comes. It's quite simple."

"Oh, Betty, do stop. You're as bad as a schoolmistress," said Nicholas.

He and Edward exchanged their usual glances of long suffering.

"You know better than anyone I could never be a schoolmistress. All my class would be in a perpetual turmoil. How ridiculous you are. It's just that I can see these days or dates quite clearly in my head, but it's hard to explain it to other people. Other people have minds which see things differently from my own, I think."

The next day, in an odd moment at the sink, I was thinking, "I suppose we don't really know very much about St Andrew. He's not like St Paul whom we can't help knowing well because he wrote so much. Or like St John the Evangelist, because his Gospel is imbued with his personality. Or even like the other John, the Baptist, who told of the coming of Christ, and pointed him out when he did come, who lived in the desert and wore a camel's hair garment and ate locusts (only it's possible, I read, it's the locust *plant* which would be more nourishing and easier to find than the insect), and wild honey. He's totally memorable. So I planned, that evening, I'd sit down again with my Bible and Concordance, but after supper this time, and try to discover what there is we do know about Andrew.

So, after supper on that dark evening I did sit down, and I discovered one great thing about St Andrew: he brings people to Jesus. In the Gospel story this bringing begins when John baptises people in Bethabara beyond Jordan. When he sees Jesus coming towards him John calls out,

'Behold the Lamb of God, who taketh away the sin of the world. This is he of whom I said that after me cometh a man who is preferred before me, for he was before me.' John sees the Spirit descending on Jesus from heaven like a dove, and it abides upon Jesus. And the next day, two of John's disciples are there with him, John. Jesus is there too. John says again 'Behold the Lamb of God'. These two disciples follow Jesus and spend the day with him. One of these two is Andrew. He goes to fetch his brother Simon. 'We have found the Messiah,' he tells Simon, and brings him to Jesus. Jesus tells Simon straightaway he will be called Cephas, or Peter, a stone. (It's easier to think of this in French, where Pierre means both Peter and a stone or rock).

Another time, after a great crowd has been listening to his preaching, Jesus wonders aloud how they will be able to feed so many hungry people. (Though he already knows what he will do). It's Andrew, then, who finds a boy with five barley loaves and two fishes and brings him to Jesus. (Were they very small loaves, more like big buns, if the boy were intending to eat them all himself for lunch? Not that this question affects the story). This boy must have been more than surprised to see Jesus take his small contribution and with it feed all the five thousand gathered there; and what is more, to see twelve basketfuls of left-over bits collected afterwards.

The next mention of Andrew is a few days before the first Good Friday. Some Greeks (who have become interested in the Jewish religion) have come to Jerusalem to worship at the Feast of the Passover. They want to see Jesus, so they ask Philip where they will find him. Philip goes to fetch Andrew, and it's he, Andrew, who brings the Greeks to Jesus. Bringing people to Jesus is Andrew's characteristic action.

After the resurrection, when Jesus has been appearing to many of his believers, he comes to that part of the Sea of Galilee where Andrew and Simon keep their fishing boat. This is where, at the beginning of his ministry, he had come to call them to leave their work of catching fish and follow him, and become fishers of men. I've often thought they must, probably, from time to time, have come back here to continue their fishing, even if only for short spells. This time, Jesus is already there on the shore, he has prepared a barbecue breakfast of fish and bread for the disciples who have been out all night and caught nothing. When they come near to the shore, Jesus tells them to cast their net on the right-hand side of the boat, which they do, and they catch one hundred and fifty three fishes. I like to think Andrew is with them too, for all the other well-known disciples are there: Simon Peter, (Andrew's own brother), and James and John, the sons of Zebedee: Thomas and Nathaniel are there, and two others who are unnamed. It's very likely one of these is Andrew.

He died on a cross as Jesus did, but traditions has made his a saltire cross, the diagonal one, with which in Scotland we are so familiar.

After all this, though, I decided, it might be helpful to look in my aged encyclopaedia, and there I discovered this might not be true. 'The relic of the cross,' I read, 'is exhibited in the convent of St Victoire near Marseille. It's placed at such an angle the observer has to view it diagonally and this creates in his mind a visual image of the famous cross we know.' Well, well, I thought. One lives and learns!

And then my thoughts wandered a little from the point. I thought perhaps it was Edward who should be called Andrew, for he spends his life bringing people to Christ.

And then it was Advent Sunday, followed on the Monday by St Andrew's Day itself, our patronal festival. In the evening there was a Sung Eucharist, or it could be called a High Mass. As usual there was a large congregation assembled.

"It must be the very best service we can put on," said Edward. And so it was, with choir and vestments and favourite hymns and many arrangements of chrysanthemums, which for once were not looking impossibly stiff and stand-offish as they usually do, but warmly cheerful and welcoming.

Afterwards we had a party in the hall; wine or fruit drinks (for those who would be driving home) or tea or coffee and cheese and sandwiches and salads and excellent cakes of many delicious kinds. There was much lively talk. This cheerful gathering of all the congregation brightened a rather dreary month when darkness comes early, as it especially had this year when the weather had been gloomier, more overcast and windier than usual.

Sometimes at this party we sang Scottish songs. I'd always felt a little embarrassed at that moment, not knowing the words. But, I reminded myself, I wouldn't know the words of the equivalent English songs either, so there was no need for anyone to be offended.

And once or twice, in other years, some gifted individuals had given amusing little sketches about people and happenings. This year perhaps there wasn't enough talent, nor had there been enough noteworthy events, for anything exciting to take place on that evening.

ADVENT:
CHRISTMAS PREPARATIONS

Each year Advent is the time we make our own spiritual journey to the Manger. Some of our preparations for Christmas are practical, but many have a spiritual side to them too. Very soon, on the second Sunday, comes the collect which tells us to 'read, mark, learn, and inwardly digest the Holy Scriptures which were written for our learning.' This we should do, so that:

'by patience and comfort of God's holy word, we may embrace and ever hold fast the blessed hope of everlasting life which thou has given us in our Saviour Jesus Christ.'

Then I loved to think of our own Christmas tree we'd be buying nearer the time, and the crib I would arrange in our hall, and all the holy thoughts and prayers which belonged to it.

And then, quite suddenly, so it seemed, the lovely Felicity came north to Strathlyon to see Christopher's present home and church, and to meet his friends. Everybody was delighted with her.

While Christopher had that unusual though very attractive Scottish combination of black wavy hair and blue eyes, Felicity's blue eyes were accompanied by bobbed, just not quite straight fair hair which shone in the sun or lamplight. She wasn't shy, nor noticeably bossy either, which was a great help for us who were trying to do our best for her. She knew how to show her enjoyment of being made very welcome by all whom she met. She wasn't in the least stuck up about her good looks or her good works in Melthorne. Her ambition now was to make life easier and more pleasant for the man who would be her husband, to help him have more time and energy for his ministry.

Edward gave a party for her and Christopher in the Rectory where the rooms were naturally larger and more suitable than those in the curate's flat. All those who accepted enjoyed a happy evening and looked forward to welcoming her here in a happy future.

Very shortly after this, it was time for constructive Christmas action. I looked back in my mind's eye to my last year's crib. It had stood on top of the chest by the front door. To represent the stable there was a simple cardboard carton from Sameways, saved from year to year. It was covered with foil inside and out, chopped straw was sprinkled on its floor, and held down by a sheet of transparent plastic film. The figures, though modern and clearly not handmade, were very beautiful and elegant, gently coloured in soft neutral shades. I spread sprays of ivy over the top and down the sides of the box, the ends of their stalks in water and held in place by not too obvious bits of sellotape. A string of tiny electric light bulbs was arranged inside the stable and along the front of the floor, so the whole scene was marvellously lit. At night especially, but all through the gloomy midwinter days too, the whole crib shone magically in our otherwise dark hall. All the figures made a lovely picture. I often found myself pausing in my work to stand and stare at Mary, Joseph and the baby Jesus, and the shepherds, and the ox and the ass, for minutes on end, in a kind of wordless prayer. Incorrectly, but it suited me best that way, I put the Holy Babe in his manger as soon as all was arranged. In this way I could be sure he didn't get mislaid and also I'd never really enjoyed staring at any empty manger until the appointed Christmas Day of his actual arrival. The three kings were for the moment hidden behind a small potted plant, what Sparks sold as a Parlour Palm, (the most suitable plant I'd been able to find) at the side of the crib, waiting patiently for Epiphany.

I hoped I should enjoy everything this year as much as I had last. One day, while I stood there silently, a thought came to me. If I really trusted in God, he would bring me his peace. Or, if I had already found the peace of God, I would already be trusting that all my life was already being ordered by him. They're interlocking, peace and trust, like so many other aspects of God's work in us. I do trust God will arrange things to happen in my life for the best for him, and that he will give me enough strength to do my part, whatever that may be. In this way peace should grow in me, I'd no need to be fretting or wondering. Though peace is what I still have most trouble in finding. It's very elusive, I don't trust enough in God. And that's because I'm not sure enough of his love. And I'm not sure why that should be so. Probably it's because I'm still so much a beginner. I've hardly started on my pilgrim way. I'll pray for help and confidence in all this.

It was on the evening of the Sunday before Christmas Day. Nicholas and I were on our way into Strathlyon for the Carol Service, the Nine Lessons and Carols. I was quite excited in anticipation. I loved singing the old familiar words to the old familiar and beautiful tunes. There was always, at St Andrews's, in the Carol Service, a lovely atmosphere of hope and worship and thanksgiving.

I must remember, I reminded myself, to listen hard when Edward reads the Gospel for Christmas Day, which he will do as the ninth lesson. On Christmas Day itself he will sing it, but I enjoy it much more when he speaks it. I suppose it's something to do with the subtle overtones of the speaking voice, especially when that voice is carrying a message one believes in, as also does the reader. But it is true the singing or chanting voice carries further in a full church which is the reason for its traditional use on that Christmas Day.

'In him was life, and life was the light of men. And the light shineth in darkness ... that was the true light, which lighteth everyman, coming into the world ... And the Word became flesh and dwelt among us, (and we beheld his glory, the glory as of the only begotten of the Father) full of grace and truth.'

('And we beheld his glory -' Someone once said to me, (who was it? I've forgotten), that this 'we beheld' seems to prove that the John who wrote this Gospel must be the same John who was there at Christ's resurrection).

The church was not yet decorated for Christmas but the lights were on brightly and the heating was working well, the light and warmth welcomed us all as we came in. There was a good crowd, not only of our usual congregation, but also a good sprinkling of strangers from the neighbourhood around; not strangers really, each one would be known to at least one member of our congregation. The Old Church provided cheerful services on festive occasions such as Christmas, and so many of those, whose own dour church did not, were for once attracted to ours.

The words and music of the carols soon wrapped me up in their lovely atmosphere. There were both the usual favourites and some unusual ones sung by the choir alone. The pure sound of the boys' voices seemed to float on the air towards me. The sound is real enough, but it doesn't seem to have its source in the boys, it's more a spirit sound than the voices of boys: boys   whom we know, boys who dash around and are rowdy and real enough before and after a service.

I was hoping we would sing, 'In the Bleak Midwinter', and we did. This carol makes me sad, though not in an unpleasant way, for it overcomes its sadness by the end of the last verse.

> 'What can I give him
> Poor as I am?
> If I were a shepherd
> I would bring a lamb;
> If I were a wise man
> I would do my part;
> Yet what I can I give him–
> Give my heart.'

The words were written by Christina Rossetti, but in a way it's like a George Herbert poem, direct and simple. The tune is lovely, it doesn't just go with the words, it adds to them, filling them out into a graceful pattern of curves which knot themselves together.

The reading of the Nine Lessons is, I thought, often quite amusing. It's not the best readers who are chosen, but those who fit into special categories. It's a convention, a formula. It doesn't matter if the words are not distinctly heard. No one expects to hear them clearly. It's the same words every year, and, on the whole, they're not deep or difficult, except for the reading of the Annunciation which is quite complex, and, of course, Edward's Christmas Gospel which is the most important of all and pulls the whole evening together.

I wasn't reading anything this year. I could be only a 'member of the congregation' and there was rather a lot of competition for that!

Then we sang,

> 'Hark, the herald angels sing
> Glory to the New born king',

and the service came to an end. Afterwards everybody walked round to the church hall and drank an almost non-alcoholic punch (for safety's sake) and ate hot mince pies. All of us were in a cheerful mood. Margaret Forbes was there, helping to see everyone was served.

She must be feeling this first Christmas without Duncan to be sadly strange and lonely, I thought, so I went up and spoke to her and took a mince pie from her dish.

"Yes, it's true," Margaret replied to my query. "I do feel the strangeness of being alone. But the family are being very good, the grand-children are having everything just as usual and I keep getting involved in what they're doing and all the preparations. And all the people from St Andrew's are very kind, they don't just *say* things to me, but many of them *do* something special. I've really had no time to feel sad about being lonely, and I've certainly not been forgotten."

In a short while, Nicholas and I left to drive home, where, after something a little more substantial to eat, to say nothing of a little more alcohol to drink, we sat down and read quietly until bedtime.

One morning two or three days later, we were back again in Strathlyon. After we'd parked the car, Nicholas suggested that, before doing our shopping, we would go first into St Andrew's to see how Jamie was getting on with the decorations.

We went inside and found Jamie, the sacristan, with four or so others beginning work. The tall fir tree had been placed securely upright beside the altar and was already entwined in a string of lights. A trestle table stood just inside the west door covered with a dark green cloth. On top of this the crib had been placed in position, and the straw was being encouraged to lie fairly flat on it's floor. There'd be winter greenery and a few winter flowers trailed around it later.

"Do you think," I asked Jamie, "we've got enough sets of lights for everything? Would you like another lot for the tree? It's such a grand tree, perhaps it could do with more lights. Or what about another lot for round the edge of the crib here to light up the flowers and greenery? Do you remember how super it looked last year when we were experimenting?"

Jamie looked a bit undecided, so I told him to let me know when he'd thought about it and I'd go and buy them.

On occasions such as this, Jamie was one of the mainstays of St Andrew's, or perhaps even *the* mainstay. He'd been a member of the church from time immemorial, or so it seemed to everyone. A fund of knowledge about everything to do with his job was stored in his mind. He knew all about the contents of the building itself and all about the people who had in his time worshipped there and then left or died. And, of course, he knew all the present congregation. He was short and slim and once had golden red curls which never lay down in their sparseness, but still waved around in any breeze that might be coming his way.

The big notice I'd done for the Christmas services was already placed outside the west door at the top of the steps replacing the one for the Carol Service.

"I'll bring the small notices for next week when we next come. That'll be Thursday probably, when we're in for the Mass. No, tomorrow, I'll be in for my confession. We'll bring in the greenery on Thursday for the flower ladies, it'll stay fresh forever in this cold damp weather."

On the way home Nicholas and I were talking about Jamie.

"People have no idea," I said, "how much he does. They can't see it, I suppose, because he does everything so quietly."

"The worst part is, people are always suggesting he might do more. 'Oh, Jamie can do that.' You hear it all the time. He already does much more than we can afford to pay him for. He loves St Andrew's, it's been his life and still is, but we shouldn't take advantage of this love."

"Do you remember that time when he had to be away and Edward had been away, too, for his own holiday and was hardly settled in again, and Christopher had been busy organising us as if we were his 'factory hands'. And when Sunday morning came there were many crises. There was no wine for the early service and someone had to run round to St Mary's. And the hymn boards were still showing the numbers from last Sunday's Evensong. None of the main lights were switched on until after we'd arrived, the collection plates hadn't been brought out from the Vestry. And Edward's list of readers had run out and only the readers knew this and none of them was likely to do anything about it. Except busy-body me who offered to read the Epistle. All this because of no Jamie. It was hilarious really, especially as Christopher's 'factory hands' seemed so obviously not to be very well trained. Edward, of course, was completely and obviously unmoved, maintaining his usual unflappability, which gave us all, or at least myself, confidence all would be well by the time eleven o'clock came. Which indeed it was. Just."

The next morning I drove in to St Andrew's for my pre-Christmas Confession. I was alone this time as Jane had arranged to go that evening. I was in good time and so was able quietly to kneel down and collect my thoughts before Edward arrived, which he did at twelve o'clock promptly.

I then got up and walked over to the place appointed for confessions, where I again knelt, this time with Edward at my side. I placed my piece of paper with my headlines written on it in front of me, on the sloping top of the prayer desk. But as always, it was the wrong height for me to read easily with my bifocal specs.

Everything always is at the wrong distance for bifocal specs, I realized desperately, and then, suddenly, I ceased to worry. Edward's encouraging and calm presence was working on me as usual and I found myself able to begin.

"There's nothing dramatically horrible," I said, partly to Edward who was really there, but mostly, I made myself remember, to God. He, too, was really there, though invisible. "It's just that I'm full of little horriblenesses, or not so little. I'm not kind enough to other people, especially I am not kind enough to Nicholas. I'm too short with him too often. I contradict him even when I know what he says has lots of truth in it, even if it's not totally true. I do this with other people as well. As usual I've been too critical of other people and blamed them without understanding them. I criticise people for some fault I think I can see, or for their being useless, but later I find out about their good deeds, their kindness to those in trouble, that they do much more good than I could ever do. Then I feel awful about mistakenly judging them, something we're told never to do. I still show off in my conversations with people and want to be praised, this is not right either. Thomas Merton says we should hate to be praised, we should feel it as if we were being painfully burned. I can see this. It's disturbing to be praised oneself anyway, for it's God who should have the praise. But part of myself still needs the satisfaction or reward of praise - for all these things I'm sorry.

"As usual I've failed to love God enough, and therefore to love others enough. My good works have been extremely feeble, undertaken with much half-heartedness, or else I've done them to be noticed or to acquire merit, both of which are bad reasons. I've not spent enough time in the praise of God, nor in prayer. I've saved up too many prayers for bedtime and then gone to sleep part way through.

Nor have I ever given enough thanks to God for all he has done or is doing for me. For all these things, also, I'm truly sorry."

Edward pronounced the Absolution, the words falling on my ears like sweetly soothing rain after a drought, or warming sunshine after a month of freezing dampness. He kindly told me to persevere and not to be discouraged, certainly to give more time to prayer while I was awake and not when I was just dropping off to sleep. Then, for my penance, he sent me into the Lady Chapel, to kneel in my pew and read the General Thanksgiving before he came to take the Mass.

Of course, I didn't need any longer to open my prayer book at page 88, that well-remembered number, for by now the words came easily on their own.

" '...we thine unworthy servants do give thee most humble and hearty thanks for all thy goodness and loving-kindness to us and to all men. We bless thee for our creation, preservation and all the blessings of this life; but above all for thine inestimable love in the redemption of the world by our Lord Jesus Christ, for the means of grace and for the hope of glory ... and that we shew forth thy praise not only with our lips but in our lives by giving up ourselves to thy service and by walking before thee in holiness and righteousness all our days...'"

Soon there were a few others coming in for the service. Everything was very quiet and peaceful. I felt marvellously, perfectly washed inside and out, and the words of the Mass, too, poured gently and sweetly over me and through me.

It wouldn't be possible, I thought, at the end, for a mere mortal to feel happier than I do at this moment. Now I can look forward with joy to Christmas, to celebrating the coming of the Holy Babe into this world.

CHRISTMAS:
THE EVE AND THE DAY

Christmas Eve at last. All was now set, or so I hoped. Everything in the house, so far as I could see, was prepared for the morrow. For some days the tree had been ready, its little shining ornaments hanging on the dark green branches, its lights of many colours in the shape of icicles bringing the whole to life. The crib, too, had been in its place, a bright oblong of warm light illuminating the darkness of winter in the hall. In the kitchen all was set for cooking the turkey next day when three old St Andrew's friends were coming to lunch with us.

Christmas dinner's not difficult when it's planned in good time, and experience helped me here. Every year's the same, more or less. Fortunately for me who hates nasty surprises, God created a world where the laws of physics are, for everyday purposes, constant and reliable. And electrical engineers and power station workers, not forgetting our son John, are being as humanly reliable as they can be, tomorrow especially.

That evening, soon after half past ten, we set off for the Midnight Mass at St Andrew's. There, at the service, I stood, sat or knelt almost in a dream, letting everything happen around me and feeling the Holy Spirit at work in it all.

At the appropriate moment, Edward came down the aisle, a real baby in his arms with a beautiful white Shetland shawl around his head forming a bright halo. The choir followed in procession, singing a carol as they came. At the West Door they stopped for the blessing of the crib, just as it should be. A great and mighty wonder. He handed the real baby back to the parents and placed the small figure of the Baby Jesus in his manger. The procession then moved back towards the altar.

Nicholas read the Epistle.

'God, who at sundry times and in divers manners spake in times past unto the fathers by the prophets, hath in these last days spoken unto us by his Son.'

He had a deep and clear speaking voice, it was a pleasure to hear him. It was a completely different voice from the embarrassingly unmusical, droning sound which emerged when he was singing a hymn. His understanding of what he read was well expressed as suited this occasion. It all seemed quite clear to me. There was no nonsense about it. Now we have God's true and only Son come to reveal the Truth to us. We don't have any longer to rely only on the prophets.

Edward sang the Gospel, and I took the greatest care possible to seize on the meaning of the words as they came to my ears, and then to ponder on this meaning during the small fraction of time before he was in the pulpit.

He began to speak about the power of God that's hidden in the image of the helpless babe who's lying in the manger, and of that other image of Easter, of the hidden power of God, Christ on the cross, helpless too, unable to use hands or feet in the service of the world. Both these images are of helplessness, yet they are the two most powerful images in all Christendom: Mary with her infant Son in the manger, bound in his swaddling clothes, and Christ nailed and dying on the cross. They hold the whole of our salvation, our redemption, of the whole world's salvation. We carry these images with us all the days of our life. They sustain our hope in God through all our troubles.

Then came the Communion itself, and, when I was back in my place kneeling quietly, I watched the rest of the congregation returning from the altar. I saw in my imagination each person drawing after him a silver ribbon, as if the Holy Spirit were become visible, each person taking his share of the Sacrament out into the world, each person connected always by this silver ribbon to the Spirit hidden in the Bread, consecrated on the altar.

Everyone of us brings a portion of the Spirit away in his heart and soul, ready to go out into the world to do God's work. Here in the Bread, we find God's strength and we take our share out into the world with us every time we come here and are fed.

Soon we were all wishing each other a Happy Christmas. I felt truly happy and relaxed and full of joy, and many others were, I knew, feeling the same. As Nicholas and I drove back to Ardness, unusually late at night for us, the stars were shining brightly and the car's headlights made the frosty crystals sparkle on the road.

Christmas morning came, like the night before, white and frosty. Nicholas and I were up early to prepare for our visitors whom we would collect after we'd all been to the morning Eucharist. They were three old friends, friends old in years rather than friends of long standing, for we had not been parishioners of St Andrew's long enough to have old friends in that other sense.

It was a cheerful lunch much enjoyed by all. There was no shortage of food or drink or conversation, though, neither were there crackers with paper hats nor sixpences in the plum pudding. Everyone was as bright or dull as he wished to be, but, in fact, and surprisingly, no one was bored or boring. After the meal we all relaxed in easy chairs and (I noticed, but didn't remark on this), several surreptitious naps were taken. Later, I produced cups of refreshing tea, and soon after this Nicholas drove the visitors home while I tidied up.

Fortunately there was no Evensong calling us to church again that day. We could subside and recover from the general excitement. The next day we were going to Jane's. How lovely, I thought. It would be just ourselves and Edward. I would enjoy that, only the five of us. We, who hardly needed to talk to each other, no need to 'make conversation', to be bright or especially entertaining.

CHRISTMAS: BOXING DAY

The next day was Saturday, St Stephen's Day, also Boxing Day. Poor old Stephen, I was thinking, he doesn't get much attention with his Day falling on the day after Christmas.

I was helping Jane in her kitchen after lunch. Nicholas, Jack and Edward had done a good share of the tidying, but had now retreated into comfy chairs in the sitting room. We were talking about my friend, Ruth, the one I'd written to about St Paul. She'd gone to spend Christmas with her youngest sister.

"There are lots of grandchildren there," I said, "and she enjoys them. They don't sap her strength as they would mine. Five minutes with young children and my energy is drained away."

"I was good with babies," Jane said, "or even with those up to six months or even a year old, but after that the older they got the more horrible they became. Or at least David did, until many years later. Prue wasn't so bad."

"I was a rotten mother really." It was a thought I often had but it was a bit late now to cheer myself up about it. "I did try. I thought of all kinds of things I might do, things a normal mother would do, but it was no good. I kept wanting to sit down quietly on my own and read a book. And I did. Oh, dear, I'm afraid I wasn't much good as a mother. At least as a mother of very young children."

"I don't expect you were as bad as you make out. It's amazing, though, how many people are good with the young. They're kind and unselfish naturally."

"Definitely not like me. But Ruth's kind and good with all ages of people, not only with children, and so I think is Angela. They're unconsciously Christian. Well, Angela anyway, for it's only lately that Ruth has become only doubtfully Christian. But that sounds contradictory for I don't think you can be a Christian without knowing it."

"Sometimes it seems to me," Jane suggested, "that the kind of goodness which appears naturally in people makes them not need to have any well defined religion. Do you think this could be true?"

"It might be with some people but if I had no religion I'd be selfish, that's to say self-centred, which is worse, thoughtless, even unkind, cynical, intolerant, always making snap judgments, and very inclined to sarcasm. That sounds like a very Pauline list of horrible faults, doesn't it? What I thought was surprising about Ruth was that once she told me she'd never in her life had what she would call a religious experience. It's hard to believe this, isn't it? She says she's never wanted to describe anything that's happened to her as 'out of this world.'"

"Perhaps she's never fallen in love, for that's an experience which usually makes people feel dreamlike and for a while carried away from ordinary life."

I said to Nicholas later, as we were driving home, "It was a lovely Boxing Day, Jane has everything quietly and perfectly arranged with no fuss. Her visitors enjoy themselves because they can be relaxed. Of course we had the best company today. Just the five of us, all very well known to each other. We forgot we might be worn out. It didn't matter if any of us was silent, but no one was for long. It's wintry, isn't it? All that snow on Cairn Dhu. It was gleaming in the sun this afternoon."

"Mm, mm," replied Nicholas.

Later on that evening I was beginning to think about St John the Evangelist and his Day which would come tomorrow, and of the importance of his Gospel, easily my favourite of the four. I thought of all the marvellously convincing ideas in it and what I liked to think of as 'appealing passages', those bits that appeal to that part of me which is always on the look out for words or phrases which express the spirit of truth.

I took my Bible from the shelf beside me and began searching for the passages I needed. I remembered that in St John's Gospel Jesus keeps saying 'I am'.

'I am the bread of life.'

so that

'He that cometh to me shall never hunger.'

and

'I am the door, by me if any man enter in he shall be saved, and shall go in and find pasture.'

'I am the good shepherd, the good shepherd giveth his life for his sheep ... I am the good shepherd, and I know my sheep and am known of mine ... and I lay down my life for the sheep.'
Jesus also says,
'The water that I shall give him shall be in him a well of water springing up into everlasting life.'
And he is that water.
'He that believeth on me shall never thirst.'
That word 'believeth' means truly believing Jesus to be God. He also said,
'I am the light of the world: he that followeth me shall not walk in darkness, but shall have the light of life.'
and,
'I am the way, the truth and the light, no man cometh to the Father but by me ... I am in the Father and the Father in me.'
and,
'I am the true vine and my Father is the husbandman.'
But most important of all he said,
'I am the resurrection, and the life; he that believeth in me, though he were dead, yet shall he live: and whosoever liveth and believeth in me shall never die. Believeth thou this?'
And also,
'My flesh is meat indeed and my blood is drink indeed. He that eateth my flesh and drinketh my blood dwelleth in me and I in him.'
This was the hard saying that made many of his followers leave him. There's nothing unclear about what was said. However much one might wriggle, one can't really escape. Or so I would have thought. Unless one went somewhere away altogether. But there is nowhere else to go if one wants to remain a Christian. As Peter said at the time,
'Lord, to whom shall we go? Thou has the words of eternal life. And we believe and are sure that thou art that Christ, the Son of the living God.'
I wondered how there could be anyone who'd suggest these sentences had been spoken by a mortal man, or that they might have been made up and added later. Why should anyone do so or even have had imagination enough to invent such ideas? John surely wrote all

this, and he meant us to understand that the Jesus whom he knew, who spoke these words, was the Son of God, himself God.

As I'd often wondered, I wondered again. Why had God allowed me to go on being obstinate in my belief, or rather unbelief, for so long? Who was waiting for what? Why hadn't the Spirit banged me on the head sooner and knocked a bit of sense into me?

"*Knock*! That's the word, the key word! The key to the door. Though the door is not locked, it needs no key. *Revelation*! What to find and where to find it, the two answers in one, in Revelation. The Revelation of St John.

"'Behold, I stand at the door and knock: if any man hear my voice and open the door, I will come into him, and will sup with him and he with me.'"

Very shortly after this it was bedtime and I was glad. If I didn't go to sleep at once there would be too much to think about. But I did.

CHRISTMAS:
ST JOHN
THE EVANGELIST'S DAY

The next day was Sunday, really St John the Evangelist's Day and I'd been thinking about him a lot already. I enjoyed the morning service for it was an opportunity to learn even more. John was the disciple whom Jesus especially loved, and Edward's sermon helped me see further into his thoughts then I'd been able to before.

They must have been very close, Jesus and John, Edward began, and then he went on to explain that John understood the teaching of Jesus better than any other of the Apostles did. He'd written it down in his Gospel, summarizing everything he knew into a marvellously helpful and poetic book. He wrote in such a way that its message could be taken into our hearts and minds.

John remembered many details in Jesus's life; that the house, where Mary had anointed Jesus's feet, was filled with the fragrance of the expensive ointment of spikenard: and when Judas led the band of men and officers to capture Jesus, the High Priest's servant's name was Malchus, whose right ear was cut off by Peter. He remembered the chronology of events: that, on one day, Jesus had been baptised by the other John, the Baptist, that on the next day it was Andrew and our John who had followed Jesus to where he was staying and that Andrew had brought his brother Simon to meet Jesus, and that he had been renamed Peter; that, again, on the day following Jesus had found Philip in Galilee, that Philip had found Nathaniel under a fig tree and brought him to Jesus: and on the third day, came the wedding at Cana. And, with his sense of time, John also had a sense of place, he remembered that at the Feast of the Dedication it was winter, and that Jesus had walked in the temple in Solomon's porch and he'd argued there with the Jews about God's being his Father. And there are many other examples of his carefulness.

Edward ended by saying, as he had begun, that here, in this country, we read this Gospel in English words printed in black ink on white paper, but in these words, as we come to study and understand them, we find John's story of Christ's life and teaching, the spirit of Christ, ready to enter our hearts, a story which can escape from our English language and the printed word and our century and become universal and timeless.

That evening Nicholas had arranged to meet Jack at the church early to discuss some repairs to the backdoor steps which were becoming dangerous. A new light was needed there too. This suited me, because the church itself would be deserted enough on our arrival for me to pray quietly at the crib. That morning there had, by the time we'd got there, been a talkative crowd already gathered in the doorway and I'd not thought it practicable to kneel and pray so near to their distracting noise.

But now, for the moment, the church was empty except of course for Jamie, but he was quietly getting on with his jobs and anyway he was used to my being around on my own. I put a lighted candle on the pricket stand near the crib, especially for Mary, who was pondering all those things in her heart, about her child and his being born here in this stable, and the shepherds' coming to worship him.

I'd pondered too, as I knelt there, on this mystery of the incarnation. Somewhere hidden in this crib was an idea that had come to me last year, only it escaped before I could get it clearly into my mind. Now, this year I'd begin again, and see if I could find it.

There was the Babe in his little basket or manger, in his swaddling clothes. He's tiny and helpless. He needs Mary to look after him, and she needs Joseph. I feel they all need our prayers even today, they need our help to protect them from the evil forces still abroad in this world. We should make a sheltering circle of prayer around the crib to keep in the good, to keep out the evil. It all seemed so real to me here in Strathlyon on that evening, at that very moment, so real I could imagine I was almost in Bethlehem myself. If I really were, I might be able to pick up the real true Babe and nurse him and comfort him when he cried. I was sure there must have been many people visiting Mary, expressing concern and kindness, who'd held him in their arms, all that long time ago.

So far all was clear and simple, but if I looked beyond the Babe, into the meaning of his coming and his growing up, his teaching about the Kingdom and about the Father and the Son being one, about the

Holy Spirit, and about his death on the cross and resurrection, I saw these are all ideas which are familiar to us even though we can hardly say we understand them. However, that evening, I could see also, beyond Christ on the cross, an abyss of darkness that frightened me. There was a gap, an unfathomable ravine, a rift valley of blackness, in front of me, and it was making me dizzy; I felt totally lost. If I jumped over the edge of this cliff I'd be out of touch with everything I normally relied on, it would be as if I were jumping from a plane into the night with my parachute not yet opened, and I didn't know whether it would open or not; as if I were falling into the cold spaces between the stars. I was afraid. I didn't want to jump at that moment. This space I was thinking about is the unknown darkness between Good Friday and Easter Sunday. We all have to journey across this space when we die. Some will venture a little way into it before their last day on earth, but I'm not ready yet. I need to come back to where I began, to the crib. I *could* run away from here altogether, out into the mindless busy world, but then I would be running away from the Babe whose arrival we have just been celebrating with love and adoration. I'd be running away from my true self.

One day I'd be able to let the Holy Babe take me by the hand and ask him to lead me to the edge of the abyss and with him jump out into the darkness, his hand in mine, and safely and quickly I'd come to land with him in Paradise. Will it be like that? Or must there be, as Christ found on the cross, a time of anguish, a feeling of desertion, of being abandoned, which has to be gone through before the lonely human soul is brought into the everlasting, ever-welcoming arms on the other side? Who knows? But this time I was asking to be brought back here to the crib, now, to all the friendliness of the church I knew so well.

Through the littleness of the Babe I'd caught a glimpse of the bigness of THINGS, an ungraspable greatness, almost wholly beyond my understanding, the infinite glory of God. Perhaps this blackness of space - beyond death, is connected to the dark of the garden at night into which once, (was it last year?) in my imagination, I'd stepped from my lighted room, and for a fraction of a moment I'd seemed to meet God there on the dark lawn, among the dark trees, under a starlit sky. I could remember the occasion clearly, though I'd not often thought of it since. It was a moment of love exchanged, if that's the right word, there had been something between God and myself. I felt God's love for me and gave back mine for him. If the blackness of the great unknown abyss is the same as the darkness of that garden, I've no need to be afraid. But is it? I wondered.

I opened my eyes again and looked at the little figures in the crib and thought of all the depth of feeling they stood for. I'd been part way on a journey and seen the unknown but had not ventured into it. Another time perhaps ... whenever that might come ...

I remembered the words Christ had spoken as he hung on the cross.

'My God, why hast thou forsaken me?'

And the psalm goes on:

'But be not thou far from me ... Deliver my soul from the sword ... Save me from the lion's mouth ... O praise the Lord, ye that fear him... For the Kingdom is the Lord's.' '...They shall come, and the heavens shall declare his righteousness unto a people that shall be born, whom the Lord hath made.'

I've not explained all this adventure very well. And I hadn't even to myself, so I didn't see how I would ever begin to explain it to anyone else, except of course to someone who'd already been to the edge of the abyss themselves, had been drawn into its depths or read a description of it by a master hand, and had then drawn back. Edward would listen and understand. Jane would listen but not understand.

I felt dizzy when I began to realize how much I did believe, or rather, all that followed from what I believed. The immensity of what I thought I believed and its consequences for me in life and in death is still more than I can grasp. It's certainly more than I could ever express in earthly words, so it wasn't surprising I felt frightened. Other people must feel the same.

Mary was at the very centre of the coming of God to earth. She was the person through whom Jesus's coming to earth took place, she must have felt more frightened, more out of her depth than I have ever felt, when she heard the angel's words. I'm only one in a long, long line of people who've come to the edge of this darkness and either dared to take off into the blackness or, like me, not dared but asked to come back to the world - for the present anyway. The Angel says,

'Fear not,' to all of us, but will people like myself ever have faith enough to believe him?

I got up from the crib and went to our usual pew where Nicholas soon joined me. (Jane and Jack were already sitting, as they always did, on the other side of the aisle and a little further back). I was sad and happy, both at the same time, which, I supposed, is the usual state of most of us most of the time. But I felt it was especially so for me, especially that evening. I enjoyed the service but, as you can expect, I was often deep in my own thoughts. Canon Harper preached the sermon, but I didn't try to listen. I was sure it was interesting and about St John, but I'd no energy left to concentrate on anything.

Instead I thought about Mary and how frightened she must have been when the archangel Gabriel appeared to her, and even more when he spoke to her with his astonishing message. We're used to imagining an infinitely holy and powerful God holding up the stars, or a loving Father bringing comfort to our hearts, but we're not used to God's greatest Messenger in his shining Majesty standing on the sitting-room carpet, announcing to us that we've been chosen for a leading part in God's redemption of the world.

Mary replied, and we often repeat the words,

'Behold the Handmaid of the Lord, be it unto me according to thy word...'

And then we add,

'Hail, Mary, full of grace, the Lord is with thee,
Blessed art thou among women,
Blessed is the fruit of they womb, Jesus.'

We also say,

'The Word was made flesh and dwelt among us.'

It's trying impossibly to grasp these ideas that makes me dizzy. It's something for which we have no words however hard we search for them. It's for this reason there are images to help us, symbols and pictures. There's the stable of gentle warm light and outside there's a cold winter darkness. The crib is here and the ox and the ass. Mary is here, pondering in her heart the future of the Word, not long born, the

Word made flesh dwelling among us, wrapped like a papoose in his swaddling clothes.

On the way home after the service I said to Nicholas, "Next Friday, it'll be New Year's Day, a whole New Year more on the calendar and in our lives. I'm glad we haven't got anything arranged. I definitely feel like a spot of doing nothing very much. Though it'll be time for all those New Year resolutions all over again."

"I know you and your resolutions. What have you planned this year?"

"Nothing really. All the things I ought to do are too ambitious for how I feel. At the moment anyway."

"That's good. We'll be able to catch up on the house and garden. There's a great deal to do. I could do with some help."

My heart sank just a little. That was not what I'd intended. I'd been vaguely considering, and Edward and I had rather jokingly discussed, my writing something about a pilgrimage through the church's year. But I didn't want just yet to say anything about something so embryonic, even to Nicholas. So I made no reply except a rather Nicholas-like 'Mm, mm.'

At home, after supper, I was again with my thoughts. I remembered Austin Farrer. He had written about the incarnation. His book was at my side in a pile I'd not yet put away. I took it and after I'd found my place I read that the incarnation of Jesus

'is so vivid and particular and real, as much so as any incarnation recorded in mythology, such as that of Jupiter, a mythical 'god' who had to step down only from a definable place above the glassy floor of heaven. The Eternal Word has to be gathered from all immensity and begin a human life in Mary. He who is coming in Mary's womb is not measurable, he is not conceivable in any way as anything spatial, and yet he takes place and body to himself when the Word is made Flesh.'

EPILOGUE

As I'd reminded myself, New Year's Day fell on the following Friday. That morning I'd written my Kalendar for the next week's services but had left the photocopying of it for the Sunday when we'd be at St Andrew's for the eleven o'clock Mass.

So on Sunday morning just before half past ten I was at the rectory door, ringing the bell.

"Happy New Year, Edward," I said as he opened the door to me. "Though I know we've said it before on the phone."

"Happy New Year to you too," he replied.

"There are no excitements this week, not till Epiphany, so there's only the one notice to copy. And it wasn't worth coming in specially yesterday to use the photocopier, so I've come now on my way to church."

"That's fine. When you've finished, we can walk along together. Have you decided yet to write your book? What about it?"

"Were we really being serious? I thought it was perhaps, maybe, only a vague idea for the future."

"No, no. It's been in my mind for some time. You could do it very well, you know."

"I've begun to have a little idea about its shape. Will you encourage me if or when I begin to lose heart?'

"Of course I will."

"But I've no time really. I'm too busy. Also I'm not quite ready. Everything's in a flux in my mind."

"Well, you can make time. Don't rush. Make an actual pilgrimage through the year as it goes on, and see what happens. Your flux may crystallize into something good."

"I've been thinking, though, if God wanted a book written, he would have organised me to have a broken leg or something similar, and I'd recline comfortably with my leg securely in a great plaster, and you and Nicholas and everybody would all wait on me hand and foot, and there'd be plenty of time for the words to flow out of my pen onto the paper. I know a broken leg would mend sooner than a book could be written, but I'd have made a start and got a little confidence in the

291

job. Maybe. Maybe, too, I could take after St Teresa and write under obedience. She never otherwise would have found time to write her books. As it was, she was much too busy to read over what she'd written. Though that's certainly one thing I'll have to do. Of course, I'm far from being another St Teresa in every other possible way, as you well know. I'll see. I was thinking too of all the things I do for St Andrew's at the moment anyway; they are really only very superficial jobs, nothing which gets hold of me deep down or wraps up my mind totally like creating a book would do. It would give my hands something to occupy them, or one hand anyway. I can still wield a pen even if people have trouble reading the result. Or I could acquire a word processor. That's an idea! Though I could start without one. I think I can see how to do it. That's if *you* don't think it'll be boring."

"Of course it won't be boring if you're honest with yourself, about yourself," Edward said encouragingly.

(I hadn't, of course, as I was speaking to him, composed my sentences even as semi coherently as those I've written above, but the meaning of the words I had used probably came to much the same thing).

By now the photocopying was finished, so we left the house and soon covered the short distance to the church. I'd only to replace last week's notices with the new ones, and this I quickly accomplished.

We each lit a candle at the crib and Edward went on towards the vestry while I said a quick prayer.

I knew if I wrote anything, I was bound to be honest with myself. I was even in those days no good at dissembling and I'm still not. Everything would have to be described just as it was, and all the characters would be my friends, except for a very few funny people I'd have to disguise. That's a good idea about a pilgrimage through the year and what I'd learnt on my way. I was sure God would help me choose something that would be within my strength - if I was meant to write anything at all.

I knelt down in our pew. Before me in my mind lay the morning service and the rest of the day and all the days to come after that. But there was to be an addition to my usual jobs, a new kind of work for me to do for God. It all seemed very interesting and hopeful. Soon I joined in the prayer:

'Cleanse the thoughts of our hearts by the inspiration of thy Holy Spirit, that we may perfectly love thee and worthily magnify thy Holy Name.'

I'd so often wondered in what way I could ever magnify God's holy name, even if the thoughts of my heart had been cleansed by the inspiration of his Holy Spirit. There seemed to be nothing I could ever do to open anyone's eyes a bit more to his Holy Name. But if I wrote a book and in it I was able to show a little about how to come to God, and it was a good enough book for some people to buy and enjoy reading, I might then be magnifying his Holy Name. Of course we can do nothing worthily without God. In the same way it's God who provides the perfection that should be in our love for him, perfection without God is impossible. I shall try to make both these ideas, having perfect love for God and worthily magnifying his Holy Name, be the thread running through my book, holding it all together. For normally, up to now, I've never felt I could ever show forth anything very much for God at all.